UNITED STATES POSTAL SERVICE

STAMPS & STORIES

The ENCYCLOPEDIA OF U.S. STAMPS

Produced by: CUSTOMER SERVICES DEPT.
UNITED STATES POSTAL SERVICE
WASHINGTON, D.C. 20260

Published by: SCOTT PUBLISHING CO.
3 EAST 57th STREET
NEW YORK, N.Y. 10022

Executive Editor FRANK S. TRUMBOWER
Art Director LEO LESSER
Chief Illustrator JIM SHARPE
Story Editor ELEANOR KASMIR

Stamp quotations and other philatelic reference material reprinted from the Scott U.S. Specialized Catalogue, 1979 Edition and the Scott Standard Postage Stamp Catalogue, 1980 Edition.

Chief Catalogue Editor JAMES B. HATCHER
New Issues Editor LILLY B. FREED
Staff Editors WILLIAM W. CUMMINGS, RICHARD GORDON, IRVING KOSLOW, STEVEN Y. MARDIGUIAN, IRWIN SIEGEL & BERT TAUB

Library of Congress Catalogue Card Number 79-65325

ISBN: 0-89487-029-7
Printed in the United States of America

The United States Postal Service sells only commemoratives released during the past few years and current regular and special stamps and postal stationery.

Prices listed in this handbook are called "catalogue prices" by collectors and serve only as a guide to market prices for fine specimens when offered by an informed dealer to an informed buyer. They are taken from the 1979 and 1980 Scott Catalogues whose editors have based these values on the current stamp market. Comments concerning them should be directed to the Scott Publishing Co.

The Scott numbering system for stamps is used in this book since it is the identification system used by most stamp dealers and collectors in the United States.

Note: When minimum price of a used stamp is fixed at 3 cents it reflects dealer's labor and service costs. The sum of these minimum prices does not properly indicate the value of an accumulation of stamps consisting only of cheaper stamps. Price of actual stamp sales are dependent upon supply and demand, changes in popularity, local custom, quality of the stamp itself and many other factors.

TABLE OF CONTENTS

INTRODUCTION TO STAMP COLLECTING

Philately, according to the dictionary, is the collecting or study of stamps. A philatelist is someone who does one or both of these. Some 20,000,000 of us in the United States fit that category, pursuing what is said to be the world's most popular hobby. A large proportion of that number collect United States stamps.

How do you join that happy throng? It's easy. You can begin by saving the stamps from mail delivered to your home or you can go to your local post office and buy each new issue of stamp as it is released. You can trade with other people who collect, join a stamp club, or buy from stamp dealers. It's as simple as that.

You, of course, do not have to collect only United States stamps. You have the whole world to choose from. No matter what your collecting area, you will find that these colorful bits of paper, wherever they come from, capture the spirit and history of their place of origin. To look at them is to take a journey into the far-distant and near-distant past . . . to relive the exciting days of chivalry and buccaneers, explorers and kings . . . man's journey into space.

Whatever the type of stamps you choose to collect, you will find that these bits of postal paper are educational, inspiring, enjoyable and entertaining. Wherever they are from, stamps offer you a fun-filled way to utilize your leisure time.

HOW TO BEGIN

There are many ways to collect. You can collect a specimen of each stamp issued by a country. You can expand on that and collect the various varieties of such stamps. Varieties are subtle differences in color or design or perhaps perforations. You can collect stamps "on cover"—that is the entire envelope containing the stamp, the postmark and the cancellation, showing how and where it went on its assignment to deliver the mail.

Topical collecting is very popular today. To form such a collection you should choose a subject or topic that interests you deeply. Do you like sports? Dogs? Ships? All are fine subjects for a topical collection. What about music? Flags? Space exploration? Transportation? All are perfect. If you have chosen one that is broad enough, you will find it quite easy to create a fascinating and personally meaningful collection. Many groups of specialized topical stamp collectors have prepared lists of stamp issues dealing with their subject, and these lists can easily be obtained to help you in starting.

TYPES OF STAMPS

You may limit your collection to a simple type of stamp or to stamps of any kind. Stamp issues are normally divided into the following types:

REGULAR OR DEFINITIVE STAMPS

These are the stamps you'll find on most day-in, day-out mail. They are printed in huge quantities and are kept in use by the post office for sizable stretches of time—several years, usually. Definitives usually appear in a series, with values from 1 cent to higher values, say $5.00, with as many intermediate values as are needed for the postal rates then in effect.

COMMEMORATIVE STAMPS

These are issued to honor an important event, person or special subject. They are usually larger than the definitives, more colorful and are circulated for a limited time. Often they depict famous people but, did you know, U.S. stamps never depict a living person.

AIR MAIL STAMPS

Air Mail stamps are no longer issued for postage within the U.S., Canada and Mexico. But "Air Mail" formed a fascinating part of stamp collecting and some U.S. Air Mail stamps for use in sending mail overseas are still issued. Collectors of Air Mail issues not only collect the stamps, but go in for such things as "First Flight Covers," "Airport Dedications" and "Crash Covers."

SPECIAL DELIVERY STAMPS

These stamps, sold to the sender at a premium price to secure extra-fast delivery for a letter or package, provide another avenue of collecting.

POSTAGE DUE STAMPS

Affixed to mail at the post office to indicate that the prepaid postage was not enough to carry the letter to its destination and more is to be paid for delivery, postage due stamps make an interesting branch of collecting.

COIL STAMPS

These are stamps issued in rolls, so that each stamp has two straight edges and two perforated edges. Many collectors specialize in this type of stamp.

EQUIPMENT

ALBUMS

As with most hobbies, to enjoy them fully, you must have the proper equipment. Stamp collecting is no exception. To get started, you should acquire an album to keep your stamps in, stamp hinges or stamp mounts to hold them in the album, and a pair of tongs so that they may be handled without damage. A magnifying glass helps to see important details. First, the album. There are many on the market geared for every pocketbook, every taste, every specialty. Choose yours wisely and well. Make sure your album is well-illustrated on pages of good quality paper. Make sure the album is designed to do what you wish it to do. Better albums do much to sustain your interest in collecting, and display your stamps to the best advantage. Albums with loose-leaf pages are best because they allow for convenient expansion of your collection. Annual supplements to bring your loose-leaf album up-to-date are available from most stamp dealers.

HINGES AND MOUNTS

Mounts are special plastic envelopes that hold the stamp. Most mounts are pre-glued and can be placed into your album over the stamp illustration. Mounts should be used for never cancelled stamps to preserve their value. For less expensive stamps you can use very low cost stamp hinges. If you use hinges, fold back about one fourth of the hinge with the sticky side out. Moisten the folded-back part lightly and place it on the back of the stamp, centered at the top. Then, holding the hinged stamp with your tongs, moisten the bottom part and fasten the stamp in position on the album page.

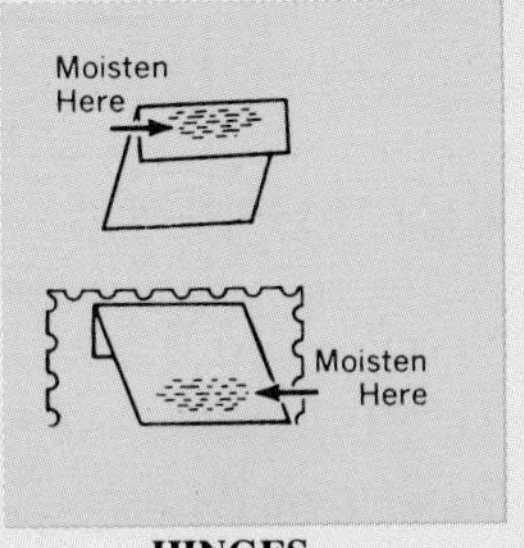

HINGES

MOUNTS

OTHER TOOLS

As you progress, there are other tools you will want. The perforations found around the edges of a stamp can often be the sole means of determining the difference between two *similar* stamps. A gauge to measure the size of these perforations is, therefore, a very useful device, indeed. A strip of paper or plastic is marked so that, when a stamp is laid over the markings, the number of teeth in a two centimeter stretch of stamp is indicated. The gauge usually contains, as well, a millimeter measurement so that the dimensions of a stamp can be accurately determined.

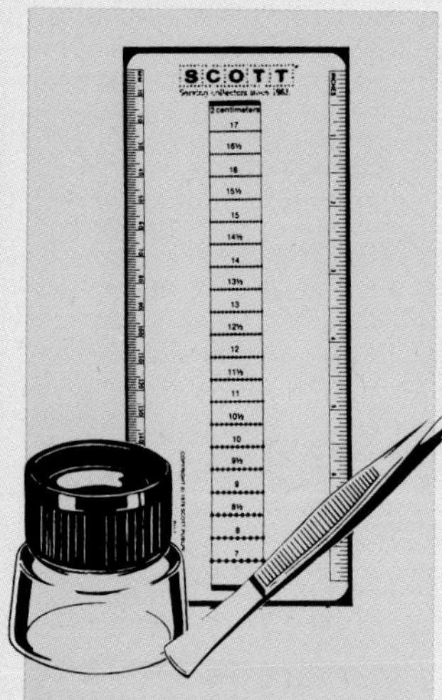

A watermark is a device or design pressed into the paper on which a stamp is printed. Often, it may be seen by holding the stamp up to a bright light. As with perforations, there are times when the only way to distinguish between two stamps is by the watermark. Each may have a different watermark, or one may have none at all.

To see a watermark clearly you must use a watermark detector. In its simplest form, this is a small black tray. The stamp is placed face down in the tray, a few drops of lighter fluid are poured over it and the watermark becomes visible. Be sure to air-dry the stamp before putting it back into your album and be careful of fire.

CATALOGUES

The more you explore the fascinating world of stamps, the more you will find there is much to learn about them. The best source of basic information about stamps and stamp collecting is the *Standard Postage Stamp Catalogue* or other worldwide and specialized catalogues that are published for collectors. Even if you are a beginner, a catalogue is one of the most important adjuncts in forming a collection. The catalogue not only identifies a stamp and its major varieties by color and denomination, but also supplies such information as its date of issue, the method used to print it, and its perforation size and watermark, if any. It identifies the subject depicted on the stamp and often gives the reason for which it was issued. Added to all this, it provides the value of the stamp, both used and unused. The catalogue also contains descriptive identifying numbers for each stamp. These numbers are used by dealers and collectors as a shorthand way of identifying the stamp they wish to buy or sell. For U.S. stamps, *Stamps & Stories* is a wonderful catalogue that contains all the information needed to learn about and collect these items of American history.

STAMP CONDITION

Condition, in the philatelic sense, means the state of a stamp—that is, whether it is a superb specimen, a mediocre specimen or a specimen that is below average. A stamp in fine condition is always more valuable than one that has been less well cared for.

When selecting a stamp to be placed in your collection, always make sure that it is the best you can obtain. Unused stamps should, if possible, be well-centered, fresh looking and have the original gum intact. Gum is the proper term for the adhesive applied to the back of the stamp. Remember, too, that unused stamps that have been hinged or with only part of the original gum are priced below a never hinged stamp with its original gum intact. Used stamps should be well-centered, lightly cancelled and never faded, dirty or stained. There should be no thinning of the paper. Thinning often occurs when stamps are improperly removed from envelopes or album pages and part of the stamp is removed as well.

Most dealers designate stamp condition by such terms as "Superb," "Fine," and "Good." There are many gradations in the range from "Exceptionally Fine," "Very Fine," and "Very Good" through "Fair," "Poor," and "Spacefiller." However, for our purposes, "Superb," "Fine," and "Good" cover the ground for most newer collectors.

SUPERB

Perfect Centering

Lightly Cancelled

"Superb" means a stamp that is of the finest quality, has perfect centering, brilliant color and perfect gum. Used copies in this category also have perfect centering. They are fresh looking, are lightly cancelled, and are sound of body.

FINE

"Fine" means a stamp without flaws, average centering, gum with light hinge marks. Used copies in this category are not quite as fresh, cancels are heavier, and centering is average.

GOOD

"Good" means stamps that are off-center, but fairly attractive and there may be minor defects such as disturbed gum, tiny thins, heavy hinge marks. Used copies, except for the gum, fall into this classification.

Stamps that fall below these standards should be ignored and are not worth acquiring. Of course, there are exceptions to these rules, but they do not come into the province of a new collector and will not be discussed here.

STAMP COLOR GUIDE

A slight difference in the color of a stamp can make it not only a different variety, but sometimes a thing of great rarity. The ability to recognize such color differences requires a practiced eye, but being able to ascertain a valuable shade is one of the real enjoyments of stamp collecting.

Common Shade
Worth $9.00

Color Variety
Worth $25.00

It is difficult to reproduce stamp color 100% accurately. Printing processes such as the ones used in *Stamps & Stories* use different kinds of ink and paper than the original stamps. As a result, the colors shown in the book are not exact reproductions.

In most catalogues the illustrations are only in black and white. The catalogue editors use many descriptive phrases to indicate the color of the stamps listed. Below we list some of the more popular names for the colors found on stamps along with some stamps that go with them.

Blue  **Dark Blue**  **Bright Blue**  **Ultramarine**

Turquoise  **Blue Green**

Green  **Light Green**  **Slate Green**  **Olive Green**

Olive Bister  **Olive**

Red

Rose

Carmine

Brick Red

Orange

Orange Red

Yellow Orange

Brown

Henna Brown

Sepia

Gray

Gray Brown

Purple

Lilac

Violet

Black

STAMP COLLECTORS' TERMS

Terms to describe condition and color are only a part of the language of stamp collectors. Following is a glossary of basic philatelic terms that every stamp collector should know.

Approvals: Stamps sent to a collector for examination. Approvals must be bought or returned to the dealer within a specific time.

Bisect: Half of a stamp used to pay postage of half the face value of the original stamp. This variety must appear on its original cover with the cancellation or postmark covering the cut.

Block: An unsevered group of stamps at least two stamps wide and two stamps high.

Booklet Pane: A small pane of stamps especially printed and cut to be sold in booklets.

Cachet: A special handstamp or printed device on a cover to denote the special circumstances in which it was mailed.

Cancellation: A mark placed on a stamp by a postal authority to prevent its reuse.

Cancelled to Order (CTO): Stamps which are cancelled by the postal authorities without being sent through the mails. They are normally less desirable than stamps which have served their postal function.

Coils: Stamps issued in rolls for use in dispensers, affixing or vending machines.

Color Changeling: A stamp whose color has been changed, either accidentally or intentionally.

Commemoratives: Stamps which honor anniversaries, important people, or special events. Commemoratives are usually sold for a specific length of time.

Compound Perforations: A stamp with perforations of different sizes on different sides.

Condition: The state of a stamp in regard to centering, color, freshness, cancellation, and other related characteristics.

Cover: The entire wrapping or envelope in which a letter has been sent through the mail.

Cut Square: An envelope stamp cut out with a square margin.

Definitives: Regular issues of stamps as distinct from commemoratives.

Die: An engraving from which the plates for printing stamps can be made.

Errors: Stamps with accidental mistakes in color, paper, inscription, watermark, etc. Errors also include bicolored stamps with inverted centers.

Essays: Designs submitted in stamp form but not accepted for issuance.

First Day Cover: A cover bearing a new stamp and cancelled with the first day of use, usually at an officially designated location.

Flat Press Stamps: Stamps printed on a flat bed press, as distinguished from a rotary press.

Booklet Pane

Freaks: Stamps which show conspicuous deviations from the normal caused by shifted perforations, heavy inking, color shifts, or similar accidents during production. Not errors.

Grill: Parallel rows of small pyramids impressed or embossed on the stamp in order to break the fibers of the paper so that the cancellation ink will soak in and make washing for reuse impossible.

Gum: The adhesive on the back of a stamp.

Hinges: Small strips of paper gummed on one side and used by collectors to mount their stamps.

Imperforate: Stamps without perforations. They must be separated with scissors and are usually collected in pairs to prove their authenticity.

India Paper: A soft, thin, silky appearing wove paper usually used for proof impressions.

Inverted Center: A stamp with the center printed upside down in relation to the rest of the design.

Laid Paper: A paper showing alternate light and dark parallel lines when held to the light or immersed in benzine.

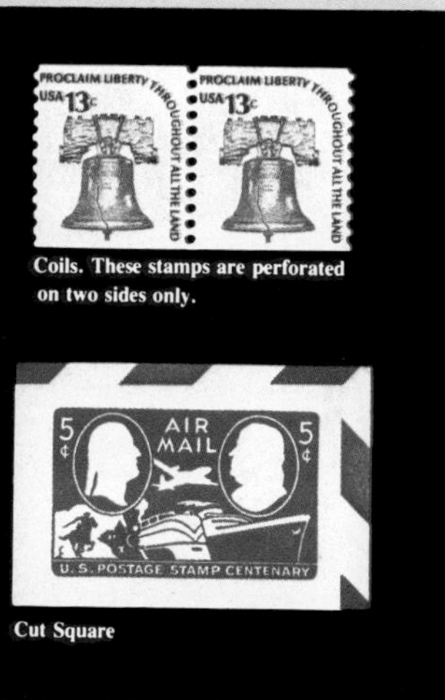

Coils. These stamps are perforated on two sides only.

Cut Square

Locals: Stamps issued for use in restricted areas either by governments or private carriers.

Margin: The border outside the printed design of a stamp, or the similar border of a pane of stamps.

Overprint: Any word, inscription, or device placed on a stamp to alter its use or locality, or to serve a special purpose.

Pair: Two unsevered stamps.

Pane: A portion of the original sheet as cut for sale at the post office.

Part-Perforate: A stamp which has perforations on one, two or three sides.

Pen Cancel: A cancellation applied to the stamp with pen and ink.

Perforations: Line of small cuts or holes placed between two rows of stamps to facilitate separation.

Plate: The actual object from which the stamps are printed.

Plate Number Block: A block of stamps with sheet margin showing a plate number or numbers. Often it is known simply as a plate block.

Postal Stationery: Envelopes, postal cards, wrappers, etc. which had nonadhesive stamps embossed or printed on them.

Postmark: A mark struck upon envelopes, generally to indicate the name of the post office, date of mailing, etc.

Precancels: Stamps with cancellations applied before the mailing of the article on which they prepay postage.

Proofs: Trial printings of a stamp made from the original die or the plate.

Provisionals: Stamps issued prior to the regular issues or to meet a temporary shortage of regular stamps.

Reissue: An official printing of a stamp, or stamps, that had been discontinued.

Remainders: Stocks of stamps on hand after the issue has been discontinued.

Reprints: Impressions from the original plates, blocks, or stones taken after the issuance of the stamps to post offices has ceased and their postal use has been voided.

Revenue Stamps: Stamps issued for use in collecting special taxes on documents, proprietary articles, products, etc.

Rotary Press Stamps: Stamps printed on a rotary type press from curved plates as compared to stamps printed from flat plates on a flat bed press. They will be slightly larger in one direction than flat press stamps.

Rouletting: Short consecutive cuts in the paper between rows of stamps to facilitate separation.

Se-tenant: An unsevered pair of stamps which differ in value, design, or surcharge.

Sheet: Complete unseparated group of stamps as originally printed.

Special Printing: Stamps of current design reissued, usually on a better grade of paper and in brilliant colors.

Stampless Cover: An envelope without stamps generally bearing a postmark and sometimes notations such as "Paid", "Paid 10", etc.

Straight Edge: The imperforate side of a stamp which is otherwise perforate.

Surcharge: An overprint which alters or restates the face value or denomination of the stamp to which it is applied.

Tied On: A stamp is "tied on" when the cancellation or postmark extends from the stamp to the envelope.

Topicals: Area of philately in which emphasis is on the subject portrayed on stamps rather than the stamps themselves.

Unused: A stamp with or without original gum which has no cancellation or other evidence of postal duty.

Used: A stamp which has done postal duty as evidenced by the cancellation.

Want List: A list of stamp numbers or philatetic items needed for a collection.

Watermark: A design or pattern incorporated into the paper during its manufacture.

Wove Paper: A paper of uniform texture throughout, showing no light or dark patterns when held to the light or immersed in benzine.

Imperforate Stamp

Perforated Stamp

Overprint

Se-tenant

Surcharge

Precancel

DEFINITION OF CATALOGUE PRICES

Stamp collectors use Catalogue prices as a guide to help them in buying items for their collections or for the purpose of trading stamps with other collectors. The values for the stamps quoted in *Stamps & Stories* are taken from the latest issue of the Catalogue used by most United States collectors. These price guides will help you to plan your stamp purchases or to evaluate the stamps that you may come across on a trip to the "attic." However, there are a few things about Catalogue prices that you must know so you will understand and use them correctly.

Catalogue values are simply guidelines to stamp values. Actual stamps may cost more or less than the values shown in the Catalogue. One reason for this, which you already know, is that stamp condition is very important in determining the value of any stamp. The Catalogue gives a price for both unused (mint) stamps and for those that have been used or cancelled. In each case, the Catalogue value is for a single stamp (except where prices of blocks or sheets of stamps are specifically noted).

Both the used and unused Catalogue price is for a stamp in **FINE CONDITION** and the Catalogue price also assumes that the copy has been hinged. If you want a stamp with **SUPERB** centering and color that has never been hinged, it could cost several times the Catalogue value. But, stamps in less than **FINE** condition or those that have been heavily hinged may be worth only a small percentage of Catalogue value.

In the case of used stamps, the Catalogue price is based on a light cancellation. Heavy cancellations, as you already know, lessen a stamp's value. But, you may not know that sometimes used stamps are worth more than unused stamps. This frequently happens when the cancellation is of a special type or for a significant date. Of course, this could mean that the stamp is worth more **only** if it is still on the original envelope.

So, if you find old envelopes, be sure to have them evaluated before simply tearing off the stamp and discarding its "cover."

There are other important things that you should know about Catalogue prices. One is that they are estimates of how much you should expect to pay for a copy of the stamp from a regular dealer. If you should wish to sell the same stamp to a dealer, he may offer you much less than the Catalogue price. The dealer's quote will be based upon his own interest in owning your stamp: he may have a full supply of this stamp at the moment and he will only buy more at a very low price. Also, the dealer will have to evaluate the time and costs involved to make a profit when he resells your stamp. The stamps of countries or topics that are more popular among collectors normally can be sold for a price closer to the Catalogue values than stamps from less popular areas.

Another point about Catalogue prices concerns very low priced stamps. Frequently the Catalogue will show that a stamp is worth a small or "minimum" value, like $.03. This means that a stamp dealer cannot afford to sell you an individual stamp for less than this minimum amount. However, a packet of stamps made up of numerous inexpensive stamps is not necessarily worth the total of their individual Catalogue values.

As a general rule you should try to collect only the best quality stamps. This practice will result in a hobby that can be enjoyable and rewarding for the rest of your life.

PRICE TRENDS OF SELECTED STAMP ISSUES

For the past few years the price of just about everything seems to have gone up. Just how the upward changes in stamp values compare to changes of items like food, electricity, automobiles and the other goods and services that every family requires can be seen from the picture below.

As you can see, the prices of selected stamp issues have gone up much faster than the prices of these other items. The stamp issues that have been chosen for this comparison represent a broad index of the stamps being purchased by U.S. collectors. Many issues have increased by greater amounts; but it is also true that many issues are worth no more today than they were on the day they were first put on sale at a post office. Overall, however, the trend in stamp values has been upward. If you had begun your collection a few years ago and chosen your stamps wisely, it is possible that your stamps today would be worth several times the amount you paid.

Scott No.	Description	Price 1968	Price 1978	Price 1979	11 yr. average 1968-1979	% increase 1978-79
1	1847 5c red brown	$250.00	$1200.00	$2000.00	20.8%	66.6%
2	1847 10c black	1100.00	8500.00	11,000.00	23.3	29.4
112-122	1869 Pictorials	1781.00	7505.00	9645.00	16.6	28.5
230-245	Columbian Issues	1568.75	7588.50	10,346.00	18.7	36.3
285-293	Trans-Mississippi Issue	734.00	3164.00	4410.00	17.7	39.4
294-299	Pan-American Issue	82.50	336.00	510.00	18.0	51.8
300-313	1902-03 Regular Issue	613.00	2714.50	3674.00	17.7	35.3
401-404	1915 Panama-Pacific (Perf. 10)	268.50	1000.00	1372.50	16.0	37.2
424-440	1914-15 Single Line Watermark	260.40	806.00	1081.00	13.8	34.0
523-524	1918 $2 & $5 Franklins	140.00	800.00	1250.00	22.0	56.2
551-573	1922-25 Regular Issue	106.86	544.65	883.15	21.2	62.2
C1-C3	1918 First Airmails	66.00	310.00	460.00	19.3	48.4
C4-C6	1923 Second Airmails	58.50	267.50	425.00	19.8	59.0
C13-C15	Graf Zeppelin Issue	600.00	2925.00	4200.00	19.4	43.6
E1-E10	1885-1916 Special Delivery	223.25	1075.00	1475.00	18.7	37.2
K1-K18	U.S. Offices in China	130.45	613.00	989.00	20.2	61.4
Q1-Q12	Parcel Post	171.15	473.50	621.50	12.4	31.3
	TOTAL	$8154.61	$39,823.25	$54,342.15	18.8%	36.0%

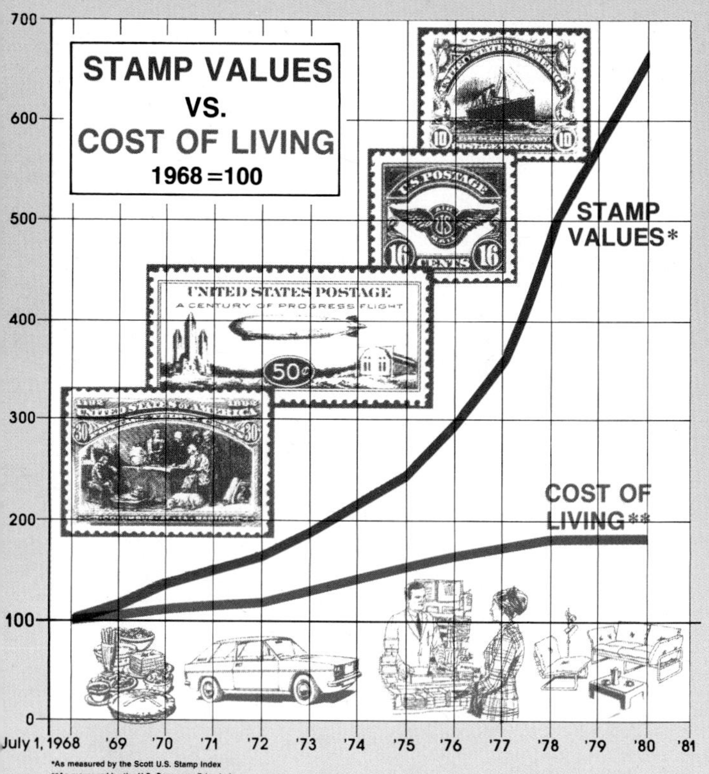

*As measured by the Scott U.S. Stamp Index
**As measured by the U.S. Consumer Price Index

The U.S. stamp issues that have gone up by the greatest percentage in the most recent period are shown in the following tables.* If stamps continue to go up at the same rates, some stamps will be worth more in a few years than they are today. But remember two things: First, not all stamps go up in value; Secondly, stamp collecting is the real fun, even when done with "space fillers," and price increases are not the purpose, but only an occasional benefit from your new hobby. And lastly, remember that any price comparisons for stamps that are taken from the Catalogues overstate the amount of gain. This is because the Catalogue prices are what you must pay to buy a copy of the stamp. When you want to sell your copy, you cannot expect to get the full Catalogue price. Seldom less than 10% and often as much as half of the current Catalogue value must be given up when you sell to another collector or stamp dealer.

* This listing includes only the stamp-types listed in *Stamps & Stories*. If other stamp-types were included, such as Migratory Bird Hunting Stamps, or U.S. stamps used in China, some of these issues would have shown greater increases.

100 LEADING STAMPS
PERCENT INCREASE 1980 vs. 1969 (11 yrs)

Rank	Scott No.	1969 Price	1980 Price	% incr	%[1]
1	J16*	.25	10.00	3900.0	39.8
2	1059*	.10	2.50	2400.0	34.0
3	375a*	4.00	100.00	2400.0	34.0
4	454*	5.00	120.00	2300.0	33.5
5	455*	.40	9.50	2275.0	33.4
6	294a*	275.00	6500.00	2263.6	33.3
7	319g*	4.50	100.00	2122.2	32.6
8	405b*	2.25	50.00	2122.2	32.6
9	463a*	3.25	65.00	1900.0	31.3
10	454°	.80	15.00	1775.0	30.5
11	406a*	3.25	60.00	1746.2	30.4
12	528A*	1.85	32.50	1656.8	29.8
13	1331*	.10	1.75	1650.0	29.7
14	1332*	.10	1.75	1650.0	29.7
15	487*	.80	13.50	1587.5	29.3
16	332a*	6.00	100.00	1566.7	29.1
17	493*	1.40	22.50	1507.1	28.7
18	331a*	7.50	120.00	1500.0	28.7
19	843*	.40	6.25	1462.5	28.4
20	300b*	32.50	500.00	1438.5	28.2
21	301c*	27.50	400.00	1354.5	27.6
22	517*	4.50	65.00	1344.4	27.5
23	C52*	.40	5.75	1337.5	27.4
24	845*	.30	4.00	1233.3	26.5
25	807a*	.65	8.50	1207.7	26.3
26	492*	.50	6.25	1150.0	25.8
27	573*	30.00	375.00	1150.0	25.8
28	847*	1.00	12.50	1150.0	25.8
29	C21*	1.60	20.00	1150.0	25.8
30	E3*	8.00	100.00	1150.0	25.8
31	E5*	6.00	75.00	1150.0	25.8
32	528B*	1.10	13.50	1127.3	25.6
33	510*	1.25	15.00	1100.0	25.3
34	701*	5.00	60.00	1100.0	25.3
35	C57*	.25	3.00	1100.0	25.3
36	JQ2*	5.00	60.00	1100.0	25.3
37	219D*	5.50	65.00	1081.8	25.2
38	583a*	6.00	70.00	1066.7	25.0
39	600*	.60	7.00	1066.7	25.0
40	834*	16.00	185.00	1056.3	24.9
41	527*	1.35	15.00	1011.1	24.5
42	J15*	1.00	11.00	1000.0	24.4
43	447*	3.65	40.00	995.9	24.3
44	502b*	2.75	30.00	990.9	24.3
45	494*	1.25	13.50	980.0	24.1
46	279Be*	32.50	350.00	976.9	24.1
47	C31*	2.00	21.00	950.0	23.8
48	1053*	12.00	125.00	941.7	23.7
49	533*	16.00	165.00	931.3	23.6
50	1254*	.10	1.00	900.0	23.3

Rank	Scott No.	1969 Price	1980 Price	% incr	%[1]
51	1255*	.10	1.00	900.0	23.3
52	1256*	.10	1.00	900.0	23.3
53	1257*	.10	1.00	900.0	23.3
54	2*	1100.00	11000.00	900.0	23.3
55	247*	2.75	27.50	900.0	23.3
56	375a°	2.50	25.00	900.0	23.3
57	452*	.75	7.50	900.0	23.3
58	623*	1.85	18.50	900.0	23.3
59	C60a*	2.25	22.50	900.0	23.3
60	C61*	.70	7.00	900.0	23.3
61	E12*	2.50	25.00	900.0	23.3
62	J22*	.25	2.50	900.0	23.3
63	J38*	.15	1.50	900.0	23.3
64	J6*	5.50	55.00	900.0	23.3
65	QE4*	2.25	22.50	900.0	23.3
66	108°	235.00	2300.00	878.7	23.0
67	412*	1.80	17.50	872.2	23.0
68	J20*	4.75	45.00	847.4	22.7
69	J58*	185.00	1750.00	845.9	22.7
70	506*	.90	8.50	844.4	22.6
71	J76*	3.75	35.00	833.3	22.5
72	301c°	21.50	200.00	830.2	22.5
73	547*	35.00	325.00	828.6	22.5
74	C9*	1.65	15.00	809.1	22.2
75	393°	.50	4.50	800.0	22.1
76	523*	100.00	900.00	800.0	22.1
77	J32*	.50	4.50	800.0	22.1
78	J46*	.50	4.50	800.0	22.1
79	J57*	5.00	45.00	800.0	22.1
80	279Be°	22.50	200.00	788.9	22.0
81	300b°	22.50	200.00	788.9	22.0
82	526*	2.25	20.00	788.9	22.0
83	J18*	6.75	60.00	788.9	22.0
84	J60*	2.25	20.00	788.9	22.0
85	570*	6.50	57.50	784.6	21.9
86	331a°	4.00	35.00	775.0	21.8
87	332a°	4.00	35.00	775.0	21.8
88	406a°	2.00	17.50	775.0	21.8
89	524*	40.00	350.00	775.0	21.8
90	J49*	2.00	17.50	775.0	21.8
91	504*	.75	6.50	766.7	21.7
92	515*	3.75	32.50	766.7	21.7
93	493°	.35	3.00	757.1	21.6
94	572*	17.50	150.00	757.1	21.6
95	634A°	1.75	15.00	757.1	21.6
96	E13*	1.75	15.00	757.1	21.6
97	J23*	.35	3.00	757.1	21.6
98	J75*	3.50	30.00	757.1	21.6
99	111°	500.00	4250.00	750.0	21.5
100	462a*	1.00	8.50	750.0	21.5

1 - Annual compound increase in percent

* unused ° used

100 LEADING STAMPS
(1 yr.) PERCENT INCREASE 1980 vs. 1979

Rank	Scott No.	1979 Price	1980 Price	% increase
1	1590a°	.03	5.00	16566.7
2	1590a*	.18	15.00	8233.3
3	1623c*	2.00	50.00	2400.0
4	1623b*	.26	1.00	284.6
5	J71*	.60	2.00	233.3
6	J69*	.50	1.50	200.0
7	O90*	.75	2.25	200.0
8	QE4*	7.50	22.50	200.0
9	393°	1.75	4.50	157.1
10	518*	35.00	90.00	157.1
11	J46*	1.75	4.50	157.1
12	633*	.50	1.25	150.0
13	J38*	.60	1.50	150.0
14	J53*	2.00	5.00	150.0
15	O92*	1.20	3.00	150.0
16	515*	13.50	32.50	140.7
17	528A*	13.50	32.50	140.7
18	O50*	1.25	3.00	140.0
19	J16*	4.25	10.00	135.3
20	O119*	1.50	3.50	133.3
21	547*	140.00	325.00	132.1
22	721*	.80	1.85	131.3
23	E13*	6.50	15.00	130.8
24	C31*	9.25	21.00	127.0
25	523*	400.00	900.00	125.0
26	611*	6.00	13.50	125.0
27	571*	22.50	50.00	122.2
28	E7*	22.50	50.00	122.2
29	J87*	6.75	15.00	122.2
30	J45*	2.50	5.50	120.0
31	301*	3.00	6.50	116.7
32	480*	150.00	325.00	116.7
33	517*	30.00	65.00	116.7
34	O91*	1.50	3.25	116.7
35	O75*	3.25	7.00	115.4
36	568*	8.25	17.50	112.1
37	502*	4.75	10.00	110.5
38	J22*	1.20	2.50	108.3
39	J39*	.60	1.25	108.3
40	J65*	1.20	2.50	108.3
41	417*	7.25	15.00	106.9
42	1*	1000.00	2000.00	100.0
43	300*	2.75	5.50	100.0
44	397*	9.00	18.00	100.0
45	398*	10.00	20.00	100.0
46	504*	3.25	6.50	100.0
47	513*	5.00	10.00	100.0
48	524*	175.00	350.00	100.0
49	567*	10.00	20.00	100.0
50	65*	12.50	25.00	100.0
51	700*	10.00	20.00	100.0
52	701*	30.00	60.00	100.0
53	J15*	5.50	11.00	100.0
54	J25*	3.75	7.50	100.0
55	J40*	3.00	6.00	100.0
56	J41*	3.00	6.00	100.0
57	J56*	5.00	10.00	100.0
58	J60*	10.00	20.00	100.0
59	J63*	1.00	2.00	100.0
60	J64*	1.00	2.00	100.0
61	J66*	5.00	10.00	100.0
62	J70*	.50	1.00	100.0
63	J73*	3.00	6.00	100.0
64	O16*	1.50	3.00	100.0
65	O88*	2.50	5.00	100.0
66	J67*	6.50	12.50	92.3
67	C15*	1100.00	2100.00	90.9
68	479*	225.00	425.00	88.9
69	506*	4.50	8.50	88.9
70	O20*	4.50	8.50	88.9
71	234*	40.00	75.00	87.5
72	514*	16.00	30.00	87.5
73	569*	16.00	30.00	87.5
74	573*	200.00	375.00	87.5
75	J74*	4.00	7.50	87.5
76	O73*	4.00	7.50	87.5
77	C13*	375.00	700.00	86.7
78	C14*	750.00	1400.00	86.7
79	516*	17.50	32.50	85.7
80	O38*	3.50	6.50	85.7
81	O74*	1.75	3.25	85.7
82	636*	1.35	2.50	85.2
83	637*	1.35	2.50	85.2
84	638*	1.35	2.50	85.2
85	639*	1.35	2.50	85.2
86	640*	1.35	2.50	85.2
87	641*	1.35	2.50	85.2
88	C1*	67.50	125.00	85.2
89	J49*	9.50	17.50	84.2
90	564*	3.00	5.50	83.3
91	699*	4.50	8.25	83.3
92	J31*	3.00	5.50	83.3
93	O55*	6.00	11.00	83.3
94	PR122*	3.00	5.50	83.3
95	PR123*	3.00	5.50	83.3
96	308*	11.00	20.00	81.8
97	552*	1.10	2.00	81.8
98	643°	.55	1.00	81.8
99	693*	2.75	5.00	81.8
100	E18*	2.75	5.00	81.8

* unused ° used

HOW TO USE STAMPS & STORIES

On this unique journey through the pages of our history, postage stamps are your guide. Illustrated stories of the famous people and events shown on stamps recreate the building of a nation from its founding to the present day.

The book also includes a color catalogue of postage stamps of the United States. This illustrated catalogue lists current market values and gives useful information that will help you to identify your stamps. Every stamp is listed chronologically by Scott catalogue number and each listing contains the following:

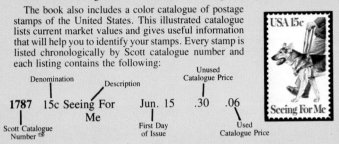

Scott Catalogue Number	Denomination	Description	First Day of Issue	Unused Catalogue Price	Used Catalogue Price
1787	15c	Seeing For Me	Jun. 15	.30	.06

USA 15c Seeing For Me

The catalogue also lists philatelic details such as watermarks, perforations, and years of issue. These will aid you in identifying stamps of similar design. Watermarks (Wmk.) are designs incorporated in the paper on which certain stamps are printed. Perforations are the number of small holes in a two centimeter space on the edge of a stamp. A stamp which has 12 such holes is listed as Perf. 12 (perforated 12), while a stamp with no perforations is listed as Imperf. (imperforate). Coil stamps are perforated on two sides only, either horizontally or vertically. **When a perforation, year of issue, or watermark is mentioned the description applies to all succeeding issues until a change is noted.**

All philatelic terms mentioned in the text are defined in the glossary. In addition, the book includes information about different types of early stamp designs. This material provides an interesting avenue of exploration for those who like the challenge of a mental puzzler.

Illustration Numbers

Some of the stamps catalogued in this book are not shown. The illustrations on such stamps are identified by a number in parenthesis. For example, in the listings which appear below Scott No. 247 has the same illustration as Scott No. 246.

246	1c	Franklin	7.50	1.25
247	1c	blue Franklin (246)	15.00	.75

How to Order Stamps

When ordering stamps from a dealer, identify items wanted by country of issue, Scott No., and condition (unused or used).

Condition is an important factor of price. Prices are for stamps in fine condition. Off center, heavily cancelled, faded or stained stamps usually sell at large discounts. Values in italics indicate latest auction prices, infrequent sales, or fluctuating market values.

COMMEMORATIVE AND DEFINITIVE POSTAGE STAMPS

GEORGE WASHINGTON

The first president of the United States was born in a brick farmhouse in Virginia, a subject of the British Crown. By the age of sixteen he was an accomplished surveyor earned the substantial sum of $7.20 a day. At 22 he was in the militia, a lieutenant colonel fighting alongside the British in the French and Indian Wars. He resigned his commission in 1758 and was a country gentleman for the next seventeen years. But during those years, relations between England and the colonists grew bitter. Washington came out of retirement in 1775 when the second Continental Congress elected him Commander in Chief of a yet-to-be-formed Continental Army.

He took command of the troops in July, forced the British to evacuate Boston in March of 1776 - and then lost and lost and lost. An expedition against Canada failed. New York fell. His troops were chased across New Jersey. They halted in December on the banks of the Delaware River, and it looked as if the British would deal them a death blow there. But Washington and his men rowed across the river under cover of darkness on Christmas night, surprise-attacked the enemy, captured 900 Hessians in the Battle of Trenton—and the first major turning point of the Revolution was reached at last.

In 1789, six years after Washington won the war, the electoral college unanimously named him United States president. As the first president of a new nation, he was forced to decide momentous questions without reference to anything but his own best judgement. Looking back from the perspective of two centuries, it is clear he decided them with infinite wisdom.

Portraits of George Washington consistently appear on United States stamps.

1

2

3

4

Issues of 1847 to 1894 are Unwatermarked
Issue of 1847, Imperf.

1	5c	Benjamin Franklin	Jul. 1	2000.00	475.00
2	10c	George Washington	Jul. 1	*11,000.00*	1300.00

Issue of 1875, Reproductions of 1 & 2

Actually, official imitations made from new plates by order of the Post Office Department. Issued without gum.

3	5c	Franklin	900.00
4	10c	Washington	1200.00

Reproductions. The letters R. W. H. & E. at the bottom of each stamp are less distinct on the reproductions than on the originals.

5c. On the original the left side of the white shirt frill touches the oval on a level with the top of the "F" of "Five." On the reproduction it touches the oval about on a level with the top of the figure "5."

10c. On the reproduction, line of coat at left points to right of "X" and line of coat at right points to center of "S" of CENTS. On the original, line of coat points to "T" of TEN and between "T" and "S" of CENTS. On the reproduction the eyes have a sleepy look, the line of the mouth is straighter, and in the curl of hair near the left cheek is a strong black dot, while the original has only a faint one.

Issue of 1851-56, Imperf.

5	1c	Franklin, type I	*70,000.00*	*12,000.00*
5A	1c	Same, type Ib	*5500.00*	*1350.00*

Nos. 6-9: Franklin (5)

6	1c	dark blue, type Ia	*7250.00*	*2000.00*
7	1c	blue, type II	300.00	55.00
8	1c	blue, type III	*2850.00*	750.00
8A	1c	pale blue, type IIIA	850.00	375.00
9	1c	blue, type IV	185.00	45.00
10	3c	orange brown Washington, type I (11)	750.00	40.00
11	3c	Washington, type I	70.00	4.50
12	5c	Jefferson, type I	4250.00	650.00
13	10c	green Washington, type I (15)	3750.00	400.00

1c Franklin Types I-IV of 1851-56

Detail of **5** Type I
Has curved, unbroken lines outside labels.
Scrollwork is complete, forms little balls at bottom.

Detail of 5A Type Ib
Lower scrollwork is incomplete, the little balls are not so clear.

Detail of **6** Type Ia
Top ornaments and outer line partly cut away.
Lower scrollwork is complete.

5

Detail of **8** Type III
Outer lines broken in the middle.
Side ornaments are complete.

Detail of **8A** Type IIIa
Outer lines broken top or bottom but not both.

Detail of **9** Type IV
Outer lines recut top, bottom, or both.

Detail of **7** Type II
Lower scrollwork incomplete (lacks little balls).
Side ornaments are complete.

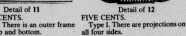

Detail of **11**
THREE CENTS.
Type I. There is an outer frame line at top and bottom.

Detail of **12**
FIVE CENTS.
Type I. There are projections on all four sides.

BENJAMIN FRANKLIN

Benjamin Franklin was the youngest son of a youngest son of a youngest son of a youngest son. His father, a Boston candlemaker, was superstitious. He figured Ben must be special. So he sent him to school for three years, which was more schooling than Ben's nine brothers ever had. At the age of twelve, Ben went to work as a printer's apprentice. He moved to Philadelphia, and by the time he was 24 he owned a printshop, a newspaper and a general store. But busy as he was, Franklin was always working on new ideas.

He formed the first circulating library in America and helped set up Philadelphia's fire department. He invented a stepladder stool, a windmill to turn the roasting spit, a lightning rod, a rocking chair with a self-activating fan, and a kind of stove that's still popular today - the Franklin stove. He published "Poor Richard's Almanack," full of wit and wisdom, and it sold like hotcakes for 25 years. When he was made Postmaster General, he cut the delivery time between Boston and Philadelphia from six weeks to six days. Then he went to London on a diplomatic mission that lasted eighteen years. But feelings between England and American went from bad to worse. Franklin was on his way home in 1775 when the Revolution began.

He was appointed to the Continental Congress and helped write the Declaration of Independence. He went to France and talked the French into entering the war on America's side. When peace came, he helped write the treaty. And at age 82, he helped write the Constitution of the United States. Franklin's father had been right: he *was* special!

Portraits of Benjamin Franklin consistently appear on United States stamps.

10c Washington Types I-IV of 1855

Detail of **13**
Type I. The "shells" at the lower corners are practically complete. The outer line below the label is very nearly complete. The outer lines are broken above the middle of the top label and the "X" in each upper corner.

Detail of **14**
Type II. The design is complete at the top. The outer line at the bottom is broken in the middle. The shells are partly cut away.

15

Detail of **15**
Type III. The outer lines are broken above the top label and the "X" numerals. The outer line at the bottom and the shells are partly cut away, as in Type II.

Detail of **16**
Type IV. The outer lines have been recut at top or bottom or both.
Types I, II, III and IV have complete ornaments at the sides of the stamps and three pearls at each outer edge of the bottom panel.

Detail of 24
ONE CENT
FRANKLIN
Type V. Similar to type III of 1851-56 but with side ornaments partly cut away.

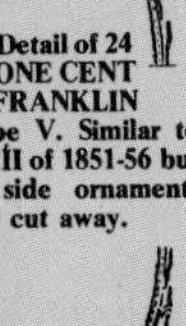

Detail of 26
THREE CENTS WASHINGTON
Type II. The outer frame line has been removed at top and bottom. The side frame lines were recut so as to be continuous from the top to the bottom of the plate.

Detail of 35
TEN CENTS
WASHINGTON
(Two typical examples).
Type V. Side ornaments slightly cut away. Outer lines complete except over right X.

Detail of 30A
FIVE CENTS JEFFERSON
Type II. The projections at top and bottom are partly cut away.

17

30A

38

39

45

No.	Description	Unused	Used
14	10c green, type II (15)	750.00	160.00
15	10c Washington, type III	725.00	150.00
16	10c green, type IV (15)	*5250.00*	800.00
17	12c Washington	900.00	125.00

Issue of 1857-61, Perf. 15

Nos. 18-24: Franklin (5)

No.	Description	Unused	Used
18	1c blue, type I	425.00	225.00
19	1c blue, type Ia	*4750.00*	1150.00
20	1c blue, type II	265.00	67.50
21	1c blue, type III	1600.00	525.00
22	1c blue, type IIIa	325.00	100.00
23	1c blue, type IV	1000.00	140.00
24	1c blue, type V	62.50	15.00

Nos. 25-26: Washington (11)

No.	Description	Unused	Used
25	3c rose, type I	375.00	15.00
26	3c dull red, type II	25.00	2.00

Nos. 27-29: Jefferson (12)

No.	Description	Unused	Used
27	5c brick red, type I	3500.00	475.00
28	5c red brown, type I	950.00	135.00
28A	5c Indian red, type I	*5000.00*	550.00
29	5c brown, type I	450.00	90.00
30	5c orange brown Jefferson, type II (30A)	400.00	525.00
30A	5c Jefferson, type II	235.00	62.50

Nos. 31-35: Washington (15)

No.	Description	Unused	Used
31	10c green, type I	2600.00	275.00
32	10c green, type II	700.00	75.00
33	10c green, type III	650.00	70.00
34	10c green, type IV	*6500.00*	600.00
35	10c green, type V	95.00	35.00
36	12c black Washington (17)	165.00	45.00
37	24c Washington	375.00	135.00
38	30c Franklin	450.00	195.00
39	90c Washington	800.00	1500.00
	90c Same, with pen cancel	——	450.00

Note: Beware of forged cancellations of No. 39. Genuine cancellations are rare.

1875: Government Reprints, Perf. 12

White Paper, Without Gum

No.	Description	Unused
40	1c bright blue Franklin (5)	*350.00*
41	3c scarlet Washington (11)	*2000.00*
42	5c orange brown Jefferson (30A)	*575.00*
43	10c blue green Washington (15)	*1500.00*
44	12c greenish black Washington (17)	*1650.00*
45	24c blackish violet Washington (37)	*1750.00*
46	30c yel. org. Franklin (38)	*1850.00*
47	90c deep blue Washington (39)	*3000.00*

Issue of 1861, Perf. 12

Following the outbreak of the Civil War, the U.S. Government demonetized all previous issues.

No.	Description	Unused	Used
55	1c Franklin	*16,000.00*	
56	3c Washington	400.00	
57	5c brown Jefferson	*10,000.00*	
58	10c Washington	*2500.00*	
59	12c Washington	*32,500.00*	
60	24c dk. vio. Washington (70)	*2750.00*	
61	30c red org. Franklin (71)	*13,000.00*	
62	90c dull blue Washington (72)	*17,000.00*	
62B	10c dark green Washington (58)	*2500.00*	*350.00*

Nos. 55-62 were not used for postage and do not exist in a cancelled state. The paper they were printed on is thin and semi-transparent, that of the following issues is more opaque.

Issue of 1861

Detail of 55

55

Detail of 56

56

57

Detail of 57

58

Detail of 58

59

Detail of 62

62

THOMAS JEFFERSON 1743-1826

In an age that produced many remarkable men, Thomas Jefferson was outstanding. Best known as a great President and the author of the Declaration of Independence, Jefferson's interests were many and his talents were varied. An eminent architect, he designed the new Virginia capitol at Richmond, the beautiful University of Virginia, and his own unique home, Monticello. Even his gardens were among the finest in America; he is credited with growing out first tomato plants. He knew foreign and classical languages, founded his state's university (1819), devised the decimal system of coinage, and still found time to play the violin in chamber music concerts.

Given the choice, Jefferson would have chosen to spend his life in pursuit of his varied interests. He preferred a modest life with his family, friends and books rather than politics, which he regarded as the "shackles of power." But his country needed him time and again, and he always answered the call. He drafted the Declaration of Independence and the Bill of Rights. He served as minister to France, Secretary of State, Vice President and, finally, President of the United States.

During his administration, 1801-1809, the new nation prospered and expanded. A war with Tripoli, 1801-1805, to end piratical attacks on American shipping, gained foreign respect for the American flag. The Lewis and Clark expedition, 1803-1805, reached the Oregon Territory, and Zebulon Pike explored the Rocky Mountains. The purchase of the Louisiana Territory from France in 1803 doubled the size of the United States.

Jefferson was devoted to the principles of freedom, which he believed were derived from the doctrines of natural law and natural rights. All men, he wrote in the Declaration of Independence, are endowed with "the right to life, liberty, and the pursuit of happiness."

Because he cherished man's inherent rights, Jefferson fought every form of tyranny. When laws deprived individuals of the opportunity to secure these ends, Jefferson advocated a change in the laws. Laws, he said, should be made by those required to obey them.

Jefferson had confidence in self-government and the necessity of a well-educated citizenry to successfully maintain it. To perpetuate democracy, he insisted on a free press and free public education for all.

Jefferson died on July 4, 1826. He asked that his tombstone be inscribed with these simple words:

> "Here was buried Thomas Jefferson, author of the Declaration of American Independence, of the statute of Virginia for religious freedom, and father of the University of Virginia."

Portraits of Thomas Jefferson consistently appear on United States stamps.

PATRICK HENRY 1736-1799

His fearless and stirring eloquence earned Patrick Henry of Virginia a reputation as a great colonial orator. He expressed the feelings of the colonists in fiery words as they prepared to fight for independence. With impassioned fervor he declared that a king who vetoes laws enacted by a colonial legislature "degenerates into a tyrant and forfeits all right to his subjects' obedience."

A leader in the Virginia House of Burgesses, Henry demanded that colonists be given the same rights as Englishmen. He also advocated the right of the colonies to legislate independently of the British Parliament. In his denunciation of the infamous Stamp Act of 1765, he lashed out at British tyranny. When critics called him a traitor to his king, he is said to have responded, "If this be treason, make the most of it."

As the time of the Revolution drew near, Patrick Henry continued to be one of the most influential leaders. In 1775, pressing for a break with the king of England and for armed resistance against the British forces, Henry answered his opponents by crying, "I know not what course others may take, but as for me, give me liberty or give me death!"

As Virginia's governor during the early uncertain years of the Revolution (1776-1778) he used his office to aid the rebel cause in the fight for liberty. Even after independence was won, Henry pursued the ideals of individual freedom. He opposed the ratification of the new Constitution because he feared it would curb the rights of both the individual and the states. The addition of the Bill of Rights to the Constitution as a basic guarantee of individual liberties is due largely to the efforts of Patrick Henry.

After the Constitution was adopted, Patrick Henry retired from public life, returning to the peace and quiet of his Virginia plantation. In 1799, however, he was again elected to the Virginia legislative assembly, but before he could take his seat this dedicated freedom fighter died.

See Scott Nos. 1052, 1144

Issue of 1861-62

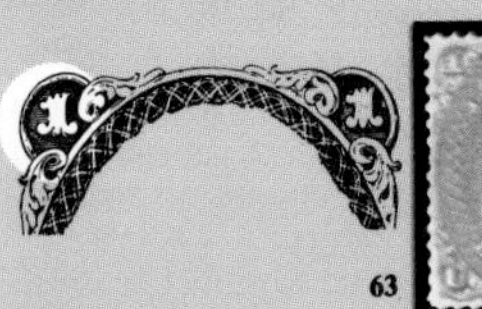

63

64

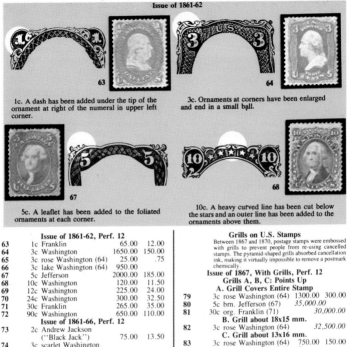

1c. A dash has been added under the tip of the ornament at right of the numeral in upper left corner.

3c. Ornaments at corners have been enlarged and end in a small ball.

67

68

5c. A leaflet has been added to the foliated ornaments at each corner.

10c. A heavy curved line has been cut below the stars and an outer line has been added to the ornaments above them.

Issue of 1861-62, Perf. 12

No.	Description	Unused	Used
63	1c Franklin	65.00	12.00
64	3c Washington	1650.00	150.00
65	3c rose Washington (64)	25.00	.75
66	3c lake Washington (64)	950.00	
67	5c Jefferson	2000.00	185.00
68	10c Washington	120.00	11.50
69	12c Washington	225.00	24.00
70	24c Washington	300.00	32.50
71	30c Franklin	265.00	35.00
72	90c Washington	650.00	110.00

Issue of 1861-66, Perf. 12

No.	Description	Unused	Used
73	2c Andrew Jackson ("Black Jack")	75.00	13.50
74	3c scarlet Washington (64)	*2500.00*	
75	5c red brown Jefferson (67)	650.00	110.00
76	5c brn. Jefferson (67)	150.00	25.00
77	15c Abraham Lincoln	300.00	35.00
78	24c lilac Washington (70)	120.00	20.00

No. 74 was not regularly issued.

Grills on U.S. Stamps

Between 1867 and 1870, postage stamps were embossed with grills to prevent people from re-using cancelled stamps. The pyramid-shaped grills absorbed cancellation ink, making it virtually impossible to remove a postmark chemically.

Issue of 1867, With Grills, Perf. 12

Grills A, B, C: Points Up

A. Grill Covers Entire Stamp

No.	Description	Unused	Used
79	3c rose Washington (64)	1300.00	300.00
80	5c brn. Jefferson (67)	*35,000.00*	
81	30c org. Franklin (71)		*30,000.00*

B. Grill about 18x15 mm.

No.	Description	Unused	Used
82	3c rose Washington (64)		*32,500.00*

C. Grill about 13x16 mm.

No.	Description	Unused	Used
83	3c rose Washington (64)	750.00	150.00

Grills, D, Z, E, F: Points Down

D. Grill about 12x14 mm.

No.	Description	Unused	Used
84	2c blk. Jackson (73)	1250.00	425.00
85	3c rose Washington (64)	600.00	135.00

Z. Grill about 11x14 mm.

No.	Description	Unused	Used
85A	1c bl. Franklin (63)		*90,000.00*
85B	2c blk, Jackson (73)	600.00	140.00

CIVIL WAR: NEW STAMPS CREATED

When the Southern states declared their independence in 1860 and 1861, the Confederacy had in its possession a fortune in U.S. postage stamps. The U.S. Post Office had to prevent the stamps that remained in Southern post offices from being sent North and converted into cash that could be used to purchase bullets for Rebel guns. So, in the summer of 1861, U.S. Postmaster General Montgomery Blair announced that the existing stamps would no longer be valid. Blair "demonetized" the stamps, turning them into worthless bits of paper. At the same time he replaced the old stamps with a complete new issue. Post offices and citizens were instructed to exchange the old, demonetized stamps for new ones. The old stamps were phased out as quickly as the new ones could be designed, printed and distributed. And by January 1, 1862, not a single U.S. stamp more than a few months old could be used as postage anywhere in the Union.

See Scott Nos. 63-73

69

12c. Ovals and scrolls have been added to the corners.

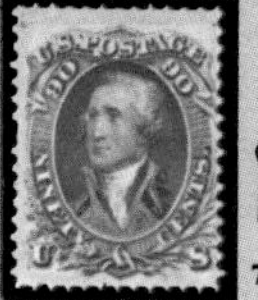
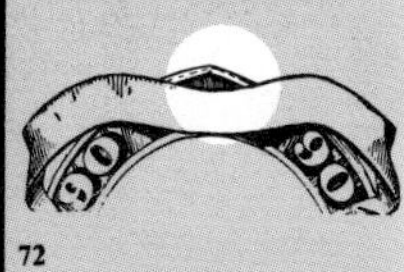
72

90c. Parallel lines form an angle above the ribbon with "U. S. Postage"; between these lines a row of dashes has been added and a point of color to the apex of the lower pair.

70

71

73

77

Grill

85C	3c rose Washington (64)	1500.00	325.00
85D	10c green Washington (68)		*22,000.00*
85E	12c black Washington (69)	850.00	250.00
85F	15c blk. Lincoln (77)		*30,000.00*

E. Grill about 11x13 mm.

86	1c blue Franklin (63)	350.00	90.00
87	2c black Jackson (73)	150.00	30.00
88	3c rose Washington (64)	95.00	4.00
89	10c grn. Washington (68)	600.00	75.00
90	12c blk. Washington (69)	650.00	75.00
91	15c black Lincoln (77)	1300.00	175.00

F. Grill about 9x13 mm.

92	1c blue Franklin (63)	135.00	35.00
93	2c black Jackson (73)	65.00	12.50
94	3c red Washington (64)	40.00	2.00
95	5c brown Jefferson (67)	450.00	100.00
96	10c yellow green Washington (68)	265.00	37.50
97	12c black Washington (69)	285.00	40.00
98	15c black Lincoln (77)	300.00	42.50
99	24c gray lilac Washington (70)	650.00	200.00
100	30c orange Franklin (71)	775.00	140.00
101	90c blue Washington (72)	1700.00	450.00

Reissues of 1875—Without Grill, Perf. 12

102	1c blue Franklin (63)	*275.00*	*400.00*
103	2c black Jackson (73)	*1650.00*	*2000.00*
104	3c brown red Washington (64)	*2000.00*	*2500.00*
105	5c brown Jefferson (67)	*1100.00*	*1100.00*
106	10c grn. Washington (68)	*1450.00*	*1750.00*
107	12c blk. Washington (69)	*2000.00*	*2300.00*
108	15c black Lincoln (77)	*2000.00*	*2300.00*
109	24c deep violet Washington (70)	*2300.00*	*2500.00*
110	30c brownish orange Franklin (71)	*2850.00*	*3000.00*
111	90c blue Washington (72)	*3600.00*	*4250.00*

112 113 114 115 116 117 118 120 121 122

FIFTY-FOUR CENTS TO $101,500

What makes a 30¢ stamp worth $29,000? Its rarity. Some of the rarest stamps—and, therefore, some of the most valuable—are stamps with printing errors. The first 30¢ U. S. pictorials issued in 1869, included some stamps printed with inverted flag. Over the years, one of these upside-down stamps passed through several collections and ended up in a dealer's stock in Portland, Oregon. But until another dealer chanced upon the stamp in 1930, nobody noticed the printing error! The Scott Number of that stamp is 121b. A used copy of 121b recently sold for $29,000, at a West Coast Auction House.

Probably the most famous U. S. philatelic misprint is the so-called "Inverted Jenny". A single sheet of the 1918 24¢ airmail stamps was printed with the picture of the biplane upside down. What was the latest price paid for a single stamp out of that legendary sheet? $72,500, sold by a New York auction house in 1978.

See Scott Nos. 121b and C3a.

Detail of 118
FIFTEEN CENTS.
Type I. Picture unframed.

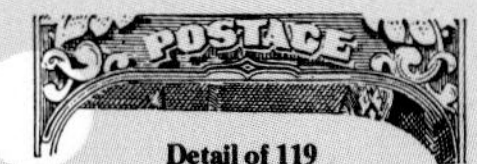

Detail of 119
Type II. Picture framed.
Type III. Same as type I but without fringe of brown shading lines around central vignette.

Issue of 1869, With Grill Measuring 9½x9 mm. Perf. 12

112	1c	Franklin	150.00	37.50
113	2c	Post Horse & Rider	90.00	15.00
114	3c	Locomotive	80.00	3.50
115	6c	Washington	500.00	60.00
116	10c	Shield and Eagle	525.00	65.00
117	12c	S.S. Adriatic	450.00	60.00
118	15c	Columbus Landing, type I	1000.00	150.00
119	15c	brown and blue Columbus Landing, type II (118)	500.00	70.00
119b		Center inverted	*80,000.00*	*10,000.00*
120	24c	Declaration of Independence	*1250.00*	*300.00*
120b		Center inverted	*60,000.00*	*10,000.00*
121	30c	Shield, Eagle and Flags	1100.00	125.00
121b		Flags inverted	*70,000.00*	*30,000.00*
122	90c	Lincoln	4000.00	700.00

Reissues of 1875, Without Grill Hard White Paper, Perf. 12

123	1c	buff (112)	225.00	125.00
124	2c	brown (113)	250.00	200.00
125	3c	blue (114)	2000.00	850.00
126	6c	blue (115)	575.00	300.00
127	10c	yellow (116)	900.00	550.00
128	12c	green (117)	950.00	600.00
129	15c	brown and blue Columbus Landing, type III (118)	900.00	375.00
130	24c	grn. & vio. (120)	900.00	300.00
131	30c	bl. & car. (121)	1200.00	700.00
132	90c	car. & blk. (122)	3000.00	3500.00

Reissues of 1880, Soft, Porous Paper, Perf. 12

133	1c	buff (112)	130.00	110.00

ABRAHAM LINCOLN

Abraham Lincoln was born in backwoods Kentucky in a one-room, dirt-floored log cabin. He moved to Illinois in 1831, clerked in a grocery store and studied law in his spare time. In 1834 he was elected to the Illinois general assembly, and two years later to Congress. Years passed, and the bitter dispute between pro-slavers and Abolitionists became uglier and uglier. By 1857, Lincoln was speaking out brilliantly against the spread of slavery to the new Western territories. In 1860 he was elected president of the United States, then the floodgates burst.

One Southern state after another seceded, declaring its independence. In his inaugural address, Lincoln said the union of states was unbreakable, but the South had made its decision and would not turn back. The war that pitted brother against brother was on. After four long bloody years, the South was beaten. On April 11, 1865, Lincoln told a cheering victory crowd that the South was "safely at home" in the union. Three days later he took his wife to Ford's Theater where the assassin, Booth, awaited him. Lincoln never went safely home again.

Portraits of Abraham Lincoln consistently appear on United States Stamps.

Issue of 1870-71
With Grill, White Wove Paper, Perf. 12

134	1c Franklin	275.00	25.00
135	2c Jackson	175.00	15.00
136	3c Washington	110.00	3.50
137	6c Lincoln	750.00	135.00
138	7c Edwin M. Stanton	575.00	115.00
139	10c Jefferson	850.00	235.00
140	12c Henry Clay	*8500.00*	*1000.00*
141	15c Daniel Webster	950.00	375.00
142	24c General Winfield Scott		*8000.00*
143	30c Alexander Hamilton	2400.00	600.00
144	90c Commodore Perry	3250.00	400.00

Without Grill
White Wove Paper, Perf. 12

145	1c ultra. Franklin (134)	70.00	4.00
146	2c red brn. Jackson (135)	25.00	2.50
147	3c green Washington (136)	40.00	.30
148	6c carmine Lincoln (137)	100.00	5.50
149	7c verm. Stanton (138)	175.00	25.00
150	10c brown Jefferson (139)	95.00	5.50

1873: Printed by the Continental Bank Note Co.

Designs of the 1870-71 Issue with secret marks on the values from 1c to 15c as described and illustrated below.

156

1c. In the pearl at the left of the numeral "1" there is a small crescent.

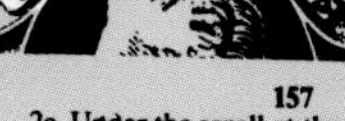

157

2c. Under the scroll at the left of "U. S." there is a small diagonal line. This mark seldom shows clearly. The stamp, No. 157, can be distinguished by its color.

158

3c. The under part of the upper tail of the left ribbon is heavily shaded.

159

6c. The first four vertical lines of the shading in the lower part of the left ribbon have been strengthened.

160

7c. Two small semi-circles are drawn around the ends of the lines which outline the ball in the lower right hand corner.

161

10c. There is a small semi-circle in the scroll at the right end of the upper label.

162

12c. The balls of the figure "2" are crescent shaped.

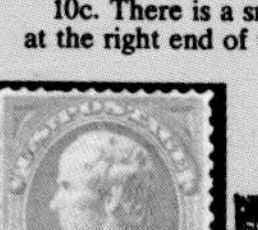

163

15c. In the lower part of the triangle in the upper left corner two lines have been made heavier forming a "V". This mark can be found on some of the Continental and American (1879) printings, but not all stamps show it.

Secret marks were added to the dies of the 24c, 30c and 90c but new plates were not made from them. The various printings of these stamps can be distinguished only by the shades and paper.

151	12c dull violet Clay (140)	300.00	22.50
152	15c bright orange Webster (141)	250.00	25.00
153	24c purple W. Scott (142)	285.00	30.00
154	30c black Hamilton (143)	550.00	50.00
155	90c carmine Perry (144)	625.00	80.00

Issue of 1873, Without Grill, Perf. 12
White Wove Paper, Thin to Thick

156	1c Franklin	25.00	1.10
157	2c Jackson	70.00	3.00
158	3c Washington	13.50	.10
159	6c Lincoln	80.00	4.25
160	7c Stanton	200.00	25.00
161	10c Jefferson	82.50	5.00
162	12c Clay	325.00	30.00
163	15c Webster	275.00	25.00
165	30c Hamilton (143)	285.00	20.00
166	90c Perry (144)	650.00	90.00

It is generally accepted as fact that the Continental Bank Note Co. printed and delivered a quantity of 24c stamps. They are impossible to distinguish from those printed by the National Bank Note Co.

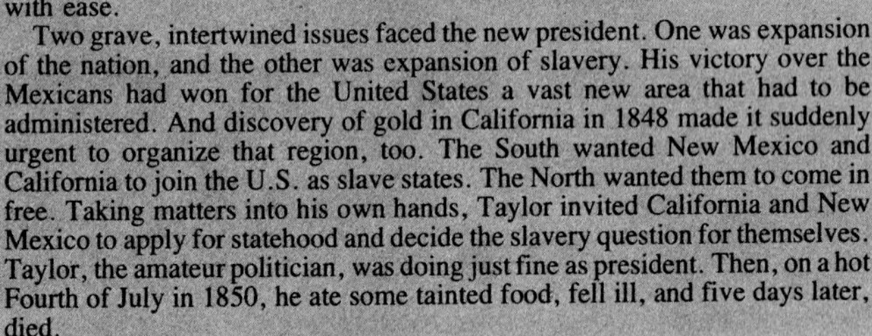

ZACHARY TAYLOR

Zachary Taylor didn't hold a single political post before he was elected president. Yet for sixteen months, he was a surprisingly effective chief executive. Taylor was the son of Virginia aristocrats who decided to strike out for Kentucky and an adventurous new life. Young Zachary grew up in a wilderness settlement, and at 23 joined the army. For forty years he was a career soldier. He commanded the forces that won the Mexican War, and emerged a national hero. In 1848 "Old Rough-and-Ready" Taylor won the presidency with ease.

Two grave, intertwined issues faced the new president. One was expansion of the nation, and the other was expansion of slavery. His victory over the Mexicans had won for the United States a vast new area that had to be administered. And discovery of gold in California in 1848 made it suddenly urgent to organize that region, too. The South wanted New Mexico and California to join the U.S. as slave states. The North wanted them to come in free. Taking matters into his own hands, Taylor invited California and New Mexico to apply for statehood and decide the slavery question for themselves. Taylor, the amateur politician, was doing just fine as president. Then, on a hot Fourth of July in 1850, he ate some tainted food, fell ill, and five days later, died.

See Scott Nos. 179, 181, 204, 817.

Issue of 1875, Special Printing
Hard, White Wove Paper, Without Gum

167	1c ultra. Franklin (156)	*4250.00*	
168	2c dark brown Jackson (157)	*2200.00*	
169	3c blue green Washington (158)	*5500.00*	
170	6c dull rose Lincoln (159)	*5500.00*	
171	7c reddish vermilion Stanton (160)	*1500.00*	
172	10c pale brown Jefferson (161)	*4500.00*	
173	12c dark violet Clay (162)	*1850.00*	
174	15c bright orange Webster (163)	*5000.00*	
175	24c dull purple W. Scott (142)	*1400.00*	
176	30c greenish black Hamilton (143)	*4750.00*	
177	90c violet car. Perry (144)	*4750.00*	

Although perforated, these stamps were usually cut apart with scissors. As a result, the perforations are often much mutilated and the design is frequently damaged.

Yellowish Wove Paper

178	2c vermilion Jackson (157)	Jun. 21	85.00	2.00
179	5c Zachary Taylor	Jun. 21	80.00	5.00

Special Printing
Hard, White Wove Paper, Without Gum

180	2c carmine verm. Jackson (157)	*12,500.00*
181	5c bright blue Taylor (179)	*20,000.00*

Issue of 1879. Printed by the American Bank Note Company. Soft, Porous Paper Varying from Thin to Thick.

182	1c dark ultramarine Franklin (156)	55.00	.75
183	2c vermilion Jackson (157)	25.00	.70
184	3c green Washington (158)	20.00	.08
185	5c blue Taylor (179)	85.00	4.00
186	6c pink Lincoln (159)	300.00	5.50
187	10c brown Jefferson (139) (no secret mark)	350.00	6.50
188	10c brown Jefferson (161) (with secret mark)	200.00	6.50
189	15c red orange Webster (163)	77.50	7.50
190	30c full black Hamilton (143)	225.00	10.00
191	30c carmine Perry (144)	600.00	60.00

Issue of 1880, Special Printing
Soft, Porous Paper, Without Gum

192	1c dark ultramarine Franklin (156)	*6250.00*

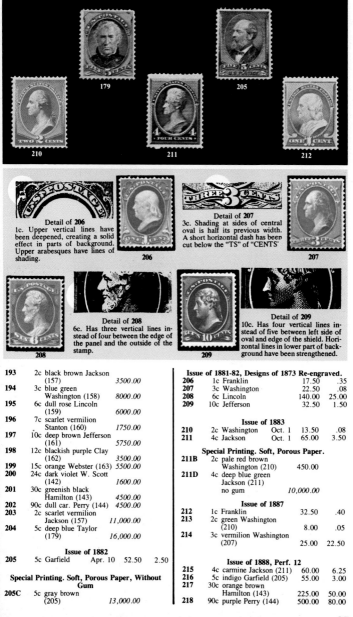

179

210

205

211

212

Detail of 206
1c. Upper vertical lines have been deepened, creating a solid effect in parts of background. Upper arabesques have lines of shading.

206

Detail of 207
3c. Shading at sides of central oval is half its previous width. A short horizontal dash has been cut below the "TS" of "CENTS"

207

208

Detail of 208
6c. Has three vertical lines instead of four between the edge of the panel and the outside of the stamp.

209

Detail of 209
10c. Has four vertical lines instead of five between left side of oval and edge of the shield. Horizontal lines in lower part of background have been strengthened.

193	2c black brown Jackson (157)		*3500.00*
194	3c blue green Washington (158)		*8000.00*
195	6c dull rose Lincoln (159)		*6000.00*
196	7c scarlet vermilion Stanton (160)		*1750.00*
197	10c deep brown Jefferson (161)		*5750.00*
198	12c blackish purple Clay (162)		*3500.00*
199	15c orange Webster (163)		*5500.00*
200	24c dark violet W. Scott (142)		*1600.00*
201	30c greenish black Hamilton (143)		*4500.00*
202	90c dull car. Perry (144)		*4500.00*
203	2c scarlet vermilion Jackson (157)		*11,000.00*
204	5c deep blue Taylor (179)		*16,000.00*

Issue of 1882

205	5c Garfield	Apr. 10	52.50	2.50

Special Printing. Soft, Porous Paper, Without Gum

205C	5c gray brown (205)	*13,000.00*

Issue of 1881-82, Designs of 1873 Re-engraved.

206	1c Franklin	17.50	.35
207	3c Washington	22.50	.08
208	6c Lincoln	140.00	25.00
209	10c Jefferson	32.50	1.50

Issue of 1883

210	2c Washington	Oct. 1	13.50	.08
211	4c Jackson	Oct. 1	65.00	3.50

Special Printing. Soft, Porous Paper.

211B	2c pale red brown Washington (210)	450.00
211D	4c deep blue green Jackson (211) no gum	*10,000.00*

Issue of 1887

212	1c Franklin	32.50	.40
213	2c green Washington (210)	8.00	.05
214	3c vermilion Washington (207)	25.00	22.50

Issue of 1888, Perf. 12

215	4c carmine Jackson (211)	60.00	6.25
216	5c indigo Garfield (205)	55.00	3.00
217	30c orange brown Hamilton (143)	225.00	50.00
218	90c purple Perry (144)	500.00	80.00

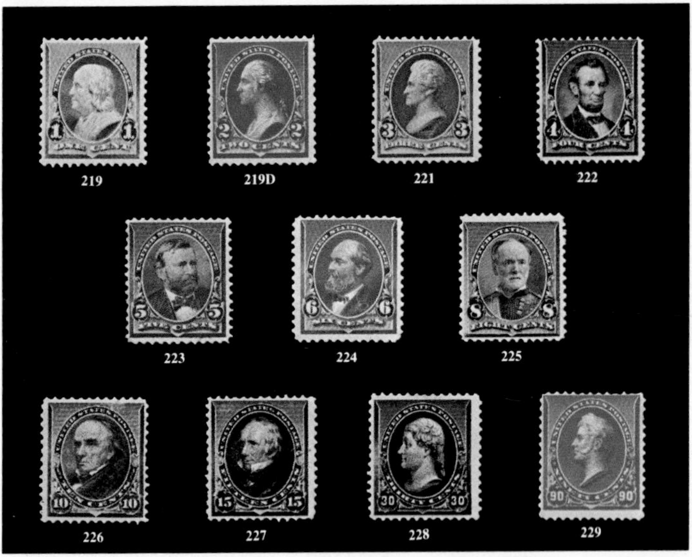

219 219D 221 222
223 224 225
226 227 228 229

Issue of 1890-93, Perf. 12

219	1c	Franklin	11.00	.05
219D	2c	Washington	65.00	.35
220	2c	carmine (219D)	8.50	.05
221	3c	Jackson	37.50	2.00
222	4c	Lincoln	35.00	1.25
223	5c	Ulysses S. Grant	36.00	1.10
224	6c	Garfield	35.00	7.00
225	8c	William T. Sherman	21.00	5.00
226	10c	Webster	67.50	1.00
227	15c	Clay	100.00	11.00
228	30c	Jefferson	135.00	13.00
229	90c	Perry	250.00	52.50

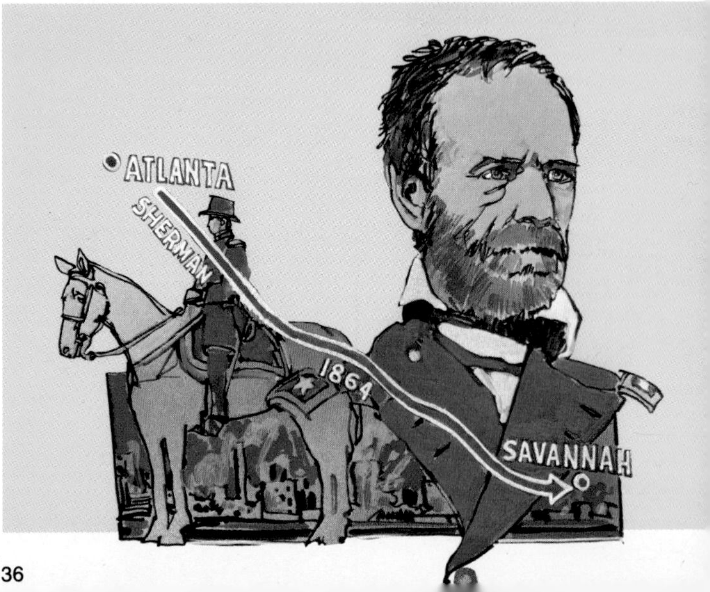

WINFIELD SCOTT

His deeds have been obscured by time, but in his day Winfield Scott was one of America's greatest heroes. And his "day" as a hero lasted over fifty years! Scott was a Virginian who won fame and his general's star for bravery during the War of 1812. He was a good peacemaker, too. In 1838 and 1839, he moved 16,000 Cherokees from the South to reservations west of the Mississippi, made peace with the Indians along the Canadian border, and settled a heated dispute with Great Britain over the boundary line of Maine.

During the Mexican War, Scott commanded a seaborne invasion of Mexico, captured Veracruz, and ended the war by marching into Mexico City in September, 1848. He ran for president in 1852 but lost. At age 74 he was still active as commander of the U.S. Army during the early months of the Civil War. Now glance back, and you'll see that the amazing Winfield Scott held the rank of general in three major American wars!

See Scott Nos. 142, 153, 175, 200, 286

WILLIAM TECUMSEH SHERMAN

Civil War general William Tecumsah Sherman waged a war of destruction that not only beat Southern forces to their knees but devastated Georgia as well. Born in Ohio and educated at West Point, Sherman was considered a disciplinary problem by his teachers; and after graduation in 1840, he found military life a bore. So he resigned his commission, tried banking and the law, and was unsuccessful at both. He rejoined the U.S. Army as a colonel at the start of the Civil War in 1861. After the first Battle of Bull Run he was made a general. But Sherman was so unsure of himself that he begged Lincoln not to give him an independent command. He was put in charge of troops in Kentucky anyway, and behaved so strangely that he was publicly called insane. But all that changed when he met General Ulysses S. Grant.

Serving as a commander under Grant, Sherman fought magnificently. Together, the two captured Vicksburg and smashed the Confederate defenses in 1862-63. Then Grant moved against Confederate general Robert E. Lee in the north, while Sherman took 60,000 troops into Georgia. He conquered Atlanta, cut a bloody path to the sea, and reached the coast in time to offer Lincoln the city of Savannah for Christmas, 1864. Now, as Grant moved to trap Lee in Virginia, Sherman swung north through the Carolinas. The vise tightened, and the Confederacy was doomed. Surprisingly, it was this ruthless fighter who said, "War is Hell."

See Scott Nos. 225, 257, 272, 787

Columbian Exposition Issue, 1893, Perf. 12

230	1c Columbus Sights Land	21.00	.25
231	2c Landing of Columbus	20.00	.06
232	3c The Santa Maria	45.00	10.00
233	4c Fleet of Columbus ultramarine	60.00	4.50
233a	4c blue (error) (233)	*5250.00*	*1800.00*
234	5c Columbus Seeking Aid	75.00	5.00
235	6c Columbus at Barcelona	70.00	12.50
236	8c Columbus Restored to Favor	40.00	6.00
237	10c Columbus Presenting Indians	90.00	5.00

238	15c Columbus Announcing His Discovery	160.00	35.00
239	30c Columbus at La Rabida	240.00	55.00
240	50c Recall of Columbus	300.00	80.00
241	$1 Isabella Pledging Her Jewels	925.00	325.00
242	$2 Columbus in Chains	1000.00	300.00
243	$3 Columbus Describing His Third Voyage	1850.00	550.00
244	$4 Isabella and Columbus	2650.00	825.00
245	$5 Portrait of Columbus	2800.00	900.00

The World's Columbian Exposition was held in Chicago in 1893 to celebrate the 400th anniversary of the discovery of America by Christopher Columbus.

CHRISTOPHER COLUMBUS 1451-1506

The discovery of America was probably the luckiest "accident" in history. Christopher Columbus was excited by the unproved scientific theory that the world was round, not flat. He was convinced that by sailing West (around the globe) instead of East (across vast oceans frequented by enemy navies) he would find a shorter and safer travelling route to the rich trading grounds in the Orient. After a frustrating search for funds to finance his voyage, Queen Isabella of Spain finally agreed to sponsor him. She supplied him with a crew and three small ships.

Columbus set sail on August 3, 1492. While nature was cooperative, providing calm seas and gentle winds, the crew was not. The men, plagued by superstition and fear, thought they would never get home alive and threatened mutiny. Columbus believed his voyage was guided by divine inspiration, and did not want to turn back. On October 10, he promised his panicky crew that if land was not found within three days, he would return to Spain. On the morning of October 12, 1492, an island, which Columbus named San Salvador, was sighted. He was certain he had found the Orient.

People continue to call the natives Indians and the islands he first reached, the West Indies. He never realized he had found the new world. He pursued his explorations, hoping to find Peking so that he could present a letter from Ferdinand and Isabella to the emperor of China.

Columbus returned in triumph with promise of new riches and glory for Spain. He believed that God meant him to make great discoveries in order to spread Christianity. He made three more voyages to colonize and further explore the islands he had found.

Columbus was a man of great vision and skill who relentlessly pursued his goal in life against tremendous obstacles. Although he found America by chance, the world owes him a great debt.

See Scott Nos. 118, 230–245

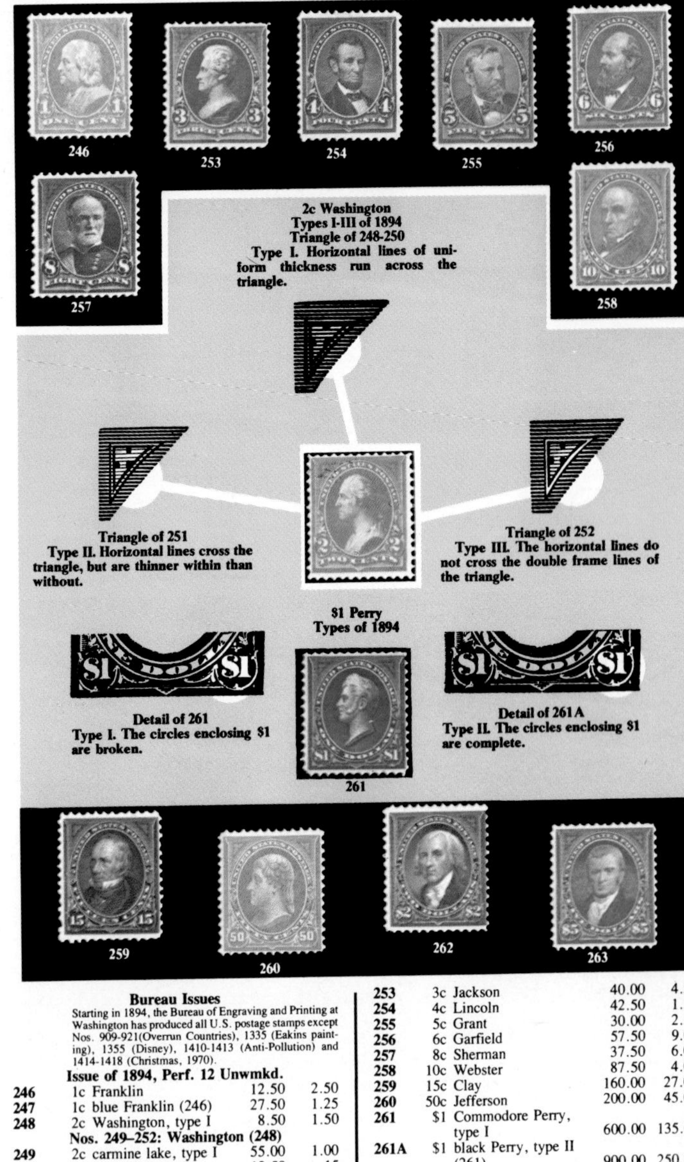

246
253
254
255
256
257
258
2c Washington
Types I-III of 1894
Triangle of 248-250
Type I. Horizontal lines of uniform thickness run across the triangle.
Triangle of 251
Type II. Horizontal lines cross the triangle, but are thinner within than without.
Triangle of 252
Type III. The horizontal lines do not cross the double frame lines of the triangle.
$1 Perry
Types of 1894
Detail of 261
Type I. The circles enclosing $1 are broken.
Detail of 261A
Type II. The circles enclosing $1 are complete.
261
259
260
262
263

Bureau Issues

Starting in 1894, the Bureau of Engraving and Printing at Washington has produced all U.S. postage stamps except Nos. 909-921(Overrun Countries), 1335 (Eakins painting), 1355 (Disney), 1410-1413 (Anti-Pollution) and 1414-1418 (Christmas, 1970).

Issue of 1894, Perf. 12 Unwmkd.

246	1c Franklin	12.50	2.50
247	1c blue Franklin (246)	27.50	1.25
248	2c Washington, type I	8.50	1.50
	Nos. 249–252: Washington (248)		
249	2c carmine lake, type I	55.00	1.00
250	2c carmine, type I	12.50	.15
251	2c carmine, type II	110.00	2.00
252	2c carmine, type III	45.00	2.00
253	3c Jackson	40.00	4.50
254	4c Lincoln	42.50	1.35
255	5c Grant	30.00	2.50
256	6c Garfield	57.50	9.00
257	8c Sherman	37.50	6.00
258	10c Webster	87.50	4.00
259	15c Clay	160.00	27.00
260	50c Jefferson	200.00	45.00
261	$1 Commodore Perry, type I	600.00	135.00
261A	$1 black Perry, type II (261)	900.00	250.00
262	$2 James Madison	1150.00	275.00
263	$5 John Marshall	2300.00	650.00

TEN CENTS.

Type I. The tips of the foliate ornaments do not impinge on the white curved line below "TEN CENTS."

Type II. The tips of the ornaments break the curved line below the "E" of "TEN" and the "T" of "CENTS."

Wmkd. USPS (191)

Issue of 1895, Perf. 12

264	1c blue Franklin (246)	3.25	.06
	Nos. 265-267: Washington (248)		
265	2c carmine, type I	13.50	.30
266	2c carmine, type II	16.50	1.25
267	2c carmine, type III	2.25	.05
268	3c purple Jackson (253)	15.00	.65
269	4c dk. brown Lincoln (254)	15.00	.65
270	5c chocolate Grant (255)	15.00	1.10
271	6c dull brn. Garfield (256)	35.00	2.50
272	8c vio. brn. Sherman (257)	12.50	.60
273	10c dk. green Webster (258)	28.50	1.00
274	15c dark blue Clay (259)	100.00	5.00
275	50c orange Jefferson (260)	140.00	11.00
276	$1 black Perry, type I (261)	425.00	30.00
276A	$1 blk. Perry, type II (261)	800.00	65.00
277	$2 brt. blue Madison (262)	600.00	150.00
278	$5 dk. grn. Marshall (263)	1200.00	190.00

Issue of 1898, Perf. 12

279	1c dp. green Franklin (246)	5.00	.06
279B	2c red Washington, type III (248)	4.50	.05
279Be	Booklet pane of 6	350.00	*200.00*
280	4c rose brn. Lincoln (254)	13.50	.70
281	5c dark blue Grant (255)	15.00	.50
282	6c lake Garfield (256)	20.00	1.50
282C	10c Webster, type I	75.00	1.50
283	10c Webster, type II	55.00	1.25
284	15c olive green Clay (259)	65.00	4.25

JAMES MADISON 1751-1836

War clouds hung over the young nation when James Madison became the fourth President in 1809. America's maritime rights were being violated by Great Britain. Ships at sea were being stopped and searched and American seamen pressed into foreign service. Anxious to avoid war, Madison attempted negotiation and peaceful coercion, but the British continued the attacks.

No longer willing to tolerate these insults to its sovereignty, the United States declared war on Great Britain in 1812. For almost three years the war raged on. In 1814 the British invaded Washington, burned the White House and made Madison the only President ever forced to flee to avoid capture. The successful outcome of the War of 1812, often called the second war for independence, established worldwide respect for American sovereignty.

During Madion's presidency, the United States grew considerably with the addition of the states of Louisiana (1812) and Indiana (1816) and the new territories of Missouri (1812) and Alabama (1817).

James Madison loved his country and devoted his life to public service. He was active in the Revolution and served in the Continental Congress. Known as "The Father of the Constitution," he played a prominent role in drafting the document and was largely responsible for its ratification.

See Scott Nos. 312, 479, 808, 843

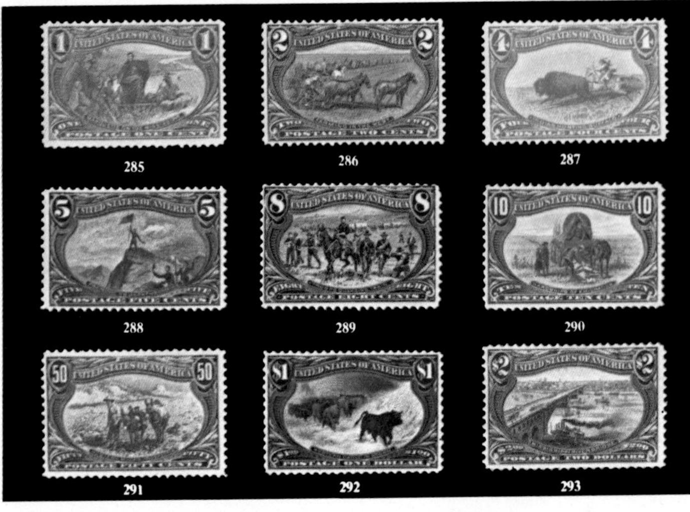

Trans-Mississippi Exposition Issue, Jun. 17
Perf. 12

No.	Denom.	Description	Unused	Used
285	1c	Marquette on the Mississippi	23.00	3.75
286	2c	Farming in the West	22.00	1.00
287	4c	Indian Hunting Buffalo	110.00	14.00
288	5c	Frémont on the Rocky Mountains	90.00	13.50
289	8c	Troops Guarding Train	140.00	25.00
290	10c	Hardships of Emigration	150.00	13.50
291	50c	Western Mining Prospector	575.00	75.00
292	$1	Western Cattle in Storm	1300.00	400.00
293	$2	Mississippi River Bridge at St. Louis	2000.00	575.00

The Trans-Mississippi Exposition was held in Omaha, Nebr. from June 1 to November 1, 1898. For this reason, the stamps in the set have been nicknamed "Omahas."

U.S. CAVALRY

The Arapahos, Cheyennes, Comanches, Kiowas and Katakas were all peacefully settled down on reservations, if you could believe the 1867 Treaty of Medicine Lodge. Trouble was, a lot of braves didn't care for such a quiet life. So they took to raiding pioneer settlements and wagon trains. In 1874, sixty Texans lost their lives to the Indians. Time to send for the Cavalry! That fall, 3,000 Federal troops converged on the Indians in Red River Valley, Texas. Fourteen pitched battles and several months later, the Indians surrendered and quietly returned to the reservations. The U.S. Cavalry had done it again.

See Scott No. 289

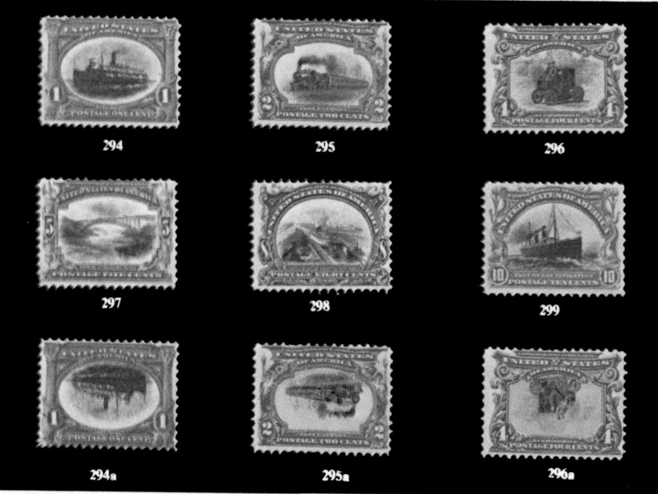

Pan-American Exposition Issue, 1901, May 1

Wmkd. USPS (191)

No.		Description	Unused	Used
294	1c	Great Lakes Steamer	17.50	3.50
294a		Center inverted	*6500.00*	*2000.00*
295	2c	An Early Locomotive	17.50	.75
295a		Center inverted	*30,000.00*	*18,000.00*
296	4c	Closed Coach Automobile	95.00	12.00
296a		Center inverted	*9500.00*	
297	5c	Bridge at Niagara Falls	95.00	12.50
298	8c	Sault Ste. Marie Canal Locks	120.00	35.00
299	10c	American Line Steamship	165.00	17.50

The Pan-American Exposition was held in Buffalo, N.Y., in 1901. It stressed engineering progress in the Western hemisphere in the nineteenth century.

NIAGARA

Niagara Falls, known for its beauty and splendor, is one of the world's greatest natural wonders. Actually there are two falls, the larger Canadian Horseshoe Falls and the smaller American Falls. Every minute, about 380,000 tons of water cascade over the cliffs, filling the air with a silvery mist.

Many daring and unique ways have been used to ride over the falls. Some have attempted the trip in a barrel; An acrobat even stretched a tightrope across the gorge and walked over.

The safer and more conventional way, however, is to use one of the Falls' many bridges. The first bridge, finished in 1848, was only a footbridge. A suspension bridge, designed by Augustus Roebling, was opened in 1855. The Cantilever Bridge, in 1883, spanned the gorge above the whirlpool. The famous Rainbow Bridge, completed in 1941, spans the river and joins Niagara Falls, N.Y. with Niagara Falls, Ontario. The bridge spans the longest unguarded border in world history and symbolizes the good will, friendship and peace existing between the United States and Canada.

See Scott Nos. 297, 568, 699, 961, 1721

AMERICAN FALLS

HORSESHOE FALLS

Regular Issue of 1902-03

Wmkd USPS (191)

Perf. 12

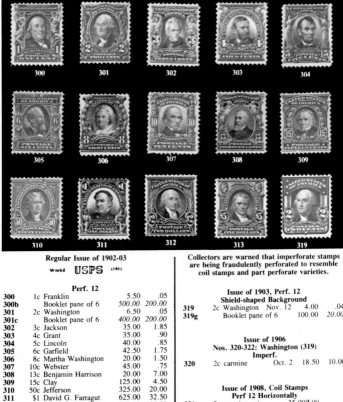

No.	Description	Unused	Used
300	1c Franklin	5.50	.05
300b	Booklet pane of 6	*500.00*	*200.00*
301	2c Washington	6.50	.05
301c	Booklet pane of 6	*400.00*	*200.00*
302	3c Jackson	35.00	1.85
303	4c Grant	35.00	.90
304	5c Lincoln	40.00	.85
305	6c Garfield	42.50	1.75
306	8c Martha Washington	20.00	1.50
307	10c Webster	45.00	.75
308	13c Benjamin Harrison	20.00	7.00
309	15c Clay	125.00	4.50
310	50c Jefferson	325.00	20.00
311	$1 David G. Farragut	625.00	32.50
312	$2 Madison	800.00	125.00
313	$5 Marshall	1550.00	425.00

For listings of 312 and 313 with Perf. 10, see Nos. 479 and 480.

Issues of 1906-08

Imperf.

No.	Description	Unused	Used
314	1c blue green Franklin (300)	21.00	12.50
314A	4c brown Grant (303)	*10,000.00*	*5000.00*
315	5c blue Lincoln (304)	525.00	225.00

No. 314A was issued imperforate, but all copies were privately perforated with large oblong perforations at the sides. (Schermack type III).

Coil Stamps

Perf. 12 Horizontally

No.	Description	Unused	Used
316	1c blue green pair Franklin (300)	*14,500.00*	
317	5c blue pair Lincoln (304)	*3000.00*	

Perf. 12 Vertically

No.	Description	Unused	Used
318	1c blue green pair Franklin (300)	*2250.00*	

With this series the Post Office Department began issuing stamps in coils for use in vending and affixing machines. The stamps in coils are perforated on two sides only, either horizontally or vertically, and are imperforate on the other sides.

Collectors are warned that imperforate stamps are being fraudulently perforated to resemble coil stamps and part perforate varieties.

Issue of 1903, Perf. 12

Shield-shaped Background

No.	Description	Date	Unused	Used
319	2c Washington	Nov. 12	4.00	.04
319g	Booklet pane of 6		100.00	*20.00*

Issue of 1906

Nos. 320-322: Washington (319)

Imperf.

No.	Description	Date	Unused	Used
320	2c carmine	Oct. 2	18.50	10.00

Issue of 1908, Coil Stamps

Perf 12 Horizontally

No.	Description	Unused	Used
321	2c carmine pair	*25,000.00*	——

Perf. 12 Vertically

No.	Description	Unused	Used
322	2c carmine pair	*3000.00*	——

Issue of 1904, Perf. 12

Louisiana Purchase Exposition Issue, Apr. 30

No.	Description	Unused	Used
323	1c Robert R. Livingston	23.00	4.00
324	2c Thomas Jefferson	21.00	1.25
325	3c James Monroe	67.50	20.00
326	5c William McKinley	82.50	15.00
327	10c Map of Louisiana Purchase	175.00	22.50

The Louisiana Purchase Exposition was held in St. Louis in 1904 in conjunction with the World's Fair of that year. President William McKinley (1843-1901), who died before the Exposition opened, authorized the Fair.

Issue of 1907, Perf. 12

Jamestown Exposition Issue

No.	Description	Unused	Used
328	1c Captain John Smith	17.50	4.50
329	2c Founding of Jamestown	22.50	3.25
330	5c Pocahontas	105.00	23.50

The first permanent English settlement in North America was established in 1607, at Jamestown, Virginia.

323 324 325 326 327 328 329 330

POCAHONTAS 1597-1617

When only twelve years old, Pocahontas, an Indian girl, intervened just in the nick of time to save the life of Captain John Smith, the leader of the colonists at Jamestown. Her father, Indian chief Powhatan, was about to strike the death blow with a war club when Pocahontas threw herself between the two men and begged her father to spare Smith's life.

A few years later, in 1613, hostilities between the settlers and the Indians recurred. Pocahontas was captured and held prisoner by the colonists who intended to use her as hostage to negotiate peace between themselves and her tribe. During her captivity, she met and fell in love with John Rolfe, who introduced the tobacco crop to the colony. After she converted to Christianity, the two were married at the Episcopal Church in Jamestown. Their marriage brought about an eight year peace with the Indians.

After the birth of their only child, Thomas, in 1615, the couple went to England where Pocahontas was treated as an Indian princess. While awaiting a ship to take them back to Virginia, she fell ill with smallpox and died.

See Scott No. 330

Regular Issues of 1908-09, Perf. 12

Wmkd. USPS (191)

331	1c	Franklin	4.50	.05
331a		Booklet pane of 6	120.00	*35.00*
332	2c	Washington	4.25	.05
332a		Booklet pane of 6	100.00	*35.00*
333	3c	Washington, type I	13.50	2.00

Nos. 334-342: Washington (333)

334	4c	orange brown	15.00	.75
335	5c	blue	21.00	1.00
336	6c	red orange	26.00	3.75
337	8c	olive green	15.00	1.75
338	10c	yellow	35.00	.65
339	13c	blue green	20.00	15.00
340	15c	pale ultramarine	32.50	3.25
341	50c	violet	160.00	8.00
342	$1	violet brown	275.00	40.00

Imperf.

343	1c	green Franklin (331)	6.25	2.50
344	2c	car. Washington (332)	8.00	1.25

Nos. 345-347: Washington (333)

345	3c	deep violet, type I	18.50	6.75
346	4c	orange brown	42.50	10.00
347	5c	blue	62.50	20.00

Coil Stamps of 1908-10
Nos. 350-351, 354-356: Washington (333)
Perf. 12 Horizontally

348	1c	green Franklin (331)	15.00	7.75
349	2c	car. Washington (332)	27.50	4.50
350	4c	orange brown	75.00	35.00
351	5c	blue	95.00	50.00

1909, Perf. 12 Vertically

352	1c	green Franklin (331)	35.00	11.00
353	2c	car. Washington (332)	30.00	4.25
354	4c	orange brown	62.50	25.00
355	5c	blue	85.00	40.00
356	10c	yellow	750.00	200.00

Issues of 1909, Bluish Paper, Perf. 12
Nos. 359-366: Washington (333)

357	1c	green Franklin (331)	60.00	50.00
358	2c	car. Washington (332)	55.00	35.00
359	3c	deep violet, type I	800.00	550.00
360	4c	orange brown	*10,000.00*	
361	5c	blue	2250.00	—
362	6c	red orange	600.00	375.00
363	8c	olive green	*10,000.00*	
364	10c	yellow	650.00	375.00
365	13c	blue green	1350.00	500.00
366	15c	pale ultramarine	550.00	275.00

Lincoln Memorial Issue, Feb. 12

367	2c	Lincoln, Perf. 12	6.50	2.75
368	2c	Lincoln, Imperf.	37.50	15.00
369	2c	Lincoln, Perf. 12, Bluish Paper	225.00	100.00

Alaska-Yukon Exposition Issue

370	2c	William Seward, Perf. 12	8.75	2.00
371	2c	William Seward, Imperf.	50.00	15.00

William H. Seward (1801-72), Lincoln's Secretary of State, bought Alaska for the U.S., in 1867.

Hudson-Fulton Celebration Issue, Sep. 25

372	2c	Half Moon and Clermont, Perf. 12	8.75	2.75
373	2c	Half Moon and Clermont, Imperf.	60.00	15.00

Henry Hudson discovered the New York river named for him in 1609. Robert Fulton's *Clermont* was the first commercially successful steamboat.

Issues of 1910-13
Perf. 12

Wmkd. USPS (190)

Nos. 376-382: Washington (333)

374	1c	green Franklin (331)	4.00	.06
374a		Booklet pane of 6	110.00	*30.00*
375	2c	car. Washington (332)	3.75	.03
375a		Booklet pane of 6	100.00	*25.00*
376	3c	deep violet, type I	8.00	1.10
377	4c	brown	11.50	.50
378	5c	blue	11.50	.50

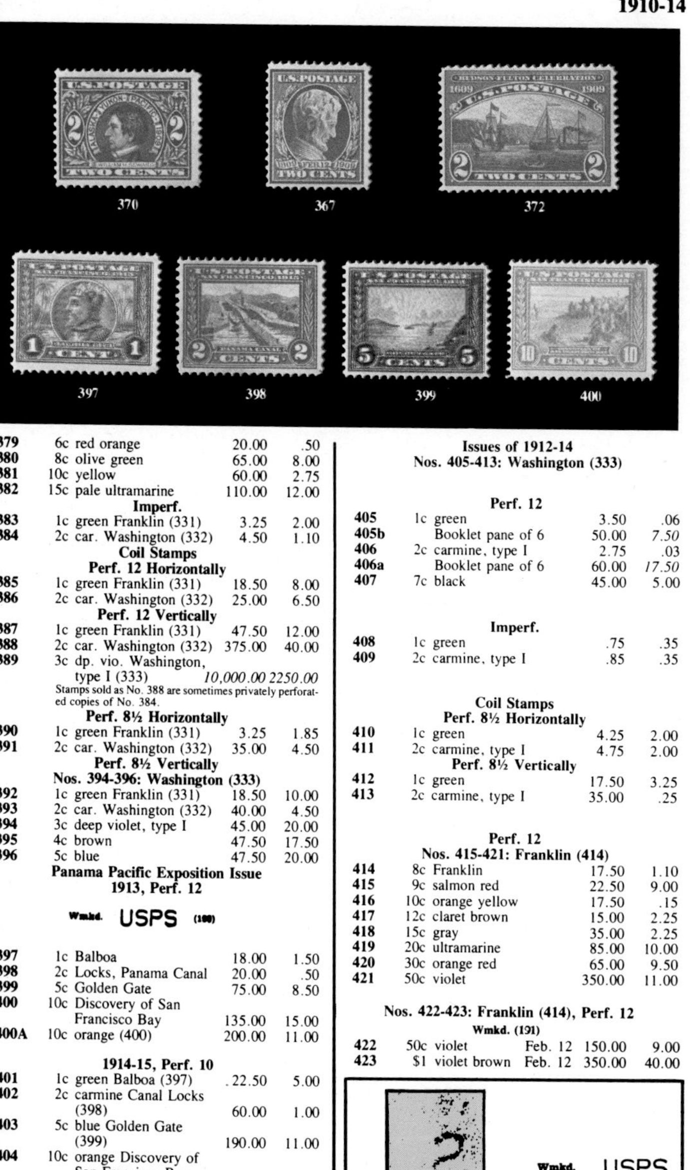

370 367 372

397 398 399 400

379	6c red orange	20.00	.50
380	8c olive green	65.00	8.00
381	10c yellow	60.00	2.75
382	15c pale ultramarine	110.00	12.00
	Imperf.		
383	1c green Franklin (331)	3.25	2.00
384	2c car. Washington (332)	4.50	1.10
	Coil Stamps		
	Perf. 12 Horizontally		
385	1c green Franklin (331)	18.50	8.00
386	2c car. Washington (332)	25.00	6.50
	Perf. 12 Vertically		
387	1c green Franklin (331)	47.50	12.00
388	2c car. Washington (332)	375.00	40.00
389	3c dp. vio. Washington, type I (333)	*10,000.00*	*2250.00*

Stamps sold as No. 388 are sometimes privately perforated copies of No. 384.

	Perf. 8½ Horizontally		
390	1c green Franklin (331)	3.25	1.85
391	2c car. Washington (332)	35.00	4.50
	Perf. 8½ Vertically		
	Nos. 394-396: Washington (333)		
392	1c green Franklin (331)	18.50	10.00
393	2c car. Washington (332)	40.00	4.50
394	3c deep violet, type I	45.00	20.00
395	4c brown	47.50	17.50
396	5c blue	47.50	20.00

Panama Pacific Exposition Issue
1913, Perf. 12

Wmkd. USPS **(190)**

397	1c Balboa	18.00	1.50
398	2c Locks, Panama Canal	20.00	.50
399	5c Golden Gate	75.00	8.50
400	10c Discovery of San Francisco Bay	135.00	15.00
400A	10c orange (400)	200.00	11.00
	1914-15, Perf. 10		
401	1c green Balboa (397)	22.50	5.00
402	2c carmine Canal Locks (398)	60.00	1.00
403	5c blue Golden Gate (399)	190.00	11.00
404	10c orange Discovery of San Francisco Bay (400)	1100.00	45.00

Spanish explorer Vasco Nuñez de Balboa discovered the Pacific Ocean in 1513. The Panama Canal, which links the Pacific and Atlantic Ocean, was opened in 1914.

Issues of 1912-14
Nos. 405-413: Washington (333)

	Perf. 12		
405	1c green	3.50	.06
405b	Booklet pane of 6	50.00	*7.50*
406	2c carmine, type I	2.75	.03
406a	Booklet pane of 6	60.00	*17.50*
407	7c black	45.00	5.00
	Imperf.		
408	1c green	.75	.35
409	2c carmine, type I	.85	.35
	Coil Stamps		
	Perf. 8½ Horizontally		
410	1c green	4.25	2.00
411	2c carmine, type I	4.75	2.00
	Perf. 8½ Vertically		
412	1c green	17.50	3.25
413	2c carmine, type I	35.00	.25
	Perf. 12		
	Nos. 415-421: Franklin (414)		
414	8c Franklin	17.50	1.10
415	9c salmon red	22.50	9.00
416	10c orange yellow	17.50	.15
417	12c claret brown	15.00	2.25
418	15c gray	35.00	2.25
419	20c ultramarine	85.00	10.00
420	30c orange red	65.00	9.50
421	50c violet	350.00	11.00

Nos. 422-423: Franklin (414), Perf. 12
Wmkd. (191)

422	50c violet	Feb. 12	150.00	9.00
423	$1 violet brown	Feb. 12	350.00	40.00

Wmk. 190

Wmkd. USPS **in Single lined Capitals. (190)**

Issues of 1914-15, Perf. 10
Wmkd. (190)
Nos. 424-430: Washington (333)

424	1c green	2.00	.06
424d	Booklet pane of 6	3.00	.75
425	2c rose red. type I	1.50	.04
425e	Booklet pane of 6	12.50	*2.00*
426	3c deep violet, type I	6.50	.75
427	4c brown	23.00	.18
428	5c blue	12.50	.30
429	6c red orange	25.00	.75
430	7c black	47.50	3.25

Nos. 431-440: Franklin (414)

431	8c pale olive green	17.50	1.10
432	9c salmon red	23.50	6.00
433	10c orange yellow	18.50	.06
434	11c dark green	11.00	4.00
435	12c claret brown	11.00	2.50
437	15c gray	65.00	5.25
438	20c ultramarine	110.00	2.75
439	30c orange red	150.00	8.50
440	50c violet	450.00	10.00

Nos. 431-440: Franklin (414)

431	8c pale olive green	17.50	1.10
432	9c salmon red	23.50	6.00
433	10c orange yellow	20.00	.06
434	11c dark green	11.00	4.00
435	12c claret brown	11.00	2.50
437	15c gray	65.00	5.25
438	20c ultramarine	125.00	2.75
439	30c orange red	165.00	8.50
440	50c violet	525.00	10.00

Coil Stamps, Washington (333)
1915-16, Perf. 10 Horizontally

448	1c green	4.00	1.75
449	2c red, type I	900.00	85.00
450	2c carmine, type III	8.50	1.50

1914-16, Perf. 10 Vertically

452	1c green	7.50	1.20
453	2c red, type I	110.00	3.75
454	2c carmine, type II	120.00	15.00
455	2c carmine, type III	9.50	.50
456	3c violet, type I	200.00	55.00
457	4c brown	22.50	10.00
458	5c blue	22.50	10.00

Issue of 1914 Washington (333), Imperf. Coil

459	2c carmine, type I Jun. 30	300.00	325.00

Issues of 1915, Perf. 10

Wmkd USPS (191)

460	$1 violet black Franklin (414) Feb. 8	600.00	42.50

Perf. 11

Wmkd. USPS (191)

461	2c pale carmine red, type I. Washington (333) Jun. 17	45.00	35.00

Privately perforated copies of No. 409 have been made to resemble No. 461.

From 1916 all postage stamps except Nos. 519 and 832b are on unwatermarked paper.

Issues of 1916-17, Perf. 10
Nos. 462-469: Washington (333)

462	1c green	4.00	.20
462a	Booklet pane of 6	8.50	*1.00*
463	2c carmine, type I	2.00	.06
463a	Booklet pane of 6	65.00	*15.00*
464	3c violet, type I	45.00	8.00
465	4c orange brown	25.00	1.25
466	5c blue	42.50	1.10
467	5c car. (error in plate of 2c)	625.00	350.00
468	6c red orange	60.00	5.50
469	7c black	75.00	10.00

Nos. 470-478: Franklin (414)

470	8c olive green	35.00	5.00
471	9c salmon red	22.50	9.00
472	10c orange yellow	65.00	.75
473	11c dark green	16.50	9.75
474	12c claret brown	25.00	4.25
475	15c gray	100.00	8.50
476	20c light ultramarine	150.00	9.50
476A	30c orange red	——	——
477	50c light violet	750.00	50.00
478	$1 violet black	600.00	12.00

Issues of 1917, Perf. 10, Mar. 22

479	$2 dark blue Madison (312)	425.00	21.00
480	$5 light green Marshall (313)	325.00	25.00

Issues of 1916-17, Washington (333), Imperf.

481	1c green	.60	.50
482	2c carmine, type I	1.00	.80
482A	2c carmine, type Ia	——	*4500.00*
483	3c violet, type I	12.00	5.50
484	3c violet, type II	6.75	3.50
485	5c car. (error in plate of 2c)	*7000.00*	

Coil Stamps, Washington (333)
1916-19, Perf. 10 Horizontally

486	1c green	.60	.15
487	2c carmine, type II	13.50	2.00
488	2c carmine, type III	2.00	1.20
489	3c violet, type I	2.50	1.00

1916-22, Perf. 10 Vertically

490	1c green	.35	.15
491	2c carmine, type II	900.00	120.00
492	2c carmine, type III	6.25	.15
493	3c violet, type I	22.50	3.00
494	3c violet, type II	13.50	.60
495	4c orange brown	11.50	2.75
496	5c blue	2.25	.60
497	10c orange yellow Franklin (414)	18.50	6.50

Issues of 1917-19, Perf. 11
Nos. 498-507: Washington (333)

498	1c green	.25	.04
498e	Booklet pane of 6	1.75	*.35*
498f	Booklet pane of 30	*450.00*	
499	2c rose, type I	.25	.03
499e	Booklet pane of 6	2.00	.50
499f	Booklet pane of 30	*4750.00*	
500	2c deep rose, type Ia	225.00	85.00
501	3c light violet, type I	7.50	.08
501b	Booklet pane of 6	65.00	*15.00*
502	3c dark violet, type II	10.00	.15
502b	Booklet pane of 6	30.00	*10.00*
503	4c brown	9.00	.10
504	5c blue	6.50	.08
505	5c rose (error in plate of 2c)	425.00	225.00
506	6c red orange	8.50	.12
507	7c black	20.00	1.00

Nos. 508-518: Franklin (414)

508	8c olive bistre	9.00	.50
509	9c salmon red	15.00	1.85
510	10c orange yellow	15.00	.05
511	11c light green	5.75	2.75
512	12c claret brown	5.75	.30
513	13c apple green	10.00	5.50

JAMESTOWN

Under a charter granted by King James I, approximately one hundred brave Englishmen set sail in three small ships to start a colony in the New World. The settlers were cautioned to select their site with care. Unfortunately, they did not heed this advice. The settlement, established on May 14, 1607, named Jamestown for their king, was difficult to defend and unsuitable for farming. Famine, disease, and Indian attacks threatened the colony's survival. Less than half of the original settlers lived through the first winter. Disheartened by the hardships they encountered, the remaining colonists wanted to return home. Only the efforts of their leader, Captain John Smith, kept the colony from being abandoned.

With a ready market in England, the colonists began to cultivate a tobacco crop and Jamestown prospered. It became the capital of Virginia. In 1619, the House of Burgesses, the first representative form of government in America, was established there.

But when agriculture became the mainstay of Virginia's economy, the city of Jamestown declined in importance. The capital was moved to Williamsburg in 1699. By the time of the American Revolution, Jamestown had fallen into near decay. In 1900, all that remained of this once bustling community was a church and some crumbling gravestones.

Today Jamestown looks much like it did when it was a thriving English settlement. Jamestown, the first permanent English colony in America, has been restored as a national historic site. Replicas of seventeenth century buildings and artifacts of the colonial settlement recapture the nature of the original colony.

See Scott Nos. 328-330, 1091

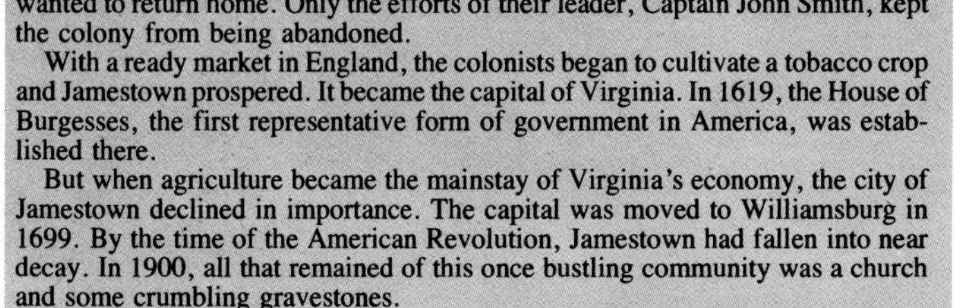

405

406

414

420

WORLD WAR I

John J. Pershing
Woodrow Wilson

In 1916, two years after Europe plunged into war, Woodrow Wilson won a second term as president of the United States. "He kept us out of the war," said his successful campaign slogan. And Wilson intended to go right on doing just that. But the following year, American lives were lost when German submarines torpedoed unarmed merchant ships in mid-Atlantic. That was too much even for the peace-loving Wilson. "The world must be made safe for democracy," he said. In April, 1917, America declared war on Germany.

But the U. S. was unprepared for war, and another year passed before American doughboys in important numbers entered the fighting in France. By the time they did, America's allies—England, France and Italy—were close to defeat. An infusion in 1918 of American men and munitions turned the tide. The fresh and spirited American forces totaled over one million and were led by a stern and brilliant career officer, John "Black Jack" Pershing. Their first major victory, in the battle of Saint-Mihiel in September, 1918, was followed by another triumph in the Meuse-Argonne campaign. Germany was brought to her knees.

514	15c gray	30.00	.60
515	20c light ultramarine	32.50	.12
516	30c orange red	32.50	.65
517	50c red violet	65.00	.35
518	$1 violet brown	90.00	.75

Issue of 1917, Perf. 11

Wmkd USPS (191)

519	2c carmine Washington (332) Oct. 10	125.00	100.00

Privately perforated copies of No. 344 have been made to resemble No. 519.

Issues of 1918, Unwmkd., Perf. 11

523	$2 orange red and black Franklin (547) Aug. 19	900.00	125.00
524	$5 deep green and black Franklin (547) Aug. 19	350.00	20.00

Issues of 1918-20, Washington (333)
Perf. 11

525	1c gray green	1.50	.50
526	2c carmine, type IV	20.00	3.50
527	2c carmine, type V	15.00	1.00
528	2c carmine, type Va	5.25	.15
528A	2c carmine, type VI	32.50	.75
528B	2c carmine, type VII	13.50	.08
529	3c violet, type III	1.20	.10
530	3c purple, type IV	.70	.06

Imperf.

531	1c green	7.50	6.25
532	2c car. rose, type IV	27.50	15.00
533	2c carmine, type V	165.00	50.00
534	2c carmine, type Va	7.75	6.00
534A	2c carmine, type VI	25.00	15.00
534B	2c carmine, type VII	1100.00	275.00
535	3c violet, type IV	6.50	5.00

537

547

As president of a victorious America, Wilson had won the war. He was destined to lose the peace.

Woodrow Wilson was a man with a dream. He dreamed of a world that would never witness another war. Even before World War I ended, he presented Congress and a battle-weary world with "14 Points"—guidelines for a new kind of peace that would last forever. Among those famous "14 Points" were calls for freedom of the seas; free trade between countries; and, most important to him, the formation of a League of Nations. Wilson considered these concepts so important that he decided to head the U.S. delegation to the peace conference in Europe. Beaming with confidence, he sailed away. And for the next six months, he watched, helpless, as England, France and Italy rejected his ideas one by one, all but the one he cherished most, the League of Nations.

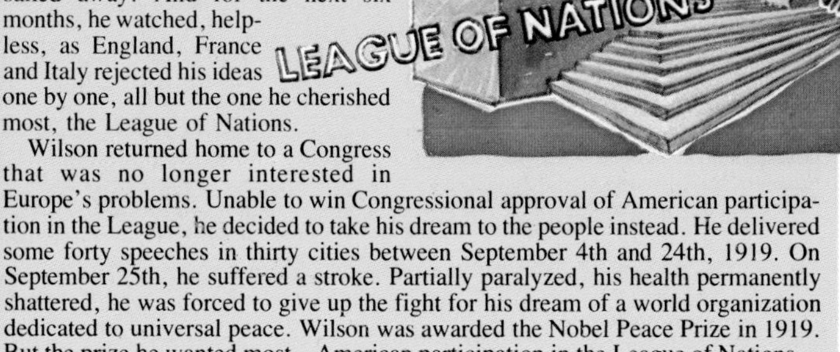

Wilson returned home to a Congress that was no longer interested in Europe's problems. Unable to win Congressional approval of American participation in the League, he decided to take his dream to the people instead. He delivered some forty speeches in thirty cities between September 4th and 24th, 1919. On September 25th, he suffered a stroke. Partially paralyzed, his health permanently shattered, he was forced to give up the fight for his dream of a world organization dedicated to universal peace. Wilson was awarded the Nobel Peace Prize in 1919. But the prize he wanted most—American participation in the League of Nations—eluded him.

See Scott Nos 623, 627, 832, 1040, 1042A

Issues of 1919
Perf. 12½

536	1c gray green Washington (333)	Aug. 15	11.00	9.00

Perf. 11

537	3c Allied Victory	Mar. 3	9.00	3.50

The Armistice of Nov. 11, 1918 ended World War I on a note of triumph for the Allies.

Nos. 538-546: Washington (333)
1919, Perf. 11x10

538	1c green	6.50	6.50
539	2c carmine rose, type II	1100.00	450.00
540	2c carmine rose, type III	6.50	6.50
541	3c violet, type II	25.00	25.00

1920, Perf. 10x11

542	1c green	May 26	3.50	.60

1921, Perf. 10

543	1c green	.25	.06

1921, Perf. 11

544	1c green, 19x22½mm.	*5500.00*	*1000.00*
545	1c grn., 19½–20mm.x22mm.	90.00	65.00
546	2c carmine rose, type III	60.00	45.00

Issues of 1920
Perf. 11

547	$2 Franklin	325.00	20.00

Pilgrims 300th Anniv. Issue, Dec. 21

548	1c Mayflower	6.00	2.50
549	2c Pilgrims Landing	9.50	2.00
550	5c Signing of Compact	52.50	16.50

In 1620 the Pilgrims landed in Massachusetts, with the Mayflower Compact as the basis for their government.

548

549

550

INDIANS EAST

Arkansas and Alibamu. Cherokee, Chickasaw, Choctaw and Catawba, Delaware, Erie, Huron. Susquehanna and Tuscarora. These were just a few of the numerous Indian tribes dwelling in the eastern part of the country when the colonists touched shore. They spoke hundreds of different languages and dialects, and their cultures varied greatly. But most of them were farmers and hunters, and their "long houses" were clustered together to form permanent villages. The men were expert hunters and, when necessary, expert warriors. The women tended the fields, tanned hides and did the work of the household. They grew corn, beans and squash. Both men and women created beautiful handicrafts.

They were deeply religious people and staunch followers of their laws and codes of behavior. In the very early days of colonization, the friendship and guidance offered by Indian tribes were often the prime factor in the continued survival of the colonists. The Pilgrims, wintering in 1620-21 in cold and inhospitable Massachusetts, felt they were not alone. They had the Indian, Squanto, by their side, and they called him "a spetiall instrument sent of God for their good beyond their expectation." With pomp and honor, four Iroquois were escorted to London in 1710 to visit the queen. It was only later that the conflict in ways of life between the Indians and the colonists led to friction.

INDIANS WEST

The saga of the conflict between the Indians and white men in the American West is a tale of which neither group of Americans can be proud.

As the U.S. expanded into the Louisiana territory, pioneers were eager to settle the new lands. There seemed to be room enough for red man and white man both. But the two ways of life were destined to clash. The pioneers wanted to clear the forests and farm the land, while the Indians preferred the age-old hunting grounds of their ancestors to remain untouched. The question was settled by war after war. And each time the whites were the aggressors. But both sides were guilty of unnecessary cruelty and the killing of many innocent people.

But heroic Indian figures emerged out of these troubled times. There were such influential leaders as Sitting Bull of the Sioux, today considered one of the most able, honest and idealistic statesmen in Indian history. There were such immortal warriors as Crazy Horse, best remembered for his victory at Little Big Horn in 1876—Custer's Last Stand. There were such inspired statesmen as Chief Joseph of the Nez Percés, who signed a peace treaty with the U.S. in 1855 and, regardless of pressures to betray his word, remained at peace with the white man from then on.

See Scott Nos. 565, 695, 972, 1364

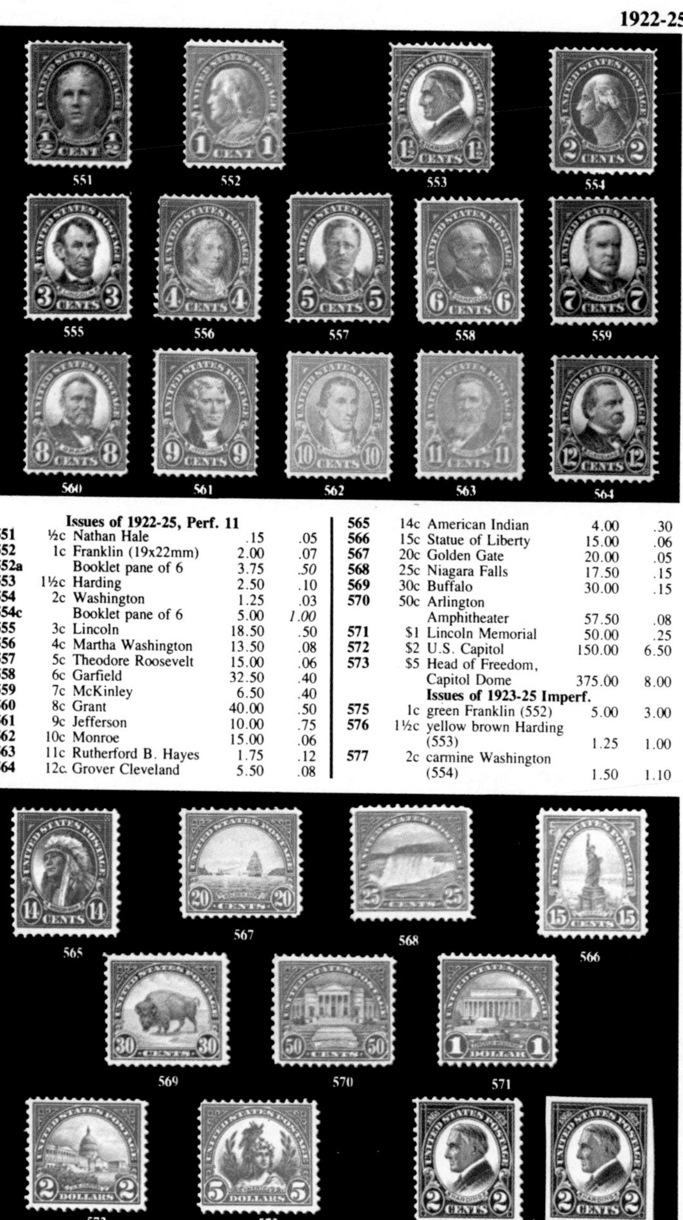

Issues of 1922-25, Perf. 11

No.	Denom.	Description	Unused	Used
551	½c	Nathan Hale	.15	.05
552	1c	Franklin (19x22mm)	2.00	.07
552a		Booklet pane of 6	3.75	*.50*
553	1½c	Harding	2.50	.10
554	2c	Washington	1.25	.03
554c		Booklet pane of 6	5.00	*1.00*
555	3c	Lincoln	18.50	.50
556	4c	Martha Washington	13.50	.08
557	5c	Theodore Roosevelt	15.00	.06
558	6c	Garfield	32.50	.40
559	7c	McKinley	6.50	.40
560	8c	Grant	40.00	.50
561	9c	Jefferson	10.00	.75
562	10c	Monroe	15.00	.06
563	11c	Rutherford B. Hayes	1.75	.12
564	12c	Grover Cleveland	5.50	.08
565	14c	American Indian	4.00	.30
566	15c	Statue of Liberty	15.00	.06
567	20c	Golden Gate	20.00	.05
568	25c	Niagara Falls	17.50	.15
569	30c	Buffalo	30.00	.15
570	50c	Arlington Amphitheater	57.50	.08
571	$1	Lincoln Memorial	50.00	.25
572	$2	U.S. Capitol	150.00	6.50
573	$5	Head of Freedom, Capitol Dome	375.00	8.00

Issues of 1923-25 Imperf.

No.	Denom.	Description	Unused	Used
575	1c	green Franklin (552)	5.00	3.00
576	1½c	yellow brown Harding (553)	1.25	1.00
577	2c	carmine Washington (554)	1.50	1.10

MARTHA WASHINGTON

Martha Custis was the wife of a wealthy tobacco planter and the mother of two small children. Suddenly and tragically, in May, 1757, her husband fell ill and died. The young widow kept busy supervising her large household and her husband's business, but she was lonely. The following spring, at the home of friends, she spent a happy few hours chatting with the young military hero, Colonel Washington. Washington began courting Martha Custis and in July, 1758, they announced their engagement. Six months later they were married.

They took up residence at Mount Vernon, the Washington estate. They lived the life of prosperous Virginia plantation folk for the next fifteen years, busy with house parties, picnics, barbecues, concerts, balls. Then the march of historical events parted them. Washington went to Boston in 1775 to take command of the Revolutionary forces while his wife remained behind. But throughout the war, he wore a gold locket holding a miniature portrait of the waiting Martha.

See Scott Nos. 306, 556, 805

For listings of other perforated stamps of issues 551-573 see:

Nos. 578 and 579	Perf. 11x10
Nos. 581 to 591	Perf. 10
Nos. 594 and 595	Perf. 11
Nos. 622 and 623	Perf. 11
Nos. 632 to 642, 653, 692 to 696	Perf. 11x10½
Nos. 697 to 701	Perf. 10½x11

Perf. 11x10

578	1c	green Franklin (552)	45.00	45.00
579	2c	carmine Washington (554)	30.00	30.00

Issues of 1923-26 Perf. 10

581	1c	green Franklin (552)	3.25	.50
582	1½c	brown Harding (553)	3.00	.40
583	2c	carmine Washington (554)	1.20	.05
583a		Booklet pane of 6	70.00	*25.00*
584	3c	violet Lincoln (555)	18.50	1.25
585	4c	yellow brown M. Washington (556)	11.00	.25
586	5c	blue T. Roosevelt (557)	11.50	.15
587	6c	red orange Garfield (558)	5.00	.25
588	7c	black McKinley (559)	6.50	4.00
589	8c	olive green Grant (560)	18.50	2.00
590	9c	rose Jefferson (561)	3.50	1.75
591	10c	orange Monroe (562)	40.00	.06

Perf. 11

594	1c	green Franklin, 19¾x22¼mm. (552)	*6000.00*	*1500.00*
595	2c	carmine Washington, 19¾x22¼mm. (554)	110.00	95.00
596	1c	green Franklin, 19¼x22¾mm. (552)		*11,000.00*

Coil Stamps 1923-29, Perf. 10 Vertically

597	1c	green Franklin (552)	.25	.06
598	1½c	brown Harding (553)	.75	.08
599	2c	carmine Washington, type I (554)	.30	.04
599A	2c	carmine Washington, type II (554)	130.00	7.00
600	3c	violet Lincoln (555)	7.00	.08
601	4c	yellow brown M. Washington (556)	3.00	.20
602	5c	dark blue Theodore Roosevelt (557)	1.10	.10
603	10c	orange Monroe (562)	2.50	.06

Coil Stamps 1923-25 Perf. 10 Horizontally

604	1c	yellow green Franklin (552)	.25	.08
605	1½c	yellow brown Harding (553)	.30	.12
606	2c	carmine Washington (554)	.30	.10

Harding Memorial Issue, 1923
Flat Plate Printing (19¼x22¼mm.)

610	2c	Harding, Perf. 11	Sep. 1	1.00	.10
611	2c	Harding, Imperf.	Nov. 15	13.50	4.00

Rotary Press Printing (19¼x22¾mm.)

612	2c	black, Perf. 10 (610)	Sep. 12	21.00	1.50
613	2c	black, Perf. 11 (610)			*9500.00*

Warren G. Harding (1865-1923) was the 28th President of the United States (1921-23).

THEODORE ROOSEVELT

At the turn of the century, Americans felt tremendously good about themselves and their country. Looking at a Europe that was still ruled mostly by royalty, Americans felt free, vigorous and morally superior. Looking at the weak and economically backward nations of Latin America, they felt powerful, prosperous, protective. In 1901 America elected a president who was the living embodiment of all those strongly nationalistic feelings. And they got him by accident!

Theodore Roosevelt was Assistant Secretary of the Navy when war with Spain was declared in 1893. He resigned his post, organized the famous "Rough Riders" and took them to Cuba to fight. His exploits there - especially his daring charge up San Juan Hill - captured the popular imagination. He came home a national hero. It was easy for him to win the governorship of New York after that. As Governor, however, Roosevelt angered the Republican Party Boss of the state by removing corrupt politicians from office. So Boss Platt had Roosevelt maneuvered into the Vice Presidency of the U. S., a powerless position at the time that was sure to lead nowhere politically. Platt thought he'd gotten rid of a troublemaker, until President McKinley was assassinated and Theodore Roosevelt became President in 1901.

The Republican party was supposed to be the party of big business. Teddy Roosevelt was a Republican, but his loyalty to the public interest came before his loyalty to the party. He began "trust busting," forcing the break-up of 44 gigantic corporations. He served as referee in the conflict between business and labor, personally arbitrating a strike in the anthracite coal industry, and establishing the precedent for governmental interference in the affairs of business and labor when the public interest was at stake. He pressured Congress into passing the first Pure Food and Drug law, and consumer protection was on its way.

In international relations, Roosevelt claimed he would "speak softly and carry a big stick." His policies paid off when he convinced Europe to stay out of Latin American affairs, but he tampered in Central American politics himself in order to pave the way for Panama Canal construction.

After he completed his second term in 1908, Roosevelt went off to Africa to hunt. He came back home, itching for action. In 1912 he ran for president on a third party ticket and lost. He always hoped he'd get another crack at a job he loved — the presidency of the United States.

See Scott Nos. 557, 586, 602, 663, 674, 830, 856, 1039.

Huguenot-Walloon 300th Anniv. Issue 1924, May 1

614	1c Ship "New Netherland"	5.25	4.25
615	2c Landing at Fort Orange	8.25	3.00
616	5c Huguenot Monument, Florida	45.00	16.50

In the seventeenth century Dutch Walloons and French Huguenots fled to America to escape religious persecution. The Walloons founded Albany, New York.

Lexington-Concord Issue, 1925, Apr. 4

617	1c Washington at Cambridge	5.00	4.00
618	2c Birth of Liberty	9.50	5.50
619	5c Statue of Minute Man	42.50	16.00

Issued for the 150th anniversary of the Battle of Lexington and Concord.

Norse-American Issue, May 18

620	2c Sloop "Restaurationen"	9.00	3.50

LEXINGTON AND CONCORD

The Minutemen were mostly farmers and shopkeepers with little formal military training, meager supplies of arms and ammunition and no uniforms. What chance did these rebels have against the highly disciplined, efficiently trained, abundantly equipped military forces of the most powerful nation in the world? Their cause seemed hopeless!

British troops had been ordered to Lexington to arrest rebel leaders Samuel Adams and John Hancock for inciting revolution and then to march on Concord to destroy the colonists' military supplies. Fortunately, word of the British plans leaked out and Paul Revere, in his famous midnight ride, warned of the approaching redcoats. By the time the British arrived at Lexington, late on the night of April 18, 1775, Hancock and Adams had already fled to safety.

... BUT IF THEY
MEAN TO HAVE A WAR
LET IT BEGIN HERE...

Although there was a skirmish at Lexington, the first real battle of the Revolution occurred at neighboring Concord. The British encountered the forewarned Minutemen at the old bridge and fired at them. The rebels responded and fired "the shot heard around the world". The war for independence had begun!

See Scott Nos. 617-619, 1593

620 621 622 628 627 623 629

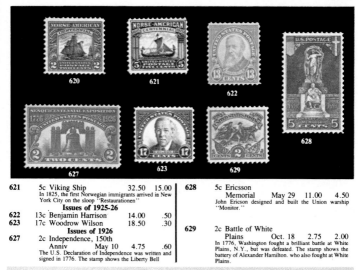

621 5c Viking Ship 32.50 15.00
In 1825, the first Norwegian immigrants arrived in New York City on the sloop "Restaurationen"

Issues of 1925-26

622 13c Benjamin Harrison 14.00 .50
623 17c Woodrow Wilson 18.50 .30

Issues of 1926

627 2c Independence, 150th Anniv May 10 4.75 .60
The U.S. Declaration of Independence was written and signed in 1776. The stamp shows the Liberty Bell

628 5c Ericsson Memorial May 29 11.00 4.50
John Ericson designed and built the Union warship "Monitor."

629 2c Battle of White Plains Oct. 18 2.75 2.00
In 1776, Washington fought a brilliant battle at White Plains, N.Y., but was defeated. The stamp shows the battery of Alexander Hamilton. who also fought at White Plains.

PAUL REVERE 1735-1818

On April 18, 1775, the British were mounting their forces in Boston preparing to raid the colonial strongholds at Lexington and Concord. The Boston patriots got word of the plans and hung two lanterns in the tower of old North Church, a prearranged signal, to announce the British were proceeding by boat. The rebels at Lexington had to be alerted.

Paul Revere mounted his horse and threaded his way through British patrols spreading the alarm "The British are coming, the British are coming." From village to village and house to house the cry of impending danger was sounded. As a result of the daring of this brave patriot, the Minutemen were waiting when the British troops arrived.

After the war, Revere resumed his many diverse interests and activities. He opened a foundry which manufactured bells and cannons. He invented a process for rolling sheet copper and made copper and brass fittings for the USS *Constitution*. His greatest talent, however, was as a silversmith. His works, displayed in many fine museums, are greatly prized for their excellent craftsmanship.

See Scott Nos. 1048, 1059A

International Philatelic Exhibition Issue, Oct. 18

Souvenir Sheet

630	2c	car. rose, sheet of 25 with selvage inscription (629)	550.00	300.00

Imperf.

631	1½c	Harding Aug. 27 18½–19mm.x22mm.	1.35	1.15

Issues of 1926-27, Perf. 11x10½

632	1c	green Franklin (552)	.15	.03
632a		Booklet pane of 6	1.00	*.25*
633	1½c	Harding	1.25	.08
634	2c	carmine Washington type 1 (554)	.15	.03
634d		Booklet pane of 6	1.00	*.15*
634A	2c	carmine Washington. type II (554)	325.00	15.00
635	3c	violet Lincoln (555)	.50	.04
636	4c	yellow brown M. Washington (556)	2.50	.08
637	5c	dark blue T. Roosevelt (557)	2.50	.03
638	6c	red org. Garfield (558)	2.50	.03
639	7c	black McKinley (559)	2.50	.08
640	8c	olive grn, Grant (560)	2.50	.05
641	9c	org. red Jefferson (561)	2.50	.05
642	10c	orange Monroe (562)	4.00	.03

Issues of 1927, Perf. 11

643	2c	Vermont 150th Anniversary Aug. 3	1.50	1.00

150th anniversary of the Battle of Bennington.

VERMONT

Unsettled land disputes with its neighbors kept Vermont from joining the newly formed United States in 1776. Instead, Vermont adopted its own declaration of independence from England on January 16, 1777. Later that same year its constitution was ratified. Vermont is proud of the fact that this was the first state constitution to forbid slavery and establish universal suffrage for men.

Vermonters fought side by side with the patriots of the original thirteen colonies in the War for Independence from Great Britain. The "Green Mountain Boys," as the Vermont fighters were called because of their being local militia from the settlements in the Green Mountains, are credited with the first aggressive initiative of the war, the capture of the fort at Ticonderoga on May 10, 1778. Later that same year the Vermonters led the victory at Bennington which started the series of British defeats that contributed to British General Burgoyne's surrender at Saratoga.

For fourteen years Vermont was not part of the new United States and functioned as an independent republic. In January of 1791, however, after settling its border disputes with neighboring states, Vermont adopted the United States Constitution and entered the Union as the fourteenth state.

See Scott Nos. 643, 903

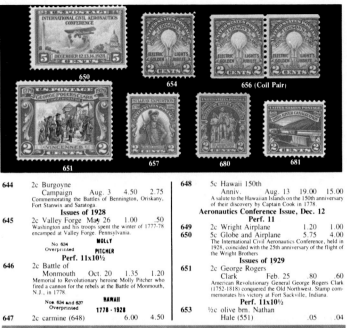

650 654 656 (Coil Pair) 651 657 680 681

644 2c Burgoyne Campaign Aug. 3 4.50 2.75
Commemorating the Battles of Bennington, Oriskany, Fort Stanwix and Saratoga.

Issues of 1928

645 2c Valley Forge May 26 1.00 .50
Washington and his troops spent the winter of 1777-78 encamped at Valley Forge, Pennsylvania.

No 634 Overprinted MOLLY PITCHER

Perf. 11x10½

646 2c Battle of Monmouth Oct. 20 1.35 1.20
Memorial to Revolutionary heroine Molly Pitcher who fired a cannon for the rebels at the Battle of Monmouth, N.J., in 1778.

Nos. 634 and 637 Overprinted HAWAII 1778 - 1928

647 2c carmine (648) 6.00 4.50

648 5c Hawaii 150th Anniv. Aug. 13 19.00 15.00
A salute to the Hawaiian Islands on the 150th anniversary of their discovery by Captain Cook in 1778.

Aeronautics Conference Issue, Dec. 12

Perf. 11

649 2c Wright Airplane 1.20 1.00

650 5c Globe and Airplane 5.75 4.00
The International Civil Aeronautics Conference, held in 1928, coincided with the 25th anniversary of the flight of the Wright Brothers

Issues of 1929

651 2c George Rogers Clark Feb. 25 .80 .60
American Revolutionary General George Rogers Clark (1752-1818) conquered the Old Northwest. Stamp commemorates his victory at Fort Sackville, Indiana.

Perf. 11x10½

653 ½c olive brn. Nathan Hale (551) .05 .04

BURGOYNE—SARATOGA

British military strategy was to seize control of New York and isolate the New England colonies. They hoped their success would result in a quick suppression of the American rebellion.

To secure this end a three-pronged offensive, slated to eventually meet in Albany, was launched. The largest of these units, about 8,000 British, Hessian and Indian troops, was led by General John Burgoyne. He laboriously marched his army through woods and swamps, encountering rebel forces along the way, and pressed on toward Albany. But he never reached it. At Freeman's farm, less than 30 miles from Albany, Burgoyne's troops suffered heavy casualties. Burgoyne attacked again at Freeman's farm in October. Short of men and supplies, Burgoyne was forced to retreat to Saratoga where the colonials, under General Gates, surrounded his troops. On October 17, 1777, Burgoyne surrendered his entire army.

Saratoga was more than America's first great battlefield victory of the Revolution. Often called the turning point of the war, it raised the morale of the patriots and induced France to aid the rebel cause.

See Scott Nos. 644, 1728

CHARLESTON, S.C.

A lot can happen to a town in three centuries. It can grow from a village to a fine city, be devastated by war, and then grow all over again. That's what happened to Charleston, S.C.

Charleston was founded in 1670. Less than twenty years later, it was a bustling port and commercial center. But in the 19th century, Charleston became the focus of the growing bitterness between North and South. In Charleston Harbor in 1861, Confederates captured Ft. Sumter, and the Civil War began. Under siege for over a year, the city suffered cruelly during the war. Recovery was slowed by a severe earthquake in 1886. But by 1900, Charleston boomed again.

Today it is a proud metropolis—a thriving center of industry and shipping, education and culture. It is also a living memorial to a gracious past, enriched by lovingly preserved old homes and marvelous formal gardens arranged just as gardens were two centuries ago. *See Scott No. 1178*

Electric Light Jubilee Issue
Perf. 11

654	2c Edison's First Lamp	Jun. 5	.90	.75

Perf.11x10½

655	2c carmine rose (654)	Jun. 11	.75	.25

Coil Stamp, Perf. 10 Vertically

656	2c carmine rose (654)	Jun. 11	22.50	1.50

Thomas A. Edison invented the first practical incandescent electric light bulb on Oct. 21. 1879.

Perf. 11

657	2c Sullivan Expedition	Jun.17	.70	.60

In 1779, General Sullivan led a daring Revolutionary War raid against the Iroquois in New York State.

Regular Issue of 1926-27

Overprinted **Kans.**

Perf. 11x10½

658	1c green Franklin (552)	1.50	1.35
659	1½c brown Harding (553)	2.75	2.50
660	2c carmine Washington (554)	2.25	.40
661	3c violet Lincoln (555)	13.50	10.00
662	4c yellow brown M. Washington (556)	14.50	5.00
663	5c deep blue T. Roosevelt (557)	10.00	7.00
664	6c red orange Garfield (558)	20.00	11.00
665	7c black McKinley (559)	20.00	17.50
666	8c olive green Grant (560)	60.00	45.00
667	9c light rose Jefferson (561)	10.00	7.50
668	10c orange yellow Monroe (562)	18.50	7.50

Overprinted **Nebr.**

669	1c green Franklin (552)	1.50	1.50
670	1½c brown Harding (553)	2.00	1.85
671	2c carmine Washington (554)	1.20	.65
672	3c violet Lincoln (555)	10.00	6.75
673	4c yellow brown M. Washington (556)	12.50	7.00
674	5c deep blue T. Roosevelt (557)	11.50	7.50
675	6c red orange Garfield (558)	27.50	16.50
676	7c black McKinley (559)	15.00	11.00
677	8c olive green Grant (560)	25.00	17.50
678	9c light rose Jefferson (561)	24.00	18.00
679	10c orange yellow Monroe (562)	70.00	15.00

Warning: Excellent forgeries of the Kansas and Nebraska overprints exist.

682

683

684

685

688

689

690

702

703

Perf. 11

680 2c Battle of Fallen Timbers Sep. 14 1.15 .90
A memorial to General "Mad" Anthony Wayne (1745-1796), who fought in the Revolution.

681 2c Ohio River Canal Oct. 19 .75 .60
Completion of the Ohio River Canalization Project between Cairo, Ill., and Pittsburgh, Pa.

Issues of 1930

682 2c Mass. Bay Colony Apr. 8 .65 .45
In 1630, English Puritans founded the Massachusetts Bay Colony. Stamp shows the seal of colony.

683 2c Carolina-Charleston Apr. 10 1.25 1.00
260th anniversary of the Carolina Province and 250th anniversary of the city of Charleston, S.C.

Perf. 11x10½

684	1½c Warren G. Harding	.20	.05
685	4c William H. Taft	.40	.06

Coil Stamps, Perf. 10 Vertically

686	1½ brown Harding (684)	.50	.07
687	4c brown Taft (685)	1.10	.25

Perf. 11

688 2c Braddock's Field Jul. 9 1.25 1.00
The Battle of Braddock's Field, fought near Ft. Duquesne, Pennsylvania in the French and Indian War, was a crushing defeat for the English.

689 2c Von Steuben Sep. 17 .75 .50
200th anniversary of the birth of the Prussian general (1730-1794), who helped train the Continental Army.

Issues of 1931

690 2c Pulaski Jan. 16 .30 .18
150th anniversary of the death of the Polish Count Casimir Pulaski (1748-1779), who was killed while fighting in our Revolution.

Perf. 11x10½

692	11c light blue Hayes (563)	2.50	.10
693	12c brown violet Cleveland (564)	5.00	.06
694	13c yellow green Harrison (622)	1.60	.10
695	14c dark blue Indian (565)	3.50	.30
696	15c gray Statue of Liberty (566)	8.50	.06

Perf. 10½x11

697	17c black Wilson (623)	4.00	.20
698	20c car, rose Golden Gate (567)	11.00	.05
699	25c blue green Niagara Falls (568)	8.25	.08
700	30c brown Buffalo (569)	20.00	.07
701	50c lilac Amphitheater (570)	60.00	.07

Perf. 11

702 2c Red Cross May 21 .15 .12
The American Red Cross was founded by Clara Barton in 1881.

703 2c Yorktown Oct. 12 .40 .25
The American Revolution ended at Yorktown, Virginia in 1781 when Washington, DeGrasse and Rochambeau defeated Cornwallis.

THE FRENCH AND INDIAN WARS

From 1689 to 1763, France and Great Britain waged war after war to determine who would control North America. Eventually the conflict spread to every part of the world where either country held territory. The last of the French and Indian Wars—one phase of the Seven Years' War raging in Europe—began in 1754. For the next four years it looked as if France would win. Then, slowly, the tide began to turn. In 1758 the British blockaded the Gulf of St. Lawrence. They won major victories at Louisburg, Ft. Frontenac, Ft. Ticonderoga. Finally, in 1759, the French forces surrendered. And France relinquished virtually all military and political power in North America.

See Scott No. 1071

Issues of 1932. Perf. 11x10½
Washington Bicentennial Issue, Jan. 1

704	½c Portrait by Charles W. Peale	.08	.05
705	1c Bust by Jean Antoine Houdon	.13	.04
706	1½c Portrait by Charles W. Peale	.40	.06
707	2c Portrait by Gilbert Stuart	.10	.03
708	3c Portrait by Charles W. Peale	.50	.06
709	4c Portrait by Charles P. Polk	.30	.06
710	5c Portrait by Charles W. Peale	2.25	.08
711	6c Portrait by John Trumbull	5.00	.06
712	7c Portrait by John Trumbull	.40	.12
713	8c Portrait by Charles B.J.F. Saint Memin	5.25	.70
714	9c Portrait by W. Williams	4.00	.25
715	10c Portrait by Gilbert Stuart	16.50	.10

200th anniversary of the birth of George Washington.

Perf. 11

716	2c Olympic Games	Jan. 25	.35	.20

The Olympic Winter Games of 1932 were held at Lake Placid in New York.

Perf. 11x10½

717	2c Arbor Day	Apr. 22	.18	.08

In Nebraska trees are planted every year on Arbor Day. Nebraskan Julius Sterling Morton created Arbor Day.

10th Olympic Games Issue, June 15

718	3c Runner at Starting Mark	.55	.06
719	5c Myron's Discobolus	.90	.20

In 1932 the Olympic Summer Games were held in Los Angeles, California.

720	3c Washington	Jun. 16	.15	.03
720b	Booklet pane of 6		22.50	*5.00*

Coil Stamps
Perf. 10 Vertically

721	3c deep violet (720)	Jun. 24	1.85	.08

Perf. 10 Horizontally

722	3c deep violet (720)	Oct. 12	1.25	.20

Perf. 10 Vertically

723	6c red orange Garfield (558)	Aug. 18	7.00	.20

Perf. 11

724	3c William Penn	Oct. 24	.30	.15

English Quaker William Penn (1644-1718) founded Pennsylvania; laid out Philadelphia in 1682.

725	3c Daniel Webster	Oct. 24	.50	.25

Issued for the 150th anniversary of the birth of the Massachusetts orator and statesman (1782-1852), who was twice Secretary of State, a Congressman, and Senator.

Issues of 1933

726	3c Georgia 200th Anniv.	Feb. 12	.35	.15

Englishman James Oglethorpe (1696-1785) established Georgia as a refuge for imprisoned debtors in 1733.

Perf. 10½x11

727	3c Peace of 1783	Apr. 19	.15	.10

In 1783, peace between the United States and the British was proclaimed.

Century of Progress Issue, May 25

728	1c Restoration of Ft. Dearborn	.12	.06
729	3c Fed. Building at Chicago 1933	.18	.04

The Century of Progress Exposition held in Chicago, Ill. in 1933, marked the "Windy City's" 100th anniversary.

American Philatelic Society Issue
Souvenir Sheets, Aug. 25 Without Gum, Imperf.

730	1c deep yellow green sheet of 25 (728)	45.00	30.00
730a	Single stamp	.75	.50
731	3c dp. vio. sheet of 25 (729)	37.50	25.00
731a	Single stamp	.60	.50

Issued in sheets of 25 with marginal inscriptions commemorating the 1933 convention of the American Philatelic Society, held in Chicago.

Perf. 10½x11

732	3c NRA	Aug. 15	.14	.03

Issued to publicize the National Recovery Act, F.D.R.'s program of aid for the depression-stricken country.

OLYMPICS

Excitement and drama surround the Olympics. Athletes from participating nations march into the stadium accompanied by the sounds of blaring trumpets and booming cannons. One of the most colorful highlights of the opening ceremonies is the lighting of the Olympic Flame. A relay of couriers carry the torch from Greece by plane, ship and foot. The final runner lights the flame, signalling the start of the competition. It burns continuously throughout the games.

Myth and history trace the origin of the Olympics to ancient Grecian religious ceremonies. After the Roman conquest of Greece, the games were abolished. There were no Olympics for 1500 years.

The modern Olympics were resumed in Athens, Greece in 1896. Since then, participating nations send their best amateur athletes to compete in a series of contests held every four years in a different country.

The Olympic games have been the scene of exciting individual achievements and dramatic events. Americans are particularly proud of their athletes. Johnny Weissmuller won 5 gold medals for swimming in 1924 and 1928. Jesse Owens took 4 gold medals in 1936 for track and field. Americans were outraged when Adolf Hitler refused to shake hands with this great black athlete. Mark Spitz set a record by winning 7 gold medals for swimming in 1972.

The Olympic flag, first flown in 1920, consists of 5 interlocking colored rings which represent the five major continents. At least one of the colors can be found on the flag of each participating nation.

See Scott Nos. 716, 718, 719, 1146, 1460-1462, 1695-1698, C85

Perf. 11

No.	Description	Date	Unused	Used
733	3c Byrd's Antarctic Expedition	Oct. 9	.85	.70

Issued in connection with Rear Admiral Richard E. Byrd's second South Pole expedition.

No.	Description	Date	Unused	Used
734	5c Tadeusz Kosciuszko	Oct. 13	.75	.30

Polish patriot Tadeusz Kosciuszko (1746-1817) fought in our Revolution and was awarded American citizenship in 1783.

Issues of 1934

National Stamp Exhibition Issue

Souvenir Sheet, Feb. 10 Without Gum, Imperf.

No.	Description	Date	Unused	Used
735	3c dk. blue sheet of 6 (733)		20.00	16.00
735a	Single stamp		2.50	2.25

Issued in sheets of six with marginal inscription commemorating the National Stamp Exhibition of 1934, held in New York City.

Perf. 11

No.	Description	Date	Unused	Used
736	3c Maryland 300th Anniversary	Mar. 23	.20	.15

Lord Baltimore founded Maryland in 1634

Mothers of America Issue, May 2

Perf. 11x10½

No.	Description	Date	Unused	Used
737	3c Whistler's Mother		.15	.06

Perf. 11

No.	Description	Date	Unused	Used
738	3c deep violet (737)		.20	.18

Issued in honor of Mother's Day. Stamp shows adaptation of the painting of Whistler's Mother

No.	Description	Date	Unused	Used
739	3c Wisconsin 300th Anniversary	Jul. 7	.20	.12

French explorer Jean Nicolet arrived at Green Bay in present-day Wisconsin in 1634.

ADM. RICHARD E. BYRD 1888-1957

Richard E. Byrd, explorer, aviator and U.S. Rear Admiral, won fame for his expeditions to the vast unknown areas of the polar regions. In 1926, Byrd and Floyd Bennett flew over the North Pole, a feat that earned them the Congressional Medal of Honor.

Byrd led his first expedition to the South Pole in 1928. From a base he called Little America, airplanes were flown over large areas, charting previously unexplored polar territory.

Byrd's second expedition to Antarctica in 1934, which emphasized scientific research, almost resulted in tragedy. In order to make weather observations, Byrd spent the five month winter alone in a cabin more than 100 miles from the safety of the base at Little America. Temperatures of –50 F and below and fumes from a faulty heating stove nearly ended Byrd's life. But he survived and made three subsequent Polar expeditions before his death in 1957.

SOUTH POLE

See Scott Nos. 733, 735, 753, 768

National Parks Issue

740	1c	El Capitan, Yosemite, Calif.	.10	.06
741	2c	Grand Canyon, Arizona	.15	.06
742	3c	Mt. Rainier and Mirror Lake, Washington	.20	.06
743	4c	Mesa Verde, Colorado	.45	.40
744	5c	Old Faithful, Yellowstone, Wyoming	1.00	.75
745	6c	Crater Lake, Oregon	1.40	.80
746	7c	Great Head, Acadia Park, Maine	1.00	.75
747	8c	Great White Throne, Zion Park, Utah	2.50	1.75
748	9c	Mt. Rockwell and Two Medicine Lake, Glacier National Park, Montana	2.25	.65
749	10c	Great Smoky Mountains, North Carolina	3.75	1.00

This series was issued in honor of National Parks Year.

GRAND CANYON

The awesome panorama of the Grand Canyon is one of the world's outstanding spectacles. The Colorado River and the forces of nature joined to chisel the barren rock into multitudes of buttes, peaks and canyons within canyon. The walls of the huge chasm have been carved into a series of cliffs and terraces much like an enormous staircase. The beauty of the canyon is heightened by layers of rock reflecting glowing bands of spectacular color. The hundreds of gorges, which join the main canyon on both sides, further enhance the canyon's splendor.

The colorful canyon rocks were formed millions of years ago. Granite and schist, which make up the inner gorge, are believed to be more than 4,000,000,000 years old.

The Grand Canyon was established as a national park in 1919. Scenic roads and trails provide access to the major attractions of the canyon. Adventure-seekers can journey through the canyon by mule or ride the roaring rapids in an inflatable raft.

See Scott Nos. 741, 757

GRAND CANYON

COLORADO

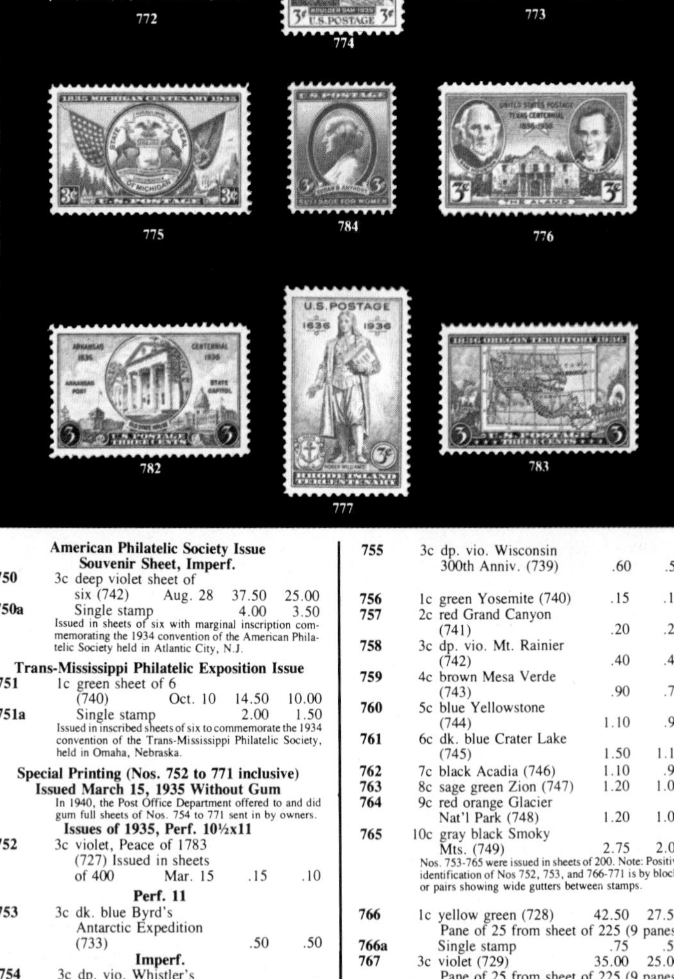

772 774 773 775 784 776 782 777 783

American Philatelic Society Issue
Souvenir Sheet, Imperf.

750	3c deep violet sheet of six (742)	Aug. 28	37.50	25.00
750a	Single stamp		4.00	3.50

Issued in sheets of six with marginal inscription commemorating the 1934 convention of the American Philatelic Society held in Atlantic City, N.J.

Trans-Mississippi Philatelic Exposition Issue

751	1c green sheet of 6 (740)	Oct. 10	14.50	10.00
751a	Single stamp		2.00	1.50

Issued in inscribed sheets of six to commemorate the 1934 convention of the Trans-Mississippi Philatelic Society, held in Omaha, Nebraska.

Special Printing (Nos. 752 to 771 inclusive)
Issued March 15, 1935 Without Gum

In 1940, the Post Office Department offered to and did gum full sheets of Nos. 754 to 771 sent in by owners.

Issues of 1935, Perf. 10½x11

752	3c violet, Peace of 1783 (727) Issued in sheets of 400	Mar. 15	.15	.10

Perf. 11

753	3c dk. blue Byrd's Antarctic Expedition (733)	.50	.50

Imperf.

754	3c dp. vio. Whistler's Mother (737)	.60	.50
755	3c dp. vio. Wisconsin 300th Anniv. (739)	.60	.50
756	1c green Yosemite (740)	.15	.15
757	2c red Grand Canyon (741)	.20	.20
758	3c dp. vio. Mt. Rainier (742)	.40	.40
759	4c brown Mesa Verde (743)	.90	.75
760	5c blue Yellowstone (744)	1.10	.90
761	6c dk. blue Crater Lake (745)	1.50	1.10
762	7c black Acadia (746)	1.10	.90
763	8c sage green Zion (747)	1.20	1.00
764	9c red orange Glacier Nat'l Park (748)	1.20	1.00
765	10c gray black Smoky Mts. (749)	2.75	2.00

Nos. 753-765 were issued in sheets of 200. Note: Positive identification of Nos 752, 753, and 766-771 is by blocks or pairs showing wide gutters between stamps.

766	1c yellow green (728)	42.50	27.50
	Pane of 25 from sheet of 225 (9 panes)		
766a	Single stamp	.75	.50
767	3c violet (729)	35.00	25.00
	Pane of 25 from sheet of 225 (9 panes)		
767a	Single stamp	.60	.50

SUSAN B. ANTHONY

Susan B. Anthony dedicated her life to two great political goals. Both lay so close to the heart of American law that they could not reach fulfillment until the Constitution of the United States was changed. Well, if that's what it takes, she decided, let's get the Constitution changed! Daughter of a zealous Massachusetts Abolitionist, young Susan took up her father's favorite cause, serving as an agent for the American Anti-Slavery Society. When black men were granted civil and political rights under the 14th and 15th Amendments to the Constitution, her first great goal was achieved. Now she could dedicate herself totally to the second one - civil and political rights for women.

In those days, America barred half its citizens - the women — from the polls. Only men could vote. This was the injustice that Susan B. Anthony fought. She collaborated in the publication of a weekly newspaper to spread the word. She led a group of women to the polls in Rochester, N.Y., to force a test of women's right to vote. And when she was arrested and convicted, she refused to pay the fine. She wrote, she lectured, she organized. She campaigned relentlessly for an amendment to the Constitution that would grant women the right to vote. That amendment - the 19th, became the law of the land fourteen years after she died. Today she remains a heroine to all those who strive for equal opportunity and equal rights for women around the world.

See Scott No. 784

768	3c dark blue (733)	20.00	16.00
	Pane of 6 from sheet of 150 (25 panes)		
768a	Single stamp	2.50	2.25
769	1c green (740)	12.00	8.50
	Pane of 6 from sheet of 120 (20 panes)		
769a	Single stamp	1.60	1.40
770	3c deep violet (742)	27.50	22.50
	Pane of 6 from sheet of 120 (20 panes)		
770a	Single stamp	3.25	3.00
771	16c dark blue Seal of U.S. (CE2), issued in sheets of 200	2.00	2.00

Perf. 11x10½

772 3c Connecticut 300th Anniv. Apr. 26 .12 .06
Connecticut was settled in 1635. The Founders hid their charter in the Charter Oak (shown).

773 3c California-Pacific Exposition May 29 .12 .06
The 1935 Exposition was held in San Diego.

Perf. 11

774 3c Boulder Dam Sep. 30 .12 .06
Boulder Dam, now Hoover Dam, was dedicated on September 30, 1935.

Perf. 11x10½

775 3c Michigan 100th Anniv. Nov. 1 .12 .06
Michigan became a state in 1835.

Issues of 1936

776 3c Texas 100th Anniv. Mar. 2 .12 .06
Texas became a Republic in 1836.

Perf. 10½x11

777 3c Rhode Island 300th Anniv. May 4 .12 .06
Rhode Island was founded in 1636 by dissenters from the Massachusetts Bay Colony led by Roger Williams.

Third International Philatelic Exhibition Issue
Souvenir Sheet, Imperf.

778 violet, sheet of 4 diff stamps (772, 733, 775 and 776) May 9 3.75 3.00
Issued in sheets of four with marginal inscription commemorating the Third International Philatelic Exhibition of 1936, held in New York.

Perf. 11x10½

782 3c Arkansas 100th Anniv. Jun. 15 .12 .06
Arkansas became a state in 1836.

783 3c Oregon Territory Jul. 14 .12 .06
The Oregon Trail, which played an important role in the settlement of the West, was opened in 1836.

784 3c Susan B. Anthony Aug. 26 .10 .05
Issued for the 16th anniversary of women's suffrage. Susan B. Anthony was a national leader in the struggle for women's rights.

Issues of 1936-37
Army Issue

785	1c George Washington and Nathanael Greene	.10	.06
786	2c Andrew Jackson and Winfield Scott	.15	.06
787	3c Generals Sherman, Grant and Sheridan	.20	.08
788	4c Generals Robert E. Lee and "Stonewall" Jackson	.65	.15
789	5c U.S. Military Academy, West Point	.70	.15

Issued to honor United States Army.

AIR FORCE

Until being made a separate and independent branch of the U.S. military forces in 1947, the U.S. Air Force had been a part of the Army. Indeed, it had been established as the Aeronautical Division of the U.S. Army in 1907, only four years after the Wright Brothers' first successful powered flight at Kitty Hawk, N.C.

In World War I, aircraft were at first used for observation only, but in the very nature of things aerial combat soon became quite common. "Dogfights," as they were called, were battles between individual pilots which usually ended in one or other of the planes plunging to earth in a fiery crash.

In World War II, the Army Air Corp (as it was then known) proved invaluable. Fighter planes sought out and destroyed the enemy craft, while bombers devastated his transportation and industry.

The warfare of the future—and possibly the course of history—was altered when, on August 6, 1945, a bombardier in a B-29 named *Enola Gay* released an atomic bomb on Hiroshima, Japan.

Today, the Air Force is ever alert to protect the United States and safeguard its citizens. In addition, through many diversified space projects the Air Force, along with private industry and the National Aeronautic and Space Agency (NASA), is engaged in space exploration, while experimenting with various rockets and spacecraft.

See Scott Nos. 1013, 1067

Navy Issue

No.	Description	Unused	Used
790	1c John Paul Jones and John Barry	.10	.06′
791	2c Stephen Decatur and Thomas MacDonough	.15	.06
792	3c Admirals David G. Farragut and David D. Porter	.20	.08
793	4c Admirals William T. Sampson, George Dewey and Winfield S. Schley	.65	.15
794	5c Seal of U.S. Naval Academy and Naval Cadets	.70	.15

Issued to honor the United States Navy.

790

791

792

793

794

U.S. MARINES

The United States Marine Corps is organized, trained and equipped for the primary purpose of engaging in integrated land-sea warfare—at any time and anywhere. Smaller than the other branches of the military services, the Marine Corps is noted for pride, dedication, spirit, and its readiness to speed to any trouble spot in the world. It has often been said that "when the Marines have landed, the situation is well in hand."

The Marine Corps was established by the First Continental Congress on November 10, 1775, and its members participated in many Revolutionary War battles.

The Corps has always been among the first to fight in every conflict and Marines have served this country in every part of the globe. The famous Marine anthem recalls this service: "From the halls of Montezuma to the shores of Tripoli." Marine heroics in 1918 at Belleau Wood are credited with saving Paris in World War I.

In World War II, the Corps led the amphibious landings in the island-to-island liberation of Japanese-held territory. The largest Marine battle of the war at Iwo Jima resulted in the greatest toll of casualties. This costly victory has been commemorated by a group statue of the Marines who raised the American flag atop Mount Suribachi during the heat of the struggle.

See Scott Nos. 929, 1315, 1569

795 796 798

800 801

799 802

Issues of 1937

795 3c Northwest Ordinance
150 Anniv. Jul. 13 .12 .06

The Northwest Territory was created in 1787. It included the present states of Ohio, Indiana, Illinois, Michigan, Wisconsin, and part of Minnesota.

Perf. 11

796 5c Virginia Dare Aug. 18 .40 .25

Marks the 350th anniversary of the birth of the first child born in America of English parents, at Roanoke Island.

Society of Philatelic Americans Souvenir Sheet, Imperf.

797 10c blue green
(749) Aug. 26 1.25 .60

Issued in sheets of one stamp with marginal inscription commemorating the 43rd Annual Convention of the Society of Philatelic Americans held in Asheville, North Carolina.

OLD HAWAIIAN KINGS

The Hawaiian Islands, which entered the Union as the 50th state in 1949, have the unique distinction of being the only state that was ever a royal kingdom.

In 1795, Kamehameha I conquered the Islands, united them into a kingdom and started a royal dynasty. During the reigns of Kamehameha II through V (1819-1874), missionaries converted most Hawaiians to Christianity. Also during this period large agricultural projects were developed on the Islands, and due to the desperate need for laborers, the Islands became a melting pot.

Kalakaua, called the "Merry Monarch," succeeded Kamehameha V. During his reign (1874-91) Hawaiian music and the hula reappeared on the cultural scene, and the pineapple and sugar cane became the staple crops of the Islands. Upon his death, his sister Liliuokalani became queen. Her attempts to increase her royal power led to a bloodless coup in 1893. Queen Liliuokalani (1891-1893), who wrote the famous *Aloha Oe* ("Farewell to Thee"), was the last Hawaiian monarch.

See Scott Nos. 647-648, 799, C46, C55, C94

PUERTO RICO

Puerto Rico ("Rich Port") is the only United States territory on which Christopher Columbus ever set foot. It was discovered on his second voyage to the New World in 1493. Ponce de Leon established the first Spanish settlement in 1508 and gave the island its name.

Puerto Rico remained a Spanish colony until 1898 when, as a result of the Spanish-American War, it became a territory of the United States.

In 1917 all Puerto Ricans became citizens of the United States and since 1948 the island has elected its own governor. In 1952, Puerto Rico was established as a self-governing commonwealth economically linked to the United States.

See Scott Nos. 801, 983

Perf. 11x10½

No.	Description	Date		
798	3c Constitution 150th Anniv.	Sep. 17	.15	.07

Issued on the 150th anniversary of the signing of the Constitution, Sep. 17, 1787.

Territorial Issues
Perf. 10½x11

No.	Description	Date		
799	3c Hawaii	Oct. 18	.15	.07

Perf. 11x10½

No.	Description	Date		
800	3c Alaska	Nov. 12	.15	.07
801	3c Puerto Rico	Nov. 25	.15	.07
802	3c Virgin Islands	Dec. 15	.15	.07

These stamps show a statue of King Kamehameha I (Hawaii), Mt. McKinley (Alaska), Fortaleza Castle (Puerto Rico), and Charlotte Amalie (Virgin Islands).

STONEWALL JACKSON

Thomas Jackson was the greatest of Robert E. Lee's Civil War generals. Born in Virginia and orphaned young, Jackson graduated from West Point and immediately joined the American army in Mexico. There he first met General Lee. After the Mexican War was won, Jackson resigned his commission and became professor of artillery at the Virginia Military Institute. When the Civil War broke out he joined the Confederate army.

A colonel now, Jackson organized a volunteer army brigade. In July 1861, Union troops invaded Virginia. On the field of Bull Run, Jackson stationed his brigade in a strong line—a wall of men that withstood attack against overwhelming odds. And he was "Stonewall" Jackson from then on. Victory followed victory—in the Shenandoah Valley, Winchester, Cross Keys, Port Republic, Bull Run a second time, Harpers Ferry, Fredericksburg. He was invincible. But after a great victory at Chancellorsville, Jackson was accidentally shot by his own men. His left arm was amputated. Pneumonia set in. One of the greatest tacticians in military history was dead.

See Scott No. 787

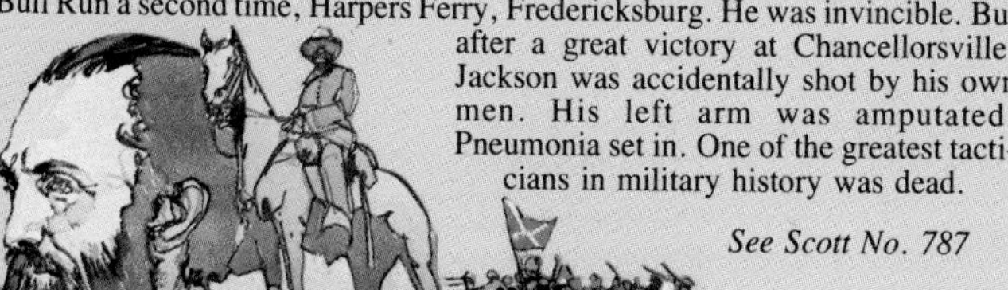

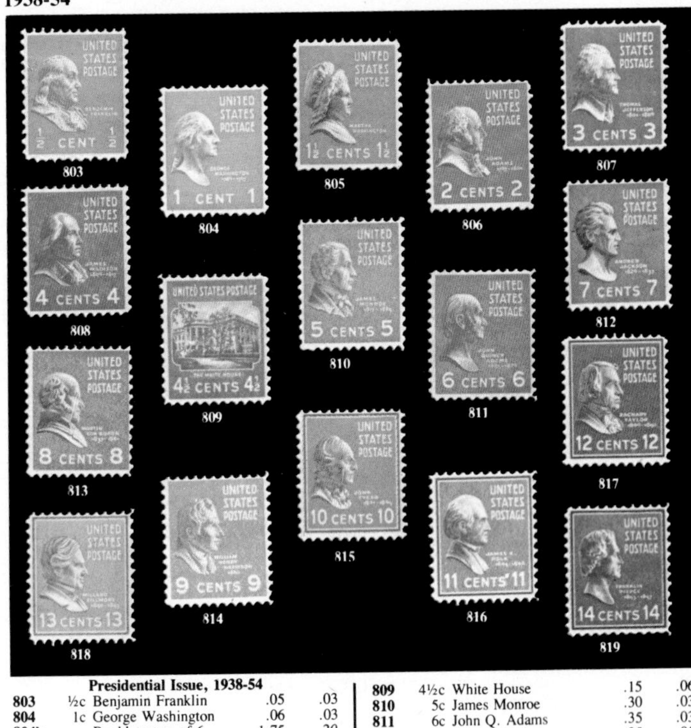

		Presidential Issue, 1938-54		
803	½c	Benjamin Franklin	.05	.03
804	1c	George Washington	.06	.03
804b		Booklet pane of 6	1.75	*.20*
805	1½c	Martha Washington	.06	.03
806	2c	John Adams	.06	.03
806b		Booklet pane of 6	4.25	*.50*
807	3c	Thomas Jefferson	.10	.03
807a		Booklet pane of 6	8.50	*.50*
808	4c	James Madison	.30	.04
809	4½c	White House	.15	.06
810	5c	James Monroe	.30	.03
811	6c	John Q. Adams	.35	.03
812	7c	Andrew Jackson	.35	.05
813	8c	Martin Van Buren	.40	.04
814	9c	William H. Harrison	.45	.04
815	10c	John Tyler	.45	.03
816	11c	James K. Polk	.65	.08
817	12c	Zachary Taylor	.90	.06

WHITE HOUSE

Construction of the "Presidential Mansion" began in 1792. Still unfinished, and drafty and uncomfortable, it was first occupied by John Adams and his family in 1800. Mrs. Adams made the most of her new home and hung the wash in the East Room.

The British burned the White House in the War of 1812. President James Madison fled, but his wife Dolley Madison saved the famous Gilbert Stuart portrait of Washington.

The White House is located in the heart of the Capital and is surrounded by beautiful park-like gardens. During the Civil War, troops protecting Washington were bivouacked on the lawn, and military quarters were set up in the East Room. During World War I there were no troops stationed there, but sheep grazed on the White House grass.

During President Harry Truman's administration in 1948, the White House was discovered to be on the verge of collapse. Massive rebuilding and renovation were required, but the original floor plan was preserved. During her husband's administration, Mrs. John F. Kennedy endeavored to restore the interior as it was in the early eighteen hundreds. *See Scott Nos. 809, 844, 932, 990*

No.	Denom.	Subject	Unused	Used
818	13c	Millard Filmore	.90	.08
819	14c	Franklin Pierce	.90	.10
820	15c	James Buchanan	.65	.03
821	16c	Abraham Lincoln	1.20	.25
822	17c	Andrew Johnson	1.20	.12
823	18c	Ulysses S. Grant	1.40	.08
824	19c	Rutherford B. Hayes	1.20	.30
825	20c	James A. Garfield	.90	.03
826	21c	Chester A. Arthur	1.35	.10
827	22c	Grover Cleveland	1.35	.35
828	24c	Benjamin Harrison	2.25	.25
829	25c	William McKinley	1.35	.03
830	30c	Theodore Roosevelt	7.00	.05
831	50c	William Howard Taft	10.50	.06
		Perf. 11		
832	$1	Woodrow Wilson	16.50	.10
832b		Wmkd. USIR	100.00	25.00
833	$2	Warren G. Harding	42.50	4.25
834	$5	Calvin Coolidge	185.00	4.00

CHESTER A. ARTHUR

Chester A. Arthur was a small-town boy who made good in the big city. Born in Fairfield, Vermont, he moved to New York in 1854 to practice law. Slowly and steadily, he rose to a position of power in New York's Republican party. The New York Republicans wanted to see Ulysses S. Grant run for a third term as president. When the reform-minded James A. Garfield won the nomination instead, Arthur was chosen vice presidential nominee to appease a disgruntled New York delegation. But in 1881, four months after taking office, Garfield was assassinated. And Arthur, an unknown factor to most Americans, was plummeted into the presidency. Many people considered him unqualified for the job. Surprisingly enough, his administration was scandal-free. In fact, he supported some important reform measures. Chester Arthur turned his back on narrow party loyalties, conducted himself judiciously, and earned the confidence of the nation.

See Scott No. 826

Issues of 1938
Perf. 11x10½

835	3c Constitution Ratification	Jun. 21	.25	.08

150th anniversary of the ratification of the Constitution.

Perf. 11

836	3c Swedish-Finnish 300th Anniv.	Jun. 27	.25	.10

In 1638 Swedish and Finnish settlers led by Peter Minuit established a settlement at Wilmington, Del.

Perf. 11x10½

837	3c Northwest Territory	Jul. 15	.25	.08

The settlement of the Northwest Territory began in 1788.

838	3c Iowa Territory 100th Anniv.	Aug. 24	.25	.08

The Iowa Territory was created in 1838.

Issues of 1939
Coil Stamps, Perf. 10 Vertically

839	1c	green Washington (804)	.20	.06
840	1½c	bistre brn. M. Washington (805)	.25	.06
841	2c	rose car. Adams (806)	.25	.05
842	3c	deep vio. Jefferson (807)	.50	.04
843	4c	red violet Madison (808)	6.25	.20
844	4½c	dk. gray White House (809)	.50	.20
845	5c	bright blue Monroe (810)	4.00	.35

835

838

852

837

855

836

WILLIAM HOWARD TAFT

In his own time, Taft was considered an arch-conservative. But history has proved that his ideas were much more progressive than even he realized! Taft was appointed Secretary of War in 1904 by Teddy Roosevelt. From that highly visible post, he won the Republican presidential nomination in 1908—an honor he never wanted. He was not enthused with the idea of running for office. Even so, he won the election.

Taft was never much of a politician, but his presidency did give the nation four years of honest government. Some of his favorite causes became everyone's favorite causes much later, such as conservation of natural resources and insistence on the right of workers to strike. After he lost his bid for reelection in 1912, Taft became a professor of law at Yale. In 1921 he was appointed chief justice of the U.S. Supreme Court. It was a role he enjoyed far more than the presidency.

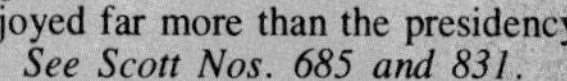

See Scott Nos. 685 and 831.

No.	Description	Date	Unused	Used
846	6c red org. J.Q. Adams (811)		1.10	.20
847	10c brown red Tyler (815)		12.50	.40
	Perf. 10 Horizontally			
848	1c green Washington (804)		.60	.12
849	1½c bistre brn. M. Washington (805)		.85	.20
850	2c rose car. Adams (806)		2.00	.20
851	3c deep violet Jefferson (807)		2.00	.25
	Perf. 10½x11			
852	3c Golden Gate Exposition	Feb. 18	.12	.06

The Golden Gate International Exposition was held at San Francisco in 1939 on man-made Treasure Island.

No.	Description	Date	Unused	Used
853	3c New York World's Fair	Apr. 1	.15	.06

Issued for the opening of the New York World's Fair of 1939.

Perf. 11

No.	Description	Date	Unused	Used
854	3c Washington's Inauguration	Apr. 30	.25	.10

In 1789 George Washington (1732-1799) became the first President of the United States.

Perf. 11x10½

No.	Description	Date	Unused	Used
855	3c Baseball Anniversary 100th	Jun. 12	.22	.08

Baseball was 100 years old in 1939. The game originated in New York at Cooperstown.

853

854

856

858

857

859 860 861 862 863

864 865 866 867 868

Perf. 11

856	3c Panama Canal Aug. 15	.22	.08

25th anniversary of opening of the Panama Canal.

Perf. 10½x11

857	3c 300th Anniv. of Printing Sep. 25	.12	.08

The first book printed in America came from the press of Stephen Daye (shown). It was *The Bay Psalm Book*.

Perf. 11x10½

858	3c 50th Anniv. of Statehood Nov. 2	.12	.08

North Dakota, South Dakota, Montana and Washington became states in 1889.

Famous Americans Issue, 1940, Perf. 10½x11

Authors

859	1c Washington Irving	.08	.06
860	2c James Fenimore Cooper	.10	.08
861	3c Ralph Waldo Emerson	.12	.06
862	5c Louisa May Alcott	.35	.30
863	10c Samuel L. Clemens (Mark Twain)	2.50	2.00

Poets

864	1c Henry W. Longfellow	.12	.08
865	2c John Greenleaf Whittier	.10	.08
866	3c James Russell Lowell	.18	.06
867	5c Walt Whitman	.35	.25
868	10c James Whitcomb Riley	3.50	2.50

Educators

869	1c Horace Mann	.09	.08
870	2c Mark Hopkins	.10	.06
871	3c Charles W. Eliot	.30	.06
872	5c Frances E. Willard	.50	.35
873	10c Booker T. Washington	2.00	1.75

Scientists

874	1c John James Audubon	.08	.06
875	2c Dr. Crawford W. Long	.10	.06
876	3c Luther Burbank	.10	.06
877	5c Dr. Walter Reed	.30	.25
878	10c Jane Addams	2.00	1.75

869 870 871 872 873

874 875 876 877 878

HENRY WADSWORTH LONGFELLOW

Henry Wadsworth Longfellow was American through and through. His family settled in Massachusetts in 1680, and his grandfather was a general in the American Revolution. When Longfellow's father suggested that young Henry enter the family law office, the son replied, "I most eagerly aspire after future eminence in literature." And eminence in literature he achieved — more than any other poet of his time.

There was a lot of glory in the life of Henry Wadsworth Longfellow, and a lot of tragedy, too. He lost two wives, the first only four years after they were wed and the second in a horrifying accident. Longfellow succumbed to depression after that. But even in the long period of melancholy that followed his second wife's death, he steadfastly produced his immensely popular narrative poems. Would you believe that a nation could be so enthused over a piece of poetry? In 1841, Longfellow's "The Wreck of the Hesperus" took America by storm. Can you imagine just about every literate family in the country buying a book-length epic poem?

He was a good deal more than just a poet. Longfellow was a linguist and translator, a professor and essayist, and an author of textbooks and novels as well as poems. Fluent in French, Italian, Spanish and German, he presided over Harvard's modern language department for 18 years. His translation into English of Dante's "Divine Comedy" is still considered one of the finest of the time. Still, it was his own narrative poems that immortalized him.

The 19th Century Americans, whose roots were comparatively new, envied the ancient heritage of their European cousins. With his poetry, Longfellow filled America's longing for a legendary past. In 1855 he set down an American Indian tale that all Americans could love — "The Song of Hiawatha". In 1858 he published a romance of colonial days that swept the nation — "The Courtship of Miles Standish". In 1863 he lifted an obscure Revolutionary hero from the dust of history and made his name shine for all time — "Paul Revere's Ride"

His poems, with their exciting plots and lilting rhythms, were loved not only in America, but everywhere English was spoken and read. After his death, a memorial to him was unveiled in Westminster Abbey, resting place of England's literary giants. And back home in the U. S., Longfellow remained far and away the most popular poet of the 19th Century.

See Scott No. 864.

879 880 881 882 883

884 885 886 887 888

		Composers		
879	1c	Stephen Collins Foster	.08	.06
880	2c	John Philip Sousa	.10	.06
881	3c	Victor Herbert	.15	.06
882	5c	Edward MacDowell	.50	.30
883	10c	Ethelbert Nevin	4.50	2.00
		Artists		
884	1c	Gilbert Charles Stuart	.08	.06
885	2c	James A. McNeill Whistler	.10	.06
886	3c	Augustus Saint-Gaudens	.10	.06
887	5c	Daniel Chester French	.40	.22
888	10c	Frederic Remington	2.50	2.25
		Inventors		
889	1c	Eli Whitney	.12	.08
890	2c	Samuel F. B. Morse	.10	.06
891	3c	Cyrus Hall McCormick	.20	.06
892	5c	Elias Howe	1.25	.40
893	10c	Alexander Graham Bell	10.50	3.25

STEPHEN COLLINS FOSTER 1826-1864

During the pre-Civil War period, Stephen Foster was one of America's most popular and prolific songwriters. He had little formal musical training, but had a great natural gift. He could sit at a piano and play almost any tune by ear. At a very early age, he began composing. One of his early compositions was "Oh! Susanna," which became quite popular and led to his being hired as songwriter for the famous Christy Minstrels. He wrote simple, moving songs inspired by Negro spirituals. Although many of these sentimental "plantation melodies" like "Swanee River" and "My Old Kentucky Home" tell of Southern life, he is known to have seen the South only once. Stephen Foster is also famous for such romantic ballads as "Beautiful Dreamer" and "Jeannie with the Light Brown Hair." In all, he composed more than 200 songs, writing lyrics as well as the music for most of them. His melodies have lived on to become an integral part of America's cultural heritage.

See Scott No. 879

ELI WHITNEY

Quick - what do you think of when you hear the name, Eli Whitney? The cotton gin, right? But Eli Whitney invented something that's had an even more profound effect on American economic history than that. Whitney invented the concept of the interchangeable part. And that led straight to the development of mass production — the basis for all modern manufacturing.

Whitney was a farmer's son, born and raised in Massachusetts. When he was 24, he graduated from Yale and accepted a teaching job in Georgia. But after he got there the job fell through and Whitney was stranded.

The mills of England were desperate for cotton at the time. The American South was not exporting large amounts of cotton because the variety that grew resisted cleaning. The cotton fibre stuck like glue to the seed. Eli Whitney figured that the inventor of a machine that would clean the cotton would make a fortune for the South and himself. No sooner said than done! A few weeks later he completed a working model of a cotton gin that took in fibre and seed at one end and deposited clean cotton fibre at the other. It was such a simple machine that any handyman could reproduce it. Unfortunately, they did. Whitney patented his invention in 1793, and with a friend, set up a factory to manufacture the gins.

Meanwhile, all over the South, Whitney's cotton gin was being pirated. The planters copied the invention and refused to pay its inventor a penny. So, by 1797, the two partners were out of business. But Eli Whitney had brought prosperity to the agricultural South, and he was destined to do the same for the industrial North.

In 1797 the U. S. government asked private contractors to manufacture 40,000 muskets. In those days, a single skilled workman made one complete musket at a time, forming each part individually. So no two muskets were exactly alike, and if a part broke, a replacement had to be specially made. Whitney designed machines with which an unskilled workman would make many pieces of one particular musket part—but each piece would be precisely the same as all the others. The parts were interchangeable, and so could be instantly replaced if broken.

In 1801 President Jefferson watched as Eli Whitney chose at random from piles of musket parts and assembled one complete and perfect musket after another. The demonstration marked the birth of American mass production.

See Scott No. 889.

889 890 891 892 893 894 895 896 897 898

PONY EXPRESS

The Pony Express, a private business enterprise established on April 3, 1860, set a goal of 10-day service between St. Joseph, Mo., where the railroad ended, and Sacramento, Calif. Skillful and daring horseback riders were recruited to carry the mail over the 1,966-mile route. Relay stations were positioned 10 to 15 miles apart, and the riders sped from one to the other with rainproof leather pouches filled with letters strapped to their saddles. The riders switched to fresh mounts as many as eight times during their dangerous dash across the American West. The most famous and picturesque of these daring horsemen was "Buffalo Bill" Cody, who was only 14 years old when he began carrying the mail for the Pony Express.

Buffalo Bill and his companions rode in all kinds of weather and often had to resist the attacks of Indians and bandits. They came through with flying colors and lost the mail only once. Like its greater counterpart, the United States Postal Service, the Pony Express delivered the mail regardless of weather conditions or obstacles.

Soon made obsolete by the completion of the transcontinental telegraph system, the short but nonetheless exciting and eventful saga of the Pony Express ended on October 24, 1861, only 18 months after it had begun.

See Scott 894, 1154

Issues of 1940
Perf. 11x10½

894 3c Pony Express Apr. 3 .50 .20
The famed Pony Express began to carry mail across the continent in 1860.

Perf. 10½x11

895 3c Pan American Union Apr. 14 .45 .15
The Pan American Union was established in 1890. The stamp shows the "Three Graces" from Botticelli's "Spring".

Perf. 11x10½

896 3c Idaho Statehood 50th Anniv. Jul. 3 .20 .08
Idaho became a state in 1890.

Perf. 10½x11

897 3c Wyoming Statehood 50th Anniv. Jul. 10 .20 .08
Wyoming became a state in 1890.

Perf. 11x10½

898 3c Coronado Expedition Sep. 7 .20 .08
In 1540, Coronado, the discoverer of the Grand Canyon, led a Spanish expedition through the Southwest, hoping to find the golden "Cities of Cibola."

National Defense Issue, Oct. 16

899 1c Statue of Liberty .05 .04
900 2c Anti-aircraft Gun .06 .03
901 3c Torch of Enlightenment .12 .03

Perf. 10½x11

902 3c Thirteenth Amendment Oct. 20 .25 .15
The Thirteenth Amendment to the Constitution, which abolished slavery, was ratified in 1865.

899 900 901 902

STATUE OF LIBERTY

The statue of "Liberty Enlightening the World" standing on Bedloe's Island (renamed Liberty Island in 1956) in New York Harbor, gateway to the New World, offers an inspirational welcome to the oppressed of all nations who have come to America's shores in search of liberty and opportunity. The statue was a gift from the people of France to the people of the United States to celebrate the 100th year of American independence and to commemorate the continuing friendship between the two nations.

The colossal statue stands on a concrete base and rises to a height of 305 feet. Broken shackles at her feet represent Liberty's victory over tyranny. Her left hand holds a tablet inscribed with the date "July 4, 1776" and her right hand, raised high, holds the torch of freedom as a beacon of hope to all mankind.

The Statue of Liberty was created by Frédéric Auguste Bartholdi, a renowned French sculptor, and on its pedestal is a sonnet "The New Colossus" written by Emma Lazarus, which closes as follows:

". . . Give me your tired, your poor,
Your huddled masses yearning to breathe free,
The wretched refuse of your teeming shore.
Send these, the homeless, tempest-tost to me,
I lift my lamp beside the golden door."

See Scott Nos. 566, 596, 1035, 1041, 1042, 1044A, 1057, 1075, 1599, 1619, C35, C58, C63, C80, C87

903

904

905

907

906

908

922

923

924

THE TELEGRAPH

The word was coined in 1792 by a Frenchman named Chappe. "Tele" meant "far," and "graph" meant "to write." To write far: telegraph. But it took almost half a century to get from the invention of the word to the invention of a working electric telegraph machine.

In 1727 an ingenious Englishman transmitted an electrical impulse over one-sixth of a mile of thread. Some researchers in Germany sent impulses over wires, releasing bubbles in a trough at the other end - but bubbles proved rather hard to read. Then, in the United States in 1835, Samuel F. B. Morse invented an electric telegraph and a signal code to use with it.

With a government appropriation, Morse built a telegraph line between Baltimore and Washington. On May 24, 1844, the first message flashed over the wires: "What hath God wrought?" The machine that clicked it out was the ancestor of the machines that today enable widely separated computers to exchange and process information, and also the machines that control space vehicles by microwave radiotelegraph.

See Scott Nos. 890 and 924.

909

910

911

912

913

914

915

916

917

918

919

920

921

Issue of 1941
Perf. 11x10½

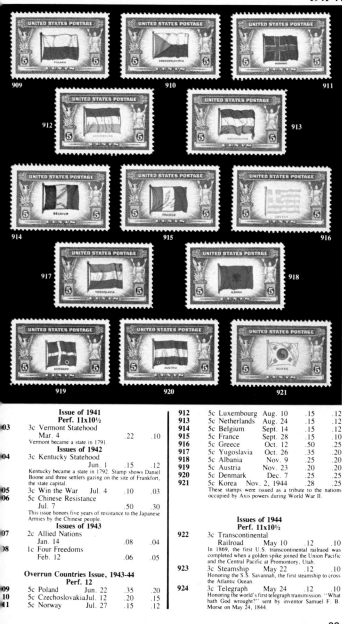

03	3c Vermont Statehood Mar. 4	.22	.10

Vermont became a state in 1791.

Issues of 1942

04	3c Kentucky Statehood Jun. 1	.15	.12

Kentucky became a state in 1792. Stamp shows Daniel Boone and three settlers gazing on the site of Frankfort, the state capital.

05	3c Win the War Jul. 4	.10	.03
06	5c Chinese Resistance Jul. 7	.50	.30

This issue honors five years of resistance to the Japanese Armies by the Chinese people.

Issues of 1943

07	2c Allied Nations Jan. 14	.08	.04
)8	1c Four Freedoms Feb. 12	.06	.05

Overrun Countries Issue, 1943-44
Perf. 12

09	5c Poland	Jun. 22	.35	.20
10	5c Czechoslovakia	Jul. 12	.20	.15
11	5c Norway	Jul. 27	.15	.12
912	5c Luxembourg	Aug. 10	.15	.12
913	5c Netherlands	Aug. 24	.15	.12
914	5c Belgium	Sept. 14	.15	.12
915	5c France	Sept. 28	.15	.10
916	5c Greece	Oct. 12	.50	.25
917	5c Yugoslavia	Oct. 26	.35	.20
918	5c Albania	Nov. 9	.25	.20
919	5c Austria	Nov. 23	.20	.20
920	5c Denmark	Dec. 7	.25	.25
921	5c Korea	Nov. 2, 1944	.28	.25

These stamps were issued as a tribute to the nations occupied by Axis powers during World War II.

Issues of 1944
Perf. 11x10½

922	3c Transcontinental Railroad	May 10	.12	.10

In 1869, the first U.S. transcontinental railraod was completed when a golden spike joined the Union Pacific and the Central Pacific at Promontory, Utah.

923	3c Steamship	May 22	.12	.10

Honoring the S.S. Savannah, the first steamship to cross the Atlantic Ocean.

924	3c Telegraph	May 24	.12	.10

Honoring the world's first telegraph transmission. "What hath God wrought?" sent by inventor Samuel F. B. Morse on May 24, 1844.

925
926
927
928
929

925 3c Philippines Sep. 27 .12 .10
A tribute to the U.S.-Philippine resistance to the Japanese at Corregidor, Jan.-May 1942.

926 3c 50th Anniversary of Motion Picture Oct. 31 .12 .10
In 1892, Edison's "Kinetoscope" the first motion picture device, had its first public showing.

Issues of 1945

927 3c Florida Statehood Mar. 3 .10 .08
Florida became a U.S. territory in 1822; a state in 1845.

928 5c United Nations Conference Apr. 25 .12 .0
The United Nations Conference of April 25, 1945 was multinational effort to establish the U.N. and to draft charter for it.

Perf. 10½x11

929 3c Iwo Jima (Marines) Jul. 11 .10 .0
A tribute to U.S. Marines who fought in World War II.

WORLD WAR II

World War II affected more people an created more social, economic and politi cal upheaval than any other major conflic in history. It was the costliest war in term of lives and property. Bombs and missile of tremendous power destroyed entir cities. Over 50 nations were directly in volved and men fought in nearly ever sector of the globe.

How did the world again become in volved in such a terrible global conflic little more than 20 years after World Wa I, the "Great War"? Problems created or left unsettled by World War I remained The League of Nations was established, with great hopes, in order to peacefull settle these disagreements. But the United States did not join and the League wa powerless.

Dictators rose to power in the wake of the economic chaos of the 1920's an '30's. Hitler in Germany, Mussolini in Italy, and Tojo in Japan sought to build grea empires and control markets and natural resources. Military aggression by thes dictators went unchecked as the rest of the world worried about their own problem at home.

War began on September 1, 1939, with the German invasion of Poland. Th United States was drawn into the conflict following the Japanese sneak attack o Pearl Harbor on Dec. 7, 1941.

In early 1942, the Allies were on the defensive on every major battlefront of th war. In this time of despair, American unity and patriotism reached a peak. Th nation rallied to achieve victory. The cause of the Allies was advanced by man persons, but two leaders emerged as outstanding military strategists, winning battl after battle.

Issues of 1945-46
Perf. 11x10½

Franklin D. Roosevelt Issue

930	1c F.D.R. and home at Hyde Park	.05	.05
931	2c Roosevelt and "Little White House," Ga.	.08	.08
932	3c Roosevelt and White House	.10	.06
933	5c F.D.R., Globe and Four Freedoms	.12	.08
	In memory of Franklin Delano Roosevelt (1882-1945), 32nd President of the United States (1933-1945).		
934	3c U.S. Army in Paris Sep. 28	.10	.05
	A tribute to U.S. soldiers who fought in World War II.		
935	3c U.S. Navy Oct. 27	.10	.05
	A tribute to U.S. sailors who served in World War II.		
936	3c U.S. Coast Guard Nov. 10	.10	.05
	Honoring U.S. Coast Guard in World War II.		

General George S. Patton Jr. (1885-1945) instructed his men: "We shall attack and attack until we are exhausted, and then we shall attack again." He made the same sacrifices of himself as he demanded of his men. Always at the front, he earned the nickname "Old Blood and Guts." He won respect and fame through spectacular battlefield victories in North Africa. But it was his driving thrusts through Europe that secured his place in history. In 1944 his Third Army stormed through German lines and liberated six countries in less than ten months. Patton's indomitable spirit and iron will prominently contributed to Allied victory in Europe.

In the Pacific, Admiral William F. ("Bull") Halsey (1882-1959) played a major role in the final conquest of Japan. As vice-admiral in command of a carrier division, he led his forces in the attacks on Gilbert, Marshall and Wake Islands in early 1942. Later that same year Halsey assumed command of the U.S. naval forces in the South Pacific. As a result of the trouncing his forces dealt the Japanese Navy in the Solomons, U.S. land forces were able to occupy the entire island chain. Halsey became Commander of the Third Fleet on June 15, 1944, and together with the Seventh Fleet at the Battle of Leyte Gulf, October, 1944, his forces rendered the Japanese Navy ineffective for the remainder of the war. Halsey's flagship, the battleship *Missouri*, was the site of the official Japanese surrender on September 2, 1945.

See Scott Nos. 905, 925, 929, 934-936, 939, 940, 956, 1026

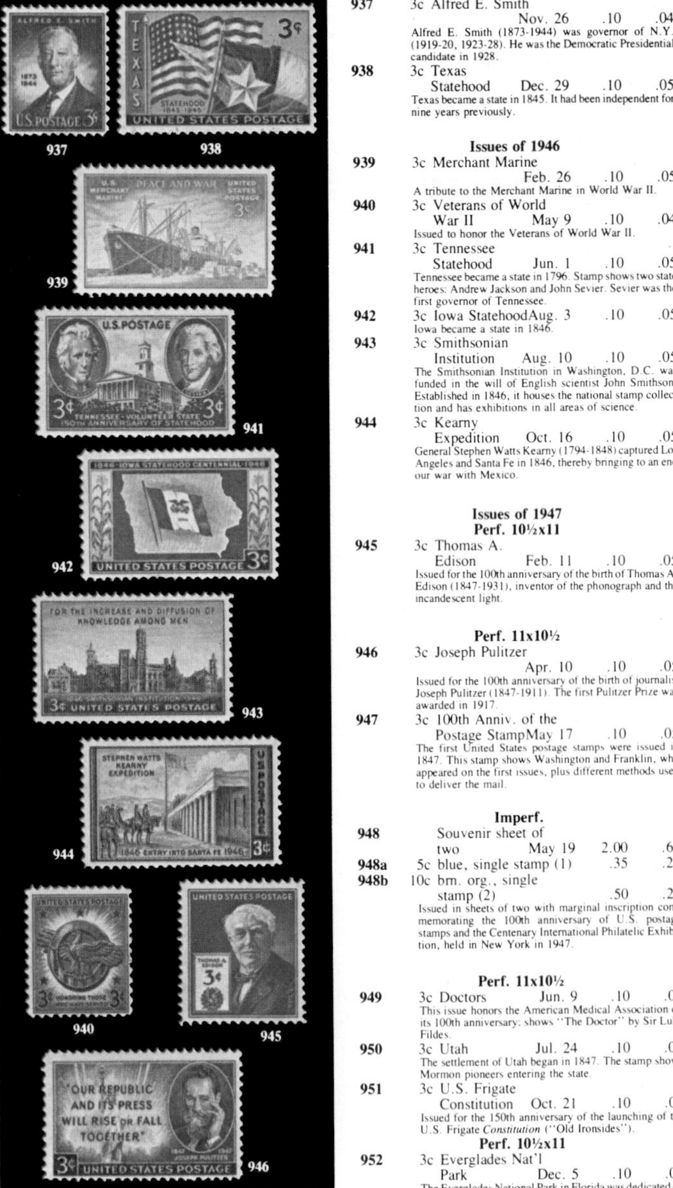

937 938 939 941 942 943 944 940 945 946

937 3c Alfred E. Smith Nov. 26 .10 .04

Alfred E. Smith (1873-1944) was governor of N.Y. (1919-20, 1923-28). He was the Democratic Presidential candidate in 1928.

938 3c Texas Statehood Dec. 29 .10 .05

Texas became a state in 1845. It had been independent for nine years previously.

Issues of 1946

939 3c Merchant Marine Feb. 26 .10 .05

A tribute to the Merchant Marine in World War II.

940 3c Veterans of World War II May 9 .10 .04

Issued to honor the Veterans of World War II.

941 3c Tennessee Statehood Jun. 1 .10 .05

Tennessee became a state in 1796. Stamp shows two state heroes: Andrew Jackson and John Sevier. Sevier was the first governor of Tennessee.

942 3c Iowa Statehood Aug. 3 .10 .05

Iowa became a state in 1846.

943 3c Smithsonian Institution Aug. 10 .10 .05

The Smithsonian Institution in Washington, D.C. was funded in the will of English scientist John Smithson. Established in 1846, it houses the national stamp collection and has exhibitions in all areas of science.

944 3c Kearny Expedition Oct. 16 .10 .05

General Stephen Watts Kearny (1794-1848) captured Los Angeles and Santa Fe in 1846, thereby bringing to an end our war with Mexico.

Issues of 1947
Perf. 10½x11

945 3c Thomas A. Edison Feb. 11 .10 .05

Issued for the 100th anniversary of the birth of Thomas A. Edison (1847-1931), inventor of the phonograph and the incandescent light.

Perf. 11x10½

946 3c Joseph Pulitzer Apr. 10 .10 .05

Issued for the 100th anniversary of the birth of journalist Joseph Pulitzer (1847-1911). The first Pulitzer Prize was awarded in 1917.

947 3c 100th Anniv. of the Postage Stamp May 17 .10 .05

The first United States postage stamps were issued in 1847. This stamp shows Washington and Franklin, who appeared on the first issues, plus different methods used to deliver the mail.

Imperf.

948 Souvenir sheet of two May 19 2.00 .65

948a 5c blue, single stamp (1) .35 .20

948b 10c brn. org., single stamp (2) .50 .25

Issued in sheets of two with marginal inscription commemorating the 100th anniversary of U.S. postage stamps and the Centenary International Philatelic Exhibition, held in New York in 1947.

Perf. 11x10½

949 3c Doctors Jun. 9 .10 .05

This issue honors the American Medical Association on its 100th anniversary; shows "The Doctor" by Sir Luke Fildes.

950 3c Utah Jul. 24 .10 .05

The settlement of Utah began in 1847. The stamp shows Mormon pioneers entering the state.

951 3c U.S. Frigate Constitution Oct. 21 .10 .05

Issued for the 150th anniversary of the launching of the U.S. Frigate *Constitution* ("Old Ironsides").

Perf. 10½x11

952 3c Everglades Nat'l Park Dec. 5 .10 .05

The Everglades National Park in Florida was dedicated on Dec. 6, 1947.

FRANKLIN DELANO ROOSEVELT 1882-1945

Roosevelt, a champion of the average American whom he called the "forgotten man," was himself born to wealth and position. Raised on an estate at Hyde Park, N.Y., he was educated at Groton Preparatory School and Harvard University. His wedding to his fifth cousin Eleanor Roosevelt in 1905 was signalized by the presence of her uncle, President Theodore Roosevelt, who gave the bride away.

In 1921, when he was 39 years old and already prominent in the national Democratic Party, tragedy struck. Roosevelt was crippled by polio. Although his legs were permanently paralyzed and he was confined to a wheelchair, he overcame this handicap and went on to become President of the United States.

When Roosevelt assumed office in 1933, the Great Depression was on and the United States was in the worst financial crisis of its history. One out of every four workers was unemployed and thousands roamed the country in search of work. Hungry men begged on street corners or waited in bread lines. Farms were abandoned by people who could not meet the mortgage demands. Panic-stricken people, hoping to salvage their savings, started runs on the banks, forcing many to close their doors. Everyone was fearful of what might happen next.

At his inauguration, Roosevelt conveyed his faith in America's future by boldly asserting, "The only thing we have to fear, is fear itself." Along with Congress, in a spectacular session known as "The Hundred Days," a series of emergency measures were swiftly enacted. These programs were the foundation of Roosevelt's "New Deal," which sought to alleviate the devastating effects of the Depression and to restore the nation's confidence and halt the downward slide of the economy. His famous "fireside chats" on radio explained government actions and reassured a frightened people.

In 1936 Roosevelt was unanimously renominated by his party and in the fall was re-elected by a landslide. In 1939 World War II began. As tensions increased in Europe, Americans grew more concerned about possible U.S. involvement in the conflict. Roosevelt promised to make every effort to keep the country out of war. In 1940 he was re-elected to an unprecedented third term as President.

The surprise attack by Japan on Pearl Harbor on December 7, 1941, threw the United States into the war. Just as he had done in peacetime, FDR assumed the leadership of his country and took command.

Even though he was in failing health, Roosevelt felt obliged to seek a fourth term in 1944 because he believed a change in leadership would demoralize the nation's war effort and endanger his peace plans. On April 12, 1945, just a few short months before final victory, FDR died and grieving people all over the world mourned the loss of a beloved leader.

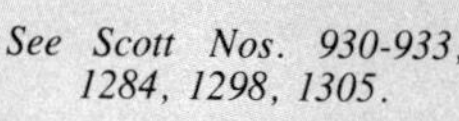

See Scott Nos. 930-933, 1284, 1298, 1305.

CALIFORNIA GOLD RUSH—THE FORTY-NINERS

Gold was discovered at Sutter's Mill, near Sacramento, Calif., on January 24, 1848. Soon the word got around and the gold rush was on. From all over the world, men arrived by boat, on foot, or horseback to seek their fortune. Many more, including whole families, came across the Great Plains in covered wagons braving the dangers of hostile Indians and the rigors of burning deserts and precipitous mountain terrain.

The forty-niners flooded into California. In one year alone, San Francisco grew from a small town to a bustling city of 25,000 population. Prospectors endured great hardships in their eagerness to be first to stake a claim and strike it rich. Many unsuccessful goldhunters became ranchers and farmers and settled in new communities. So many people poured into California that by 1850—only two years after the discovery of gold—it had a sufficient population to be admitted to the Union as the 31st state.

See Scott No. 954

Issues of 1948

953	3c Dr. George Washington Carver	Jan. 5	.10	.05

Perf. 11x10½

954	3c Calif. Gold 100th Anniv.	Jan. 24	.10	.05

In 1848 gold was found in Sutter's Mill in California.

955	3c Mississippi Territory	Apr. 7	.10	.05

The Mississippi Territory was established in 1798. It comprised the present states of Mississippi & Alabama.

947

949

950

UNDER AUTHORITY OF
ROBERT E. HANNEGAN, POSTMASTER GENERAL

PRINTED BY THE
TREASURY DEPARTMENT
BUREAU OF ENGRAVING AND PRINTING

U.S. POST OFFICE 5 FIVE CENTS 5

U.S. POST OFFICE X TEN CENTS X

IN COMPLIMENT
TO THE CENTENARY INTERNATIONAL
PHILATELIC EXHIBITION

100TH ANNIVERSARY
UNITED STATES POSTAGE STAMPS

NEW YORK, N.Y., MAY 17-25, 1947

948

951 952 954

955 956

957 953 958

956 3c Four Chaplains May 28 .10 .05
Honoring the four chaplains who lost their lives in the sinking of the S.S. *Dorchester* in World War II.

957 3c Wisconsin Statehood May 29 .10 .05
Wisconsin became a state in 1848.

958 5c Swedish Pioneer Jun. 4 .15 .10

In the nineteenth century, 1½ million Swedish pioneers helped to settle thirteen states in the Midwest.

THE FRIGATE CONSTITUTION

The most famous ship in American history was launched in Boston in 1797. She carried more than 50 guns and a crew of over 450, and the bolts fastening her timbers were made by Paul Revere. During the War of 1812, under the command of Captain Isaac Hull, she won a brilliant victory over the British frigate "Guerriere." Seeing that the British shot failed to penetrate the Constitutions's oak sides, the Americans dubbed her "Old Ironsides."

In 1828, the Constitution, old by then, was declared unseaworthy and condemned to destruction. Oliver Wendell Holmes wrote a poem of protest, "Old Ironsides." And so great was the public response that she was restored and preserved. Today, the Constitution is permanently berthed in Boston and still on the list of commissioned vessels of the U. S. Navy.

See Scott No. 951.

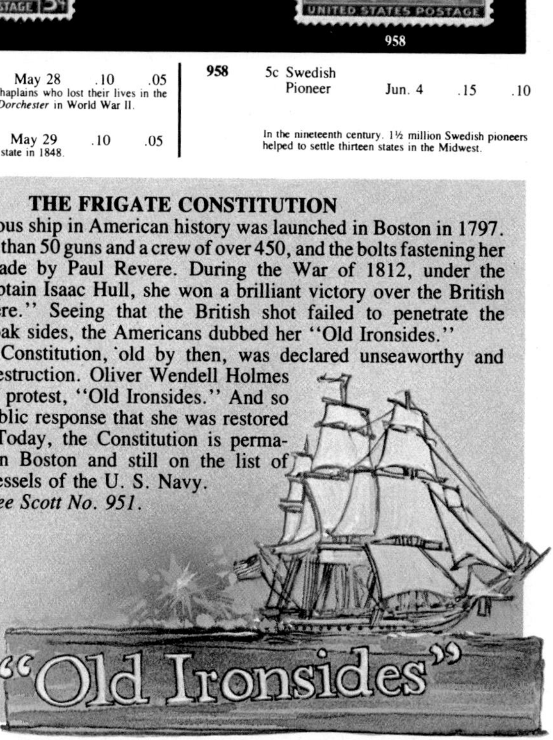

959  961  962

960  965

963

959	3c Progress of Women	Jul. 19	.10	.05
	Issued for the first Women's Rights Convention, held in 1848 at Seneca Falls, New York. The stamp shows three important leaders of the movement. Lucretia Mott, Carrie Chapman Catt and Elizabeth Stanton.			
	Perf. 10½x11			
960	3c William Allen White	Jul. 31	.10	.06
	Issued to honor William Allen White (1868-1944). American editor and author.			
	Perf. 11x10½			
961	3c U.S.-Canada Friendship	Aug. 2	.10	.05
	Issue notes a century of friendship between the United States and Canada.			
962	3c Francis Scott Key	Aug. 9	.10	.05
	Lawyer Francis Scott Key (1779-1843) composed the "Star-Spangled Banner."			
963	3c Salute to Youth	Aug. 11	.10	.06
	Honoring the Youth of America, the nation's "Leaders of Tomorrow."			
964	3c Oregon Territory	Aug. 14	.12	.10
	The Oregon Territory was established in 1848. The stamp shows pioneers Jason Lee and John McLoughlin.			

WOMAN'S PROGRESS

For centuries, women were relegated to an inferior position by society. But as a result of the social, political and economic ferment of the mid-1800's, the worldwide Women's Rights Movement developed. In the United States, Lucretia Mott and Elizabeth Cady Stanton organized the first women's convention at Seneca Falls, N.Y., in 1848. There, a Declaration of Women's Rights was adopted which closely paralleled the Declaration of Independence. Written by Mrs. Stanton, the declaration presented a list of grievances and charged "repeated injuries and usurpation on the part of men toward women" and claimed that "all men and women are created equal." Demands were made for equality in law, education and career opportunities, and especially for the right to vote.

Women's suffrage, or the right to vote, was always an important goal of the movement. When the 14th and 15th Amendments to the Constitution were adopted in 1868 and 1870 respectively, giving additional suffrage to men of different races, women were bitterly disappointed at being excluded. Yearly petitions to Congress and unsuccessful attempts to gain widespread public support marked the years leading up to 1890.

In 1890 the National American Woman's Suffrage Association was formed by a merger of many smaller women's groups, with Elizabeth Cady Stanton serving as its first president. Thus, American women continued to press for suffrage. Finally, the 19th Amendment was enacted in 1920, providing this basic democratic right for women and in part rewarding women for their long political struggle and for their valuable contribution to the war effort during World War I.

See Scott No. 959

964

967

968

Perf. 10½x11

965 3c Harlan Fiske Stone — Aug. 25 — .15 — .08
Issued to honor U.S. Chief Justice Harlan Fiske Stone (1872-1946).

966 3c Palomar Mt. Obs. — Aug. 30 — .25 — .10
Issued for the dedication of Palomar Mountain Observatory, California, home of the 200-inch Hale reflecting telescope, largest in the Western Hemisphere.

Perf. 11x10½

967 3c Clara Barton — Sep. 7 — .10 — .08
Clara Barton (1821-1912) was the founder and first president of the American Red Cross.

968 3c Poultry Industry — Sep. 9 — .12 — .08
Issued for the centennial of the establishment of the American poultry industry.

Perf. 10½x11

969 3c Gold Star Mothers — Sep. 21 — .12 — .08
Honoring the mothers of deceased servicemen.

Perf. 11x10½

970 3c Fort Kearny — Sep. 22 — .12 — .08
Established in 1848, Fort Kearny, Nebr., was a major outpost for pioneers.

966

969

970

GOLD STAR MOTHERS

One of the most deplorable aspects of war is that millions of mothers devote their lives to raising their children, only to lose them on some far-off battlefield. In 1928, as an aftermath of the First World War, the Gold Star Mothers of America was formed as an organization to honor the memory of those sons and daughters who gave their lives in the service of their country. Natural mothers whose sons or daughters have died in the line of duty while in the military service are eligible to join the organization. Service flags displayed in a window, especially during the Second World War, indicated the number of family members serving in the Armed Forces, with a blue star signifying a living member and a gold star, one who died.

In 1940 President Franklin Roosevelt, in recognition of their great sacrifice, designated the last Sunday in September as Gold Star Mothers' Day. In ceremonies at Arlington National Cemetary each year, a Gold Star wreath is placed on the Tomb of the Unknown Soldier to honor all Gold Star Mothers for their loss.

See Scott No. 969

971 972 973 974 975 976 977 978 979 980 981 982 983 984 985 986 987 988

971 3c Volunteer Firemen Oct. 4 .12 .08
America's first brigade of volunteer firemen was organized in 1648 by Peter Stuyvesant in New Amsterdam, now New York.

972 3c Five Indian Tribes Oct. 15 .12 .08
In 1848, Choctaw, Cherokee, Chickasaw, Muscogee and Seminole Indians were driven to Oklahoma from the East on the "Trail of Tears".

973 3c Rough Riders Oct. 27 .12 .10
In one of the most famous battles of the Spanish-American War, the 1st Volunteer Cavalry Regiment ("Rough Riders") stormed San Juan Hill on July 1, 1898. The stamp shows Capt. William "Bucky" O'Neill, who was killed during the conflict.

974 3c Juliette Low Oct. 29 .12 .08
Issued to honor the founder of the Girl Scouts of America.

Perf. 10½x11

975 3c Will Rogers Nov. 4 .12 .08
Issued in honor of Will Rogers (1879-1935), humorist, philosopher, author, and actor.

976 3c Fort Bliss 100th Anniv. Nov. 5 .25 .08
Fort Bliss, Texas, now a major missile center, was established in 1848.

Perf. 11x10½

977 3c Moina Michael Nov. 9 .12 .08
Moina Michael created the Memorial poppy. Countless numbers of these artificial flowers have been sold to aid disabled veterans.

978 3c Gettysburg Address Nov. 19 .12 .08
Lincoln's famous speech was given in 1863, as a dedication for the military cemetery at Gettysburg, Pa.

Perf. 10½x11

979 3c American Turners Nov. 20 .12 .08
Issued for the centennial of the American Turners Society, which promotes athletics.

980 3c Joel Chandler Harris Dec. 9 .12 .08
Joel Chandler Harris (1848-1908) created the "Uncle Remus" stories.

Issues of 1949
Perf. 11x10½

981 3c Minnesota Territory Mar. 3 .10 .05
The Minnesota Territory was established in 1849.

982 3c Washington & Lee University Apr. 12 .10 .05
Virginia's Washington and Lee University was established in 1749.

983 3c Puerto Rico Election Apr. 27 .10 .05
In 1949 Luis Muños-Marin became Puerto Rico's first elected governor.

984 3c Annapolis 300th Anniv. May 23 .10 .05
Established in 1694, Annapolis, the capital of Maryland was named for Queen Anne of England.

985 3c Grand Army of the Republic Aug. 29 .10 .05
The final encampment of the Grand Army of the Republic (Civil War Union Veterans) took place in 1949.

Perf. 10½x11

986 3c Edgar Allan Poe Oct. 7 .10 .05
Issued on the 100th anniversary of the death of Edgar Allan Poe (1809-1849), poet and short story author.

Issues of 1950
Perf. 11x10½

987 3c American Bankers Association Jan. 3 .10 .05
Issued for the 75th anniversary of the American Bankers Association.

Perf. 10½x11

988 3c Samuel Gompers Jan. 27 .10 .05
The American labor leader (1850-1924) served as president of the American Federation of Labor.

VOLUNTEER FIREMEN

Ben Franklin, who had his finger in so many 18th Century American pies, was a volunteer fireman. In fact, he was the chief of the first centralized volunteer fire company in the colonies, the Union Fire Company of Philadelphia.

The volunteer firemen of America's young days were bankers and bookkeepers, merchants and delivery boys. In return for their efforts as fire fighters they got, not money, but prestige, admiration and the thrill of facing danger in the company of other brave men. There was no municipal fire department, only a collection of separate fire companies. And each company strove to have the best-looking fire fighting equipment and the fastest horses, to get to the fire first and pump the greatest amount of water. The rivalry between companies was intense.

In the cities, the volunteer companies began to be replaced by paid fire departments in the 1850's. They proved more efficient. But more courageous, colorful or proud? Never!

See Scott No 971

990 991 989 992 993 994 995 996

National Capital 150th Anniv. Issue

Perf. 10½ x 11, 11 x 10½

989	3c Statue of Freedom	.10	.05
990	3c Executive Mansion	.10	.05
991	3c Supreme Court Building	.10	.05
992	3c U.S. Capitol Building	.10	.05

Washington, D.C. the nation's capital, was 150 years old in 1950. It was built on a site chosen by Washington.

Perf. 11 x 10½

993	3c Railroad Engineers	Apr. 29	.10	.05

Issued to honor the railroad engineers of America. Stamp shows Casey Jones who ran the crack "Cannonball Express."

994	3c Kansas City, Mo.	Jun. 3	.10	.05

Incorporated in 1850, Kansas City is a leading midwest city known for commerce, industry and transportation.

995	3c Boy Scouts	Jun. 30	.10	.06

Issued to honor the Boy Scouts of America whose Second National Jamboree was held in 1950 at Valley Forge, Pennsylvania.

NATIONAL CAPITOL

The U.S. Capitol, where Congress convenes to enact laws and debate vital national and international issues, is the most impressive structure in Washington, D.C. Its dome, topped by the heroic 19½-foot Statue of Freedom, rises nearly 300 feet and dominates the Washington skyline.

Any citizen who pays the cost and receives official approval may have a U.S. flag raised over the Capitol. In 1937, when this custom began, six flags were flown. During the U.S. Bicentennial year of 1976 there were 62,860—10,741 on the Fourth of July.

The capital city of the United States was being planned when George Washington laid the cornerstone for the Capitol building in 1793. Congress first met in the newly constructed building in 1800. When the British besieged Washington in 1814, they burned the Capitol. It was reconstructed in 1819 and through the years separate wings for the Senate and the House of Representatives have been added. It has since been modernized into a five-story building covering 3½ acres of ground.

Massive Corinthian columns support the three porticoes at the main entrance. Magnificent bronze doors lead into the Great Rotunda where circular walls depict major events and prominent figures of America's past.

The building is set atop an 83-foot hill in the heart of Washington. From Capitol Park—the hub—beautiful treelined streets and avenues crisscross in a checkerboard pattern and spread out like the spokes of an enormous wheel.

No.	Description	Date	Unused	Used
996	3c Indiana Territory	Jul. 4	.10	.05

The Indiana Territory was created in 1800. William Henry Harrison, shown on stamp, was governor of the territory before becoming President of the United States.

No.	Description	Date	Unused	Used
997	3c California Statehood	Sep. 9	.10	.05

California joined the Union in 1850.

Issues of 1951

No.	Description	Date	Unused	Used
998	3c Confederate Veterans	May 30	.10	.05

The last reunion of the United Confederate Veterans took place in 1951 at Norfolk, Virginia

No.	Description	Date	Unused	Used
999	3c Nevada 100th Anniv.	Jul. 14	.10	.05

Nevada was settled in 1851. Stamp shows Carson Valley, named for frontiersman Kit Carson.

No.	Description	Date	Unused	Used
1000	3c Landing of Cadillac	Jul. 24	.10	.05

Detroit, the "Motor City," was founded by Antoine de la Mothe Cadillac in 1701.

No.	Description	Date	Unused	Used
1001	3c Colorado Statehood	Aug. 1	.10	.05

Colorado became a state in 1876.

No.	Description	Date	Unused	Used
1002	3c American Chem. Society	Sep. 4	.10	.05

One of the world's largest scientific societies, the American Chemical Society was established in 1876.

Visitors are drawn to the Capitol by its imposing architecture and its classical beauty, but its major attraction by far is the opportunity to see Congress put democracy into action.

The National Capitol consistently appears on United States stamps.

1003 1004 1005

1006 1008 1007

1003 3c Battle of Brooklyn Dec. 10 .10 .05
In 1776 Washington saved his troops at Brooklyn in the Battle of Long Island.

Issues of 1952

1004 3c Betsy Ross Jan. 2 .10 .05
Issued for the 200th anniversary of the birth of Betsy Ross. According to legend, she made the first official U.S. Flag in 1777.

1005 3c 4-H Club Jan. 15 .10 .05
The 4-H Club movement works to improve the head, heart, hands and health of the nation's youth.

1006 3c B&O Railroad Feb. 28 .10 .05
Chartered in 1827, the B&O used horse-drawn cars to carry its first passengers. Stamp also shows the Line's first steam engine, the "Tom Thumb," and a modern diesel.

1007 3c American Auto. Assn. Mar. 4 .10 .05
Issued to promote highway safety on the 50th anniversary of the American Automobile Association.

1008 3c NATO Apr. 4 .10 .03
The North Atlantic Treaty Organization is a mutual defense pact for the Western European nations, Canada and the United States. It was created in 1949.

1009 3c Grand Coulee Dam May 15 .10 .05
Issued on the 50th anniversary of the U.S. Bureau of Reclamation, this stamp shows Grand Coulee Dam, one of the largest in the world.

1010 3c General Lafayette Jun. 13 .10 .05
Lafayette came to America in 1777 to help the fledgling Continental Army in its fight for independence from Great Britain.

Perf. 10½ x 11

1011 3c Mt. Rushmore Mem. Aug. 11 .10 .05
Mount Rushmore in South Dakota is famous for its giant busts of Lincoln, Washington, Jefferson and Theodore Roosevelt.

Perf. 11 x 10½

1012 3c Engineering Sep. 6 .10 .05
The two bridges illustrated on this stamp symbolize 100 years of civil engineering progress in America. One is an early covered wooden bridge; the other the modern George Washington Bridge between New Jersey and New York.

1013 3c Service Women Sep. 11 .10 .05
Issued as a tribute to the women members of the Army, Navy, Air Force and Marines.

1014 3c Gutenberg Bible Sep. 30 .10 .05
Johann Gutenberg (c. 1397-1468) printed the first book from movable type in 1456. This was the Holy Bible.

1009 1011 1010

1012 1013 1014

4-H CLUBS

The 4-H Clubs were originated for America's farm youth in the early 1900's. Their "learn-by-doing" has expanded worldwide and now includes members from suburbs and cities as well as farms. The 3½ million young Americans in 4-H Clubs come from many and diverse ethnic, cultural, racial and economic backgrounds. Four-H Clubs in 85 other nations are helping young people develop useful skills and become productive members of their communities. "Learn-by-doing" gives them the opportunity to obtain practical knowledge and skills through real-life experience.

Four-H Clubs are a program of the Cooperative Extension Service of the U.S. Department of Agriculture–Land Grant University system. The program receives financial support from large and small businesses and private organizations as well as from ordinary citizens. The four-leaf clover emblem stands for "head, heart, hand, and health," as spelled out in the club ritual:

"I pledge—
My head to clear thinking,
My heart to greater loyalty,
My hands to larger service, *and*
My health to better living for my club, my community and my country."

See Scott No. 1005

GRAND COULEE DAM

The Grand Coulee Dam harnesses the roaring Columbia River and produces the largest single source of hydro-electric power in the country. It is located on the Columbia River near the Grand Coulee Ice Age channel of the river—about 90 miles northwest of Spokane, Washington.

Construction of the original dam, one of the largest concrete structures in the world, began in 1933 and was completed in 1942. The present length of the dam at the axis is 5,223 feet. It is 500 feet wide and 550 feet high. An engineering project of the United States Bureau of Reclamation, it contains enough concrete (11,975,521 cubic yards) to build a six-foot-wide, four-inch-thick sidewalk around the world at the equator.

The dam provides both effective flood control and irrigation to previously arid farmlands. Two power plants, with 18 generators, supply an enormous amount of electricity to homes and industry. With the completion of a third power plant, the Grand Coulee Dam will be the greatest hydroelectric power source in the United States.

See Scott No. 1009

NEWSBOYS

A hundred years ago, before television or even radio, newspapers were the prime source of news for an information—hungry public. They weren't sold from newsstands or coin operated machines, though. They were sold on the street by ragged young boys. "Extra! Extra!" the newsboys would shout. "Get your paper! Read all about it!" And they'd wave a newspaper hopefully before the eyes of every hurrying passer-by. In the late 1800's and early 1900's, social reformers were struggling to put an end to child labor. Such activists as Jacob Riis and Louis Hine used the new art of documentary photography to make everyone aware of the children's plight. Their Photos of the newsboys have come down to us — grimy little fellows of nine and ten, clutching their newspapers, coatless, their caps pulled down at a jaunty angle over the saddest eyes in the world.

The reformers had their way, and child labor ended. But years later, a different kind of newsboy began to appear in America: small town youngsters who'd wake up extra early, grab their bikes and ride around town tossing the local newspaper on one front porch after the other. They were earning extra money with a paper route - the traditional spare-time job for several generations of American schoolboys.

See Scott No. 1015.

1015 3c Newspaper Boys Oct. 4 .10 .05
Issued "In recognition of the important service rendered their communities and their nation by America's newspaper boys."

1016 3c Red Cross Nov. 21 .10 .05
The International Red Cross was created in 1864 by Geneva Convention at the urging of Jean Dunant, the first Nobel Peace Prize winner.

Issues of 1953

1017 3c National Guard Feb. 23 .10 .05
A tribute to the National Guard which serves the United States in peace and war.

1018 3c Ohio Statehood Mar. 2 .10 .05
Ohio joined the Union as the seventeenth state in 1803.

1019 3c Washington Territory Mar. 2 .10 .05
Organized on March 2, 1853, the Washington Territory was carved from the Pacific Northwest by courageous pioneers who went there to settle and build homes.

1020 3c Louisiana Purchase Apr. 30 10 .05
Issued for the 150th anniversary of the Louisiana Purchase.

1021 5c Opening of Japan 100th Anniv. Jul. 14 .15 .10
In 1853, Commodore Matthew Perry negotiated the first U.S.-Japanese trade agreement.

1022 3c American Bar Assn. Aug. 24 .10 .05
Issued for the American Bar Association's 75th anniversary. this stamp depicts four symbolic figures representing "Wisdom," "Justice," "Truth," and "Divine Inspiration."

1023 3c Sagamore Hill Sep. 14 .10 .05
Sagamore Hill. Theodore Roosevelt's home in Oyster Bay, New York was opened as a national shrine in 1953.

1024 3c Future Farmers Oct. 13 .10 .05
Issued on the 25th anniversary of the Future Farmers of America.

1025 3c Trucking Industry Oct. 27 .10 .05
The American Trucking Association was created in 1903.

1026 3c General Patton Nov. 11 .10 .05
General George S. Patton, Jr. (1885-1945) commanded the U.S. Third Army in the Second World War.

1027 3c New York City 300th Anniversary Nov. 20 .10 .05
Settled by the Dutch in the 17th century, New York City is the nation's largest city.

1028 3c Gadsden Purchase Dec. 30 .10 .05
The 1853 Gadsden Purchase adjusted the boundary between Mexico and the United States.

Issues of 1954

1029 3c Columbia University 200th Anniv. Jan. 4 .10 .05
Columbia University was founded in 1754 as Kings College. Stamp depicts the school's Low Memorial Library.

1015
1016
1017
1018
1019
1020
1021
1022
1023
1024
1025
1026
1027
1028
1029

MONTICELLO

Monticello ("Little Mountain") is the lovely Virginia estate that was the home of Thomas Jefferson, third President of the United States. Jefferson designed and supervised the building of this unique and impressive home which stands in Albemarle County near Charlottesville, Va. Construction of the three-story, 35-room red brick and frame mansion began in 1768. The work was done in stages because Jefferson was involved in politics and diplomacy and could not spare the time.

Monticello, a fine example of 18th-century architecture, borrowed many of its outstanding features from famous Old World structures. The Greek portico is based on the Roman Temple of Vesta. The commanding dome was inspired by the Hotel Salm in Paris. Extensive gardens, among the finest in America, further enhanced the estate's beauty.

In 1809, at the age of sixty-five, Jefferson retired from the presidency and returned home to find that as a result of his long absence Monticello had fallen into disrepair. Jefferson's diligence and concentrated efforts, however, soon restored Monticello to its former elegance.

Of his home, Jefferson said, "All my wishes end where I hope my days will end, at Monticello." When he died on July 4, 1826, Thomas Jefferson was buried at his beloved Monticello.

See Scott No. 1047

Liberty Issue, 1954-68
Perf. 11 x 10½, 10½ x 11

No.	Value	Description	Unused	Used
1030	½c	Benjamin Franklin	.05	.03
1031	1c	George Washington	.05	.03
1031A	1¼c	Palace of the Governors, Santa Fe	.05	.05
1032	1½c	Mount Vernon	.05	.04
1033	2c	Thomas Jefferson	.05	.03
1034	2½c	Bunker Hill Monument and Massachusetts flag	.08	.05
1035	3c	Statue of Liberty	.08	.03
1035a		Booklet pane of 6	3.00	*.50*
1036	4c	Abraham Lincoln	.10	.03
1036a		Booklet pane of 6	2.00	*.50*
1037	4½c	The Hermitage	.12	.08
1038	5c	James Monroe	.12	.03
1039	6c	Theodore Roosevelt	.20	.03
1040	7c	Woodrow Wilson	.20	.03
		Perf. 11		
1041	8c	Statue of Liberty	.35	.06
1042	8c	Statue of Liberty redrawn	.20	.03
		Perf. 11 x 10½, 10½ x 11		
1042A	8c	John J. Pershing	.25	.03
1043	9c	The Alamo	.25	.04
1044	10c	Independence Hall	.30	.03
		Perf. 11		
1044A	11c	Statue of Liberty	.30	.06
		Perf. 11 x 10½, 10½ x 11		
1045	12c	Benjamin Harrison	.45	.05
1046	15c	John Jay	.60	.03
1047	20c	Monticello	.70	.03
1048	25c	Paul Revere	1.50	.03
1049	30c	Robert E. Lee	1.75	.08
1050	40c	John Marshall	2.75	.10
1051	50c	Susan B. Anthony	3.25	.04
1052	$1	Patrick Henry	9.50	.06
		Perf. 11		
1053	$5	Alexander Hamilton	125.00	2.50

Coil Stamps
Perf. 10 Vertically

No.	Value	Description	Unused	Used
1054	1c	dark green Washington (1031)	.15	.06
		Perf. 10 Horizontally		
1054A	1¼c	turquoise, Palace of the Governors, Santa Fe (1031A)	.45	.10
		Perf. 10 Vertically		
1055	2c	rose carmine Jefferson (1033)	.10	.05
1056	2½c	gray blue, Bunker Hill Monument and Massachusetts flag (1034)	.55	.07
1057	3c	deep violet Statue of Liberty (1035)	.15	.03
1058	4c	red violet Lincoln (1036)	.15	.04
		Perf. 10 Horizontally		
1059	4½c	blue green Hermitage (1037)	2.50	.10
		Perf. 10 Vertically		
1059A	25c	grn. P. Revere (1048)	.70	.20

1031A 1034 1032

1037 1043 1044 1047

1035 1041 1042 1044A

1030 1031 1033 1036 1038

1039 1040 1042A 1045 1046

1048 1049 1050 1051

1052 1053

Issues of 1954, Perf. 11x10½

1060 3c Nebraska Territory — May 7 — .10 — .05

The Nebraska Territory was created in 1854 under terms of the Kansas-Nebraska Act, which gave settlers free choice in the slavery issue.

1061 3c Kansas Territory — May 31 — .10 — .05

The Kansas Territory was established in 1854.

Perf. 10½x11

1062 3c George Eastman — Jul. 12 — .10 — .05

Inventor and philanthropist, George Eastman was born in 1854.

Perf. 11x10½

1063 3c Lewis and Clark Expedition — Jul. 28 — .10 — .05

The 1804-06 Lewis and Clark Expedition charted much of the Louisiana Territory purchased by the U.S. in 1803.

Issues of 1955, Perf. 10½x11

1064 3c Pennsylvania Academy of Fine Arts — Jan. 15 — .10 — .05

The Pennsylvania Academy of Fine Arts was founded in 1805 by artist Charles Wilson Peale, whose self-portrait is depicted on the stamp.

Perf. 11x10½

1065 3c Land Grant Colleges — Feb. 12 — .10 — .05

The first two U.S. land grant colleges, Michigan State University and Pennsylvania State University, were established in 1855.

1066 8c Rotary International — Feb. 23 — .20 — .12

Issued to honor the 50th anniversary of Rotary International.

ATOMS FOR PEACE

When the awesome power of the atom was unleashed in 1945, the ominous mushroom clouds over Nagasaki and Hiroshima signaled a threat to man's very survival. But what started as a new and terrible instrument of war has since, through the efforts of devoted men and women like the late Senator Brien McMahon of Connecticut, been turned into peaceful channels as well. Today, scientific laboratories are finding new and unorthodox ways of using nuclear energy. The looming worldwide shortage of natural gas and oil has, of course, given a new urgency to this exploration of the ability of the atom to fill the worldwide needs in fuel.

In 1955 the first United Nations Conference on the Peaceful Uses of Atomic Energy was held. This conference and subsequent ones have focused on the problems inherent in the international exchange of information in the atomic energy field.

1069

1072

1068

1073

1067 3c Armed Forces Reserve May 21 .10 .05
A tribute to the Armed Forces Reserve.

Perf. 10½x11

1068 3c New Hampshire Jun. 21 .10 .05
Immortalized by Hawthorne as "The Great Stone Face," the "Old Man of the Mountains" shown on stamp is New Hampshire's best-known scenic wonder.

Perf. 11x10½

1069 3c Soo Locks Jun. 28 .10 .05
The Soo Locks of the Sault Ste. Marie Canal link Lake Huron and Lake Superior. They were opened in 1855.

1070 3c Atoms for Peace Jul. 28 .15 .05
Issued to promote President Eisenhower's Atoms for Peace policy, this stamp quotes from a speech he made to the U.N. on the peaceful uses of atomic energy.

1071 3c Fort Ticonderoga Sep. 18 .10 .05
Fort Ticonderoga was the scene of many battles in the American Revolution and the French and Indian Wars. Ethan Allen, shown on the stamp, stormed the fort and won it from the British in 1775.

Perf. 10½x11

1072 3c Andrew W. Mellon Dec. 20 .10 .05
Born in 1855. Andrew Mellon was a noted financier, industrialist and philanthropist.

Issues of 1956

1073 3c Benjamin Franklin Jan. 17 .10 .05
Issued on the 250th anniversary of the birth of Benjamin Franklin.

Perf. 11x10½

1074 3c Booker T. Washington Apr. 5 .10 .05
Black educator Booker T. Washington was born in 1856. Stamp shows cabin similar to his birthplace.

1070

1071

1074

1076

Constructive and beneficial uses of nuclear energy have been found in almost every area of science and technology. Atomic reactors generate electricity and furnish power to many cities. Submarines as well as surface vessels operate on atomic power. Doctors armed with atomic tools have more efficient ways of diagnosing and treating disease. Earth satellites and spacecraft rely on atomic power for propulsion and for their telemetry and other scientific systems.

See Scott Nos. 1070, 1200

Fifth International Philatelic Exhibition
Souvenir Sheet, Imperf.

1075	Sheet of 2	Apr. 28	6.00	3.50
1075a	3c deep violet (1035)		1.35	.80
1075b	8c dk. vio. bl. & car.(1041)		1.75	1.10

Issued in sheets of two with marginal inscription commemorating the Fifth International Philatelic Exhibition held in New York City.

Perf. 11x10½

1076	3c New York Coliseum and Columbus Monument	Apr. 30	.10	.05

Stamp honors the opening of the New York Coliseum and the Fifth International Philatelic Exhibition held there in 1956.

Wildlife Conservation Issue

1077	3c Wild Turkey	May 5	.12	.05
1078	3c Pronghorn Antelope	Jun. 22	.12	.05
1079	3c King Salmon	Nov. 9	.12	.05

The Wildlife Conservation Series calls attention to the need to save our wildlife from extinction. King salmon, pronghorn antelope and the wild turkey have been helped by conservationists.

Perf. 10½x11

1080	3c Pure Food and Drug Laws	Jun. 27	.10	.05

Chemist Harvey W. Wiley, shown on stamp, helped enact the first Pure Food and Drug Act in 1906.

Perf. 11x10½

1081	3c Wheatland	Aug. 5	.10	.05

Wheatland was the home of President James Buchanan (1791-1868). It is located in Lancaster, Pa.

Perf. 10½x11

1082	3c Labor Day	Sep. 3	.10	.05

Labor Day has been a U.S. legal holiday since 1894.

Perf. 11x10½

1083	3c Nassau Hall	Sep. 22	.10	.05

Constructed in 1756, Nassau Hall is Princeton University's most famous building.

Perf. 10½x11

1084	3c Devils Tower	Sep. 24	.10	.05

In 1906 Devils Tower in Wyoming became the first U.S. national monument.

Perf. 11x10½

1085	3c Children's Issue	Dec. 15	.10	.05

Designed by a high school student, this stamp promotes friendship as the key to peace throughout the world.

Issues of 1957

1086 3c Alexander Hamilton Jan. 11 .10 .05
Issued for the 200th anniversary of the birth of Alexander Hamilton.

Perf. 10½x11

1087 3c Polio Jan. 15 .10 .05
A tribute to the March of Dimes and the National Foundation for Infantile Paralysis.

Perf. 11x10½

1088 3c Coast and Geodetic Survey Feb. 11 .10 .05
The Coast and Geodetic Survey established in 1807, charts coasts and navigation routes, records tides.

1089 3c Architects Feb. 23 .10 .05
The American Institute of Architects was created in 1857.

Perf. 10½x11

1090 3c Steel Industry May 22 .10 .05
The U.S. is one of the world's leading steel producers. The industry was 100 years old in 1957.

Perf. 11x10½

1091 3c Int'l. Naval Review Jun. 10 .10 .05
The International Naval Review was held in 1957 in connection with the 250th anniversary of Jamestown, Virginia.

1092 3c Oklahoma Statehood Jun. 14 .15 .05
From 1828 to 1846, Oklahoma was an Indian Reservation. In 1907 it became a state.

1093 3c School Teachers Jul. 1 .10 .05
A tribute to the school teachers of America.

Perf. 11

1094 4c Flag Issue Jul. 4 .10 .05
This stamp which depicts the 48-star flag was the first U.S. issue printed on the Giori press. The press can print three colors simultaneously.

Perf. 10½x11

1095 3c Shipbuilding Aug. 15 .10 .05
The *"Virginia of Sagadahock,"* the first U.S. international trading vessel was constructed in 1607.

Perf. 11

1096 8c Champion of Liberty Aug. 31 .22 .15
Ramon Magsaysay, honored here, was president of the Philippines from 1953 to 1957.

Perf. 10½x11

1097 3c Lafayette Sep. 6 .10 .05
Issued for the 200th anniversary of the birth of the Marquis de Lafayette.

1098
1099
1100
1104
1107
1105
1106
1110
1111
1108
1109
1112
1113
1114
1115
1121
1117
1116
1119
1120
1122
1118
Religious Freedom IN AMERICA
GARDENING HORTICULTURE
UNIVERSAL AND INTERNATIONAL EXHIBITION·1958
BRUSSELS
INTERNATIONAL GEOPHYSICAL YEAR 1957-58
JAMES MONROE
MINNESOTA STATEHOOD·1858·1958
CHAMPION OF LIBERTY
ATLANTIC CABLE CENTENARY 1858·1958
LINCOLN-DOUGLAS DEBATES
FREEDOM OF THE PRESS
OVERLAND MAIL 1858 1958
FOREST CONSERVATION

Perf. 11

1098 3c Wildlife Conservation Nov. 22 .10 .05
The almost extinct whooping crane points up urgent need for wildlife conservation.

Perf. 10½x11

1099 3c Religious Freedom Dec. 27 .10 .05
The Flushing Remonstrance of 1657 helped create religious freedom in America.

Issues of 1958

1100 3c Gardening-Horticulture Mar. 15 .10 .05
Horticulture issue honors birth in 1858 of botanist Liberty Hyde Bailey.

Perf. 11x10½

1104 3c Brussels Fair Apr. 17 .10 .05
Issued for the opening of the Brussels World's Fair, this stamp shows the United States Pavilion at the Fair.

1105 3c James Monroe Apr. 28 .10 .05
Issued for the 200th anniversary of the birth of James Monroe (1758-1831), fifth President of the United States.

1106 3c Minnesota Statehood May 11 .10 .05
Minnesota became a state in 1858.

Perf. 11

1107 3c Geophysical Year May 31 .15 .05
The International Geophysical Year of 1957-58 was a team effort by world scientists for research and discovery. The stamp shows part of Michelangelo's famous fresco. "The Creation of Adam."

Perf. 11x10½

1108 3c Gunston Hall Jun. 12 .10 .05
Gunston Hall was the Virginia home of George Mason (1725-92) author of Virginia's constitution.

Perf. 10½x11

1109 3c Mackinac Bridge Jun. 25 .10 .05
Dedicated in 1958, the Mackinac Bridge connects the two peninsulas of Michigan.

1110 4c Champion of Liberty Jul. 24 .10 .05

Perf. 11

1111 8c Champion of Liberty .25 .15
Simon Bolivar (1783-1830) liberated much of South America from Spanish domination.

Perf. 11x10½

1112 4c Atlantic Cable 100th Anniversary Aug. 15 .10 .05
The first Atlantic cable between London and New York was finished in 1858.

Lincoln 150th Anniv. Issue, 1958-59

Perf. 10½x11, 11x10½

1113 1c Portrait by George Healy .05 .05

1114 3c Sculptured Head by Gutzon Borglum .10 .06

1115 4c Lincoln and Stephen Douglas Debating .10 .05

1116 4c Statue in Lincoln Memorial by Daniel Chester French .10 .05

Issues of 1958

Perf. 10½x11

1117 4c Champion of Liberty Sep. 19 .10 .05

Perf. 11

1118 8c Champion of Liberty .22 .12
Lajos Kossuth (1802-1892), patriot of Hungary, was a leading figure in that nation's revolution.

Perf. 10½x11

1119 4c Freedom of Press Sep. 22 .10 .05

Perf. 11x10½

1120 4c Overland Mail Oct. 10 .10 .05
The first overland mail coach arrived in San Francisco, Calif. in 1858. It began its journey in Tipton, Mo.

Perf. 10½x11

1121 4c Noah Webster Oct. 16 .10 .05
Noah Webster (1758-1843) was a noted scholar and a lexicographer.

Perf. 11

1122 4c Forest Conservation Oct. 27 .10 .05

ALEXANDER HAMILTON 1755-1804

Alexander Hamilton, one of the youngest, most gifted and brilliant of America's Founding Fathers, was a college student when the Revolutionary War began. Hamilton organized an artillery company and became its leader. The 22-year-old Captain Hamilton so impressed George Washington with his outstanding military skills that the General made him his aide-de-camp and adviser.

Following the Revolution, Hamilton was a vigorous spokesman for a powerful central government, and for the adoption of a strong Constitution. He wrote many of the *Federalist Papers* in defense of the Constitution, which significantly influenced its eventual ratification.

The struggling young government was further strengthened by Hamilton's financial genius. As the nation's first Secretary of the Treasury, he guaranteed payment of America's war debts and was also responsible for the establishment of the Bank of the United States.

In 1804, as the culmination of a long-standing personal and political feud between the two, Aaron Burr, U.S. Vice President, challenged Hamilton to a duel. Hamilton reluctantly accepted and on July 11, 1804, the two rivals faced each other. Burr fired the only shot, which mortally wounded Hamilton.

See Scott Nos. 1040, 1086

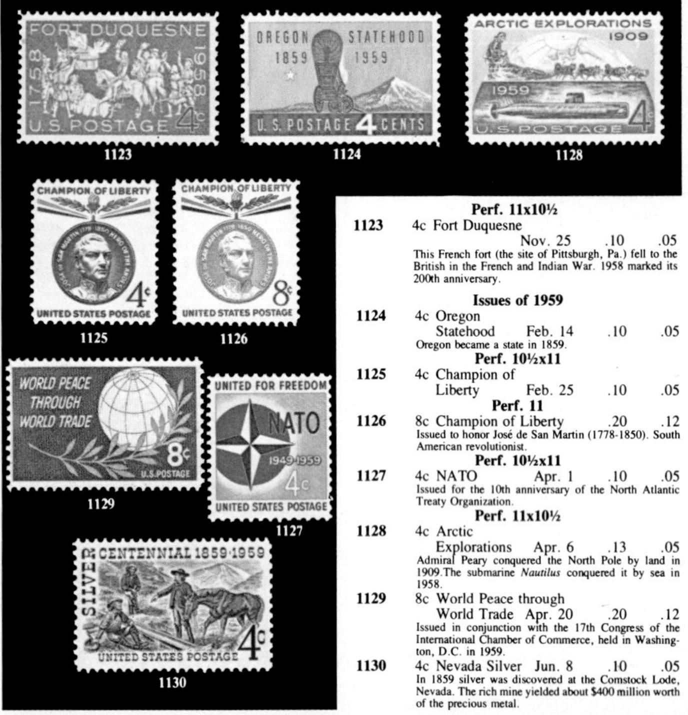

1123 1124 1128 1125 1126 1129 1127 1130

Perf. 11x10½

1123 4c Fort Duquesne Nov. 25 .10 .05

This French fort (the site of Pittsburgh, Pa.) fell to the British in the French and Indian War. 1958 marked its 200th anniversary.

Issues of 1959

1124 4c Oregon Statehood Feb. 14 .10 .05

Oregon became a state in 1859.

Perf. 10½x11

1125 4c Champion of Liberty Feb. 25 .10 .05

Perf. 11

1126 8c Champion of Liberty .20 .12

Issued to honor José de San Martin (1778-1850). South American revolutionist.

Perf. 10½x11

1127 4c NATO Apr. 1 .10 .05

Issued for the 10th anniversary of the North Atlantic Treaty Organization.

Perf. 11x10½

1128 4c Arctic Explorations Apr. 6 .13 .05

Admiral Peary conquered the North Pole by land in 1909. The submarine *Nautilus* conquered it by sea in 1958.

1129 8c World Peace through World Trade Apr. 20 .20 .12

Issued in conjunction with the 17th Congress of the International Chamber of Commerce, held in Washington, D.C. in 1959.

1130 4c Nevada Silver Jun. 8 .10 .05

In 1859 silver was discovered at the Comstock Lode, Nevada. The rich mine yielded about $400 million worth of the precious metal.

PETROLEUM INDUSTRY

Petroleum, the basis of many essentials of modern life, is often called *black gold* because of its tremendous value to mankind. Although primarily a fuel for transportation, petroleum has a myriad of other functions. It heats homes and lubricates the gears of industry. Everyday items such as detergents, synthetic materials, plastics, and tires are petroleum-based products.

The modern petroleum industry was launched in America when Edwin Drake struck oil near Titusville, Penna., in 1859. Drake's well, which pumped 10 to 35 barrels daily, attracted entrepreneurs from all over the world to drill for their fortunes; almost overnight, Titusville was transformed into a boomtown. Before railroads built branch lines to the fields, wagons and river barges transported the oil to refineries. The first successful pipeline, from an oil field in Titusville to a railroad five miles away, was constructed in 1865.

In the early days of the petroleum industry, striking oil was generally a matter of simple good luck. Making and losing fortunes overnight was commonplace. Although today's methods of finding oil are not foolproof, much of the guesswork has been reduced by modern scientific equipment.

See Scott No. 1134

1135

1138

1131

1132

1133

1137

1136

1134

Perf. 11

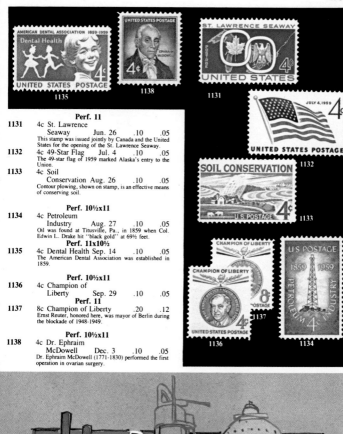

1131 4c St. Lawrence Seaway Jun. 26 .10 .05
This stamp was issued jointly by Canada and the United States for the opening of the St. Lawrence Seaway.

1132 4c 49-Star Flag Jul. 4 .10 .05
The 49-star flag of 1959 marked Alaska's entry to the Union.

1133 4c Soil Conservation Aug. 26 .10 .05
Contour plowing, shown on stamp, is an effective means of conserving soil.

Perf. 10½x11

1134 4c Petroleum Industry Aug. 27 .10 .05
Oil was found at Titusville, Pa., in 1859 when Col. Edwin L. Drake hit "black gold" at 69½ feet.

Perf. 11x10½

1135 4c Dental Health Sep. 14 .10 .05
The American Dental Association was established in 1859.

Perf. 10½x11

1136 4c Champion of Liberty Sep. 29 .10 .05

Perf. 11

1137 8c Champion of Liberty .20 .12
Ernst Reuter, honored here, was mayor of Berlin during the blockade of 1948-1949.

Perf. 10½x11

1138 4c Dr. Ephraim McDowell Dec. 3 .10 .05
Dr. Ephraim McDowell (1771-1830) performed the first operation in ovarian surgery.

1139 1140 1141

1142 1143 1144

1145 1146 1147 1148

1149 1150 1151

1152 1153 1154 1155 1156

1157 1158 1159 1160 1161

Issues of 1960-61, Perf. 11
American Credo

1139 4c Quotation from Washington's Farewell Address .18 .05

1140 4c B. Franklin Quotation .18 .05

1141 4c T. Jefferson Quotation .18 .05

1142 4c Francis Scott Key Quotation .18 .05

1143 4c Lincoln Quotation .18 .05

1144 4c Patrick Henry Quotation .18 .05

Issued to perpetuate and emphasize American ideals

1145 4c Boy Scout Jubilee Feb. 8 .10 .05

Issued for the 50th anniversary of the founding of the Boy Scouts of America.

Perf. 10½x11

1146 4c Olympic Winter Games Feb. 18 .10 .05

The Olympic Winter Games of 1960 were held in Squaw Valley, California

1147 4c Champion of Liberty Mar. 7 .10 .05

Perf. 11

1148 8c Champion of Liberty .20 .12

Thomas Masaryk (1850-1937) was the founder and first president of the Czechoslovakian Republic.

Perf. 11x10½

1149 4c World Refugee Year Apr. 7 .10 .05

World Refugee Year lasted from July 1, 1959 until June 30, 1960.

Perf. 11

1150 4c Water Conservation Apr. 18 .10 .05

Water Conservation Issue depicts the ecological water cycle: rain runoff to watershed to reservoir to city use

Perf. 10½x11

1151 4c SEATO May 31 .10 .05

The South-East Asia Treaty Organization is a mutual defense pact for some Asian nations and the U.S.

Perf. 11x10½

1152 4c American Woman Jun. 2 .10 .05

A tribute to the women of America.

Perf. 11

1153 4c 50-Star Flag Jul. 4 .10 .05

When Hawaii joined the Union (in 1959) the fiftieth star was added to the flag.

Perf. 11x10½

1154 4c Pony Express 100th Anniv. Jul. 19 .10 .05

The Pony Express was founded in 1860.

Perf. 10½x11

1155 4c Employ the Handicapped Aug. 28 .10 .05

"Employ the Handicapped" was the theme of the Eighth World Congress of the International Society for the welfare of crippled persons.

1156 4c World Forestry Congress Aug. 29 .10 .05

The Fifth World Forestry Congress was held in Seattle, Washington in 1960.

Perf. 11

1157 4c Mexican Independence Sep. 16 .10 .05

Issued for the 150th anniversary of Mexican Independence.

1158 4c U.S.-Japan Treaty Sep. 28 .10 .05

The U.S.-Japan Treaty of Amity and Commerce was ratified in 1860.

Perf. 10½x11

1159 4c Champion of Liberty Oct. 8 .10 .05

Perf. 11

1160 8c Champion of Liberty .20 .12

Issued to honor I.J. Paderewski (1860-1941), Polish pianist and statesman.

1162 1167

1163 1164

Perf. 10½x11

1161 4c Sen. Taft Memorial Oct. 10 .10 .05

Robert A. Taft (1889-1953) was a U.S. Senator from 1939-1953

Perf. 11x10½

1162 4c Wheels of Freedom Oct. 15 .10 .05

Issued in connection with the National Automobile Show, held in Detroit in 1960.

Perf. 11

1163 4c Boys' Clubs of America Oct. 18 .10 .05

The Boys' Clubs of America movement was organized in 1860.

1164 4c Automated P.O. Oct. 20 .10 .05

The first U.S. automated post office opened on October 20, 1960, in Providence, Rhode Island.

Perf. 10½x11

1165 4c Champion of Liberty Oct. 26 .10 .05

Perf. 11

1166 8c Champion of Liberty .20 .12

Baron Gustaf Mannerheim (1867-1951) was president of Finland from 1944 to 1946

1167 4c Camp Fire Girls Nov. 1 .10 .05

The Camp Fire Girls was organized in 1910.

Perf. 10½x11

1168 4c Champion of Liberty Nov. 2 .10 .05

Perf. 11

1169 8c Champion of Liberty .20 .12

Giuseppe Garibaldi (1807-1882) was a leader in the fight to unify all Italy.

1165 1168

1166 1169

1170 1171 1172 1177 1174 1173 1175 1176

CIVIL WAR

On April 12, 1861 Confederate General P.G.T. Beauregard's artillery fired on Fort Sumter to signalize the start of the Civil War. This was the culmination of a long series of disputes between the industrial North and the agricultural South, basically having to do with economic rivalry, but expressed in many ways such as arguments over the interpretation of the U.S. Constitution and, above all, in the disagreements over slavery.

Abraham Lincoln described the question that divided the South from the rest of the country as follows: "A house divided against itself cannot stand. . . . This government cannot endure permanently half slave and half free." Soon after Lincoln's election as President, the Southern states seceded and formed the Confederate States of America (CSA). Jefferson Davis was elected President of the new nation and Richmond, Va., was chosen as its capital.

The objectives of each side in the looming struggle were relatively simple: The North fought to preserve the Union, and the South fought for recognition as a sovereign nation. The North, with its larger population and greater financial and industrial resources, seemed to have the advantage. The 23 states of the Union expected a quick victory over the 11 states that comprised the Confederacy. This idea was quickly tested. The Southern forces, with their interior lines of communication and their expert military leadership under General Robert

1178

1179

1182

1180

1181

E. Lee, had all the better of the fighting in the first two years of the war. During Northern assaults at the Battle of Bull Run (July 21, 1861) the Confederate General Thomas Jonathan Jackson held his ground so firmly that he earned the nickname of "Stonewall." The Southern success at Bull Run made the overconfident North realize it was in for a long fight. At the bloody three-day battle of Gettysburg in July 1863, the Union army stopped the Confederate army under Lee and turned the tide of the war. General Lee was never able to mount enough forces to undertake another real offensive. In addition, Union forces took Vicksburg, Miss., thus ensuring control of the vital Mississippi River.

With his capable subordinates, General William Sherman, Phil Sheridan and George Thomas, General Ulysses S. Grant was able to simply grind down the then weaker Confederate forces by using the plentiful manpower and greater matériel of the North. In November 1864 General Sherman left a devastated Atlanta in flames and in 1865 General Grant took Richmond.

Robert E. Lee realized that prolonging the war would result only in an unnecessary sacrifice of lives. On April 9, 1865, at Appomattox Courthouse in Virginia, in one of the most dramatic scenes in American history, Lee surrendered to Grant. The war was over and the Union, at a terrible price, had been preserved.

See Scott Nos. 1178-1182

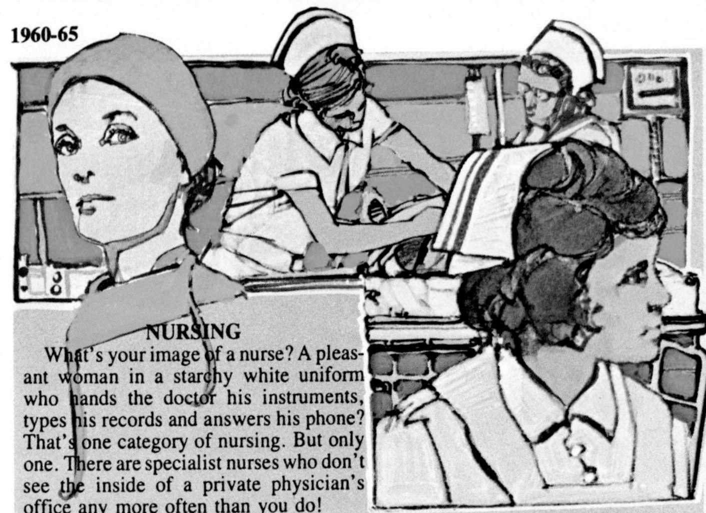

NURSING

What's your image of a nurse? A pleasant woman in a starchy white uniform who hands the doctor his instruments, types his records and answers his phone? That's one category of nursing. But only one. There are specialist nurses who don't see the inside of a private physician's office any more often than you do!

Some nurses spend their working days and nights in the hospital surgical suite or the recovery unit or the intensive care unit or the coronary care unit. They've had special training in a single facet of nursing, and that's the only kind of nursing they do. There are nurse midwives who deliver babies miles away from the nearest doctor or hospital. There are pediatric nurses who care for sick children, psychiatric nurses who tend mental patients, rehabilitative nurses who specialize in easing a patient on his way from sickness to health. Also there are military nurses, industrial nurses, public health nurses and teaching nurses.

Most nurses are women, but there's a sizeable number of men in the field, too. And some nurses take doctoral degrees in nursing, so they answer to the title "doctor"! The concept of nursing as an independent career for capable and carefully educated professionals reaches back only as far as the nineteenth century. It's a relatively new tradition, modern nursing—but a tradition that's linked to the delivery of high-quality health care in America, today and tomorrow.

See Scott Nos. 1190, 1699

Perf. 10½x11

1170 4c Sen. George Memorial — Nov. 5 — .10 — .05
Walter F. George (1878-1957) was Ambassador to NATO and a U.S. Senator.

1171 4c Andrew Carnegie — Nov. 25 — .10 — .05
Steel magnate Andrew Carnegie (1835-1919) gave $350 million to various educational institutions.

1172 4c John Foster Dulles Memorial — Dec. 6 — .10 — .05
John Foster Dulles (1888-1959) served as Secretary of State under Eisenhower.

Perf. 11x10½

1173 4c Echo I—Communications for Peace — Dec. 15 — .55 — .12
The world's first communications satellite, Echo I, was placed in orbit on August 12, 1960.

Issues of 1961
Perf. 10½x11

1174 4c Champion of Liberty — Jan. 26 — .10 — .05

Perf. 11

1175 8c Champion of Liberty — .20 — .12
Pacifist Mahatma Gandhi (1869-1948) led India to freedom from the British in 1947.

1176 4c Range Conservation — Feb. 2 — .10 — .05
Issue dramatizes the development of range conservation from the age of the pioneers to the age of modern science.

Perf. 10½x11

1177 4c Horace Greeley — Feb. 3. — .10 — .05

Civil War 100th Anniv. Issue, 1961-1965
Perf. 11x10½

1178 4c Fort Sumter Centenary, 1961 — .18 — .05

1179 4c Shiloh Centenary, 1962 — .15 — .05

Perf. 11

1180 5c Gettysburg Centenary, 1963 — .15 — .05

1181 5c Wilderness Centenary, 1964 — .15 — .05

1182 5c Appomattox Centenary, 1965 — .18 — .05

Issue dates: #1178, Apr. 12, 1961; #1179, Apr. 7, 1962; #1180, July 1, 1963; #1181, May 5, 1964; #1182, Apr. 9, 1965.

Issues of 1961

1183 4c Kansas Statehood — May. 10 — .10 — .05
Kansas became a state in 1861.

1183 1184 1185 1186 1187 1188 1189 1190 1191 1192 1193 1195 1194

Perf. 11x10½

1184 4c Sen. George W. Norris Jul. 11 .10 .05
U.S. Senator George Norris (1861-1944) helped father the Tennessee Valley Authority in 1933.

1185 4c Naval Aviation Aug. 20 .10 .05
Issued for the 50th anniversary of Naval aviation

Perf. 10½x11

1186 4c Workmen's Comp. Sep. 4 .10 .05
Issued for the 50th anniversary of the passage of the first successful Workmen's Compensation Law.

Perf. 11

1187 4c Frederic Remington Oct. 4 .15 .05
Artist Frederic Remington (1861-1909) captured the "Old West" in sculpture and on canvas. Stamp shows his work "The Smoke Signal."

Perf. 10½x11

1188 4c Republic of China Oct. 10 .10 .05
Issued for the 50th anniversary of the Republic of China. Stamp shows Sun Yat-sen (1866-1925). first president of China.

1189 4c Naismith-Basketball Nov. 6 .10 .05
James Naismith invented basketball in 1891.

Perf. 11

1190 4c Nursing Dec. 28 .10 .05
A tribute to the nursing profession.

Issues of 1962

1191 4c New Mexico Statehood Jan. 6 .10 .05
This 50th anniversary issue depicts Shiprock. sacred mountain of the Navajos, in New Mexico.

1192 4c Arizona Statehood Feb. 14 .16 .05
In 1912 Arizona joined the Union. Stamp depicts the Arizona desert.

1193 4c Project Mercury Feb. 20 .20 .10
Issued for the first orbital flight of a U.S. astronaut. Flight made by Colonel John Glenn on Feb. 20. 1962.

1194 4c Malaria Eradication Mar. 30 .10 .05
Many nations of the world, including the United States, joined the U.N.'s World Health Organization in its fight against malaria.

Perf. 10½x11

1195 4c Charles Evans Hughes Apr. 11 .10 .05
Chief Justice Charles Evans Hughes (1862-1948) also was governor of the state of New York.

1198 1197 1201

1200 1196 1199

1203 1204

1208

1206 1207

1230

Perf. 11

1196 4c Seattle World's Fair Apr. 25 .10 .05
The "Century 21" International Exposition was held at Seattle in 1962.

1197 4c Louisiana Statehood Apr. 30 .10 .05
In 1812, Louisiana joined the Union.

Perf. 11x10½

1198 4c Homestead Act May 20 .10 .05
The Homestead Act, signed into law by Lincoln in 1862, played a major role in settling the West.

1199 4c Girl Scout Jubilee Jul. 24 .10 .05
Issued for the 50th anniversary of the founding of the Girl Scouts of America.

1200 4c Sen. Brien McMahon Jul. 28 .15 .05
Senator Brien McMahon of Connecticut authored the McMahon Act for the peaceful uses of atomic energy.

1201 4c Apprenticeship Aug. 31 .10 .05
Enacted under the New Deal, the National Apprenticeship Act trained people in industry.

Perf. 11

1202 4c Sam Rayburn Sep. 16 .10 .05
Sam Rayburn of Texas (1882-1961) was Speaker of the House of Representatives for 17 years.

1203 4c Dag Hammarskjöld Oct. 23 .12 .05
Swedish diplomat Dag Hammarskjöld was Secretary General of the United Nations from 1953 until his death in 1961.

1204 4c Hammarskjöld Special Printing; black, brown and yellow (yellow inverted) .18 .08

1205 4c Christmas Issue Nov. 1 .10 .03

1206 4c Higher Education Nov. 14 .10 .05
Issued as a tribute to U.S. colleges and universities.

1207 4c Winslow Homer Dec. 15 .15 .05
Artist Winslow Homer (1836-1910) was best-known for seascapes such as "Breezing Up" shown on stamp.

Flag Issue of 1963

1208 5c Flag over White House .12 .03

1205 1209 1213 1240
1233 1232 1234
1202 1231 1235 1238
1236 1237 1239

Regular Issue of 1962-66
Perf. 11x10½

1209 1c Andrew Jackson .05 .03
1213 5c George Washington .12 .03
1213a Booklet pane of 5 + label 2.00 .75

Coil Stamps. Perf. 10 Vertically

1225 1c green Jackson (1209) .12 .03
1229 5c dark blue gray Washington (1213) .50 .03

Issues of 1963, Perf. 11

1230 5c Carolina Charter Apr. 6 .12 .05
The granting of the Carolina Charter by King Charles II gave eight Englishmen vast lands for settlement in 1663.

1231 5c Food for Peace—Freedom from Hunger Jun. 4 .12 .05
Issue publicizes joint U.S.-U.N. campaign to end starvation.

1232 5c W. Virginia Statehood Jun. 20 .12 .05
In 1863 West Virginia joined the Union.

1233 5c Emancipation Proclamation Aug. 16 .12 .05
President Lincoln's Emancipation Proclamation of January, 1863, freed all slaves in the ten Southern states.

1234 5c Alliance for Progress Aug. 17 .12 .05
Issued for the second anniversary of the Alliance for Progress.

Perf. 10½x11

1235 5c Cordell Hull Oct. 5 .12 .05
Cordell Hull (1871-1955) was Secretary of State from 1933-1944.

Perf. 11x10½

1236 5c Eleanor Roosevelt Oct. 11 .12 .05
Mrs. Franklin D. Roosevelt (1884-1962) was the 32nd First Lady (1933-1945). She also served as U.S. delegate to the U.N.

Perf. 11

1237 5c Science Oct. 14 .20 .05
The National Academy of Science was founded in 1863

1238 5c City Mail Delivery Oct. 26 .12 .05
Issued for the 100th anniversary of free city mail delivery.

1239 5c Red Cross 100th Anniv. Oct. 29 .12 .05
Issued for the 100th anniversary of the International Red Cross.

1240 5c Christmas Issue Nov. 1 .12 .03

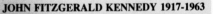

1241 1242 1243 1244 1246 1245

1241 5c John James Audubon Dec. 7 .15 .05
Audubon (1785?-1851) was a famous painter, ornithologist and conservationist. Stamp shows "Columbia Jays" from his book *The Birds of America*.

Issues of 1964, Perf. 10½x11

1242 5c Sam Houston Jan. 10 .12 .05
Sam Houston (1793-1863) was president of the Republic of Texas and later a U.S. Senator from the state of Texas.

Perf. 11

1243 5c Charles M. Russell Mar. 19 .15 .05
This stamp honors frontier artist Charles M. Russell (1864-1926). It depicts his painting, "Jerked Down."

Perf. 11x10½

1244 5c New York World's Fair Apr. 22 .15 .05
Issued for the opening of the New York World's Fair of 1964-65.

Perf. 11

1245 5c John Muir Apr. 29 .12 .05
Conservationist John Muir (1838-1914) worked to save California's redwood trees.

Perf. 11x10½

1246 5c Kennedy Memorial May 29 .12 .05
A memorial to John F. Kennedy, President of the United States from 1961 until his death in 1963.

JOHN FITZGERALD KENNEDY 1917-1963

John F. Kennedy was the youngest man ever elected to the nation's highest office. He was also the first President born in the twentieth century. At his inauguration he declared that "a new generation of Americans has taken over the leadership of America" and that they were willing to "pay any price, bear any burden . . . to assure the survival and success of liberty." He admonished his fellow citizens, "Ask not what your country can do for you—ask what you can do for your country."

During his brief tenure of office Kennedy instilled hope for the future. His "New Frontier" program established the Peace Corps, a group of dedicated volunteers who helped to improve living conditions around the world. He increased America's prestige when he confronted the Soviet Union in the Cuban missile crisis (1962) and forced the Russians to remove their missiles from Cuba. When 200,000 people staged a Freedom March for Civil Rights on Washington, D.C., in 1963 he advised the Congress to ". . . make it clear to all that race has no place in American life or law." Sadly, the great promise that millions perceived in the young President was ended by an assassin's bullets on November 22, 1963, at Dallas, Texas.

See Scott Nos. 1246, 1287

1247 1248 1249 1250 1252 1251 1253

Perf. 10½x11

1247 5c New Jersey 300th Anniv. Jun. 15 .12 .05
In 1664, the English colonized New Jersey.

Perf. 11

1248 5c Nevada Statehood Jul. 22 .12 .05
Nevada became a state in 1864.

1249 5c Register and Vote Aug. 1 .12 .05
Issued for the 1964 presidential elections.

Perf. 10½x11

1250 5c Shakespeare Aug. 14 .12 .05
English dramatist William Shakespeare was born in 1564, 400 years before this stamp was issued.

1251 5c Doctors Mayo Sep. 11 .12 .05
A tribute to the Mayo brothers, surgeons who established the Mayo Foundation. The heads on the stamp are from a sculpture by James E. Fraser.

Perf. 11

1252 5c American Music Oct. 15 .12 .05
Issued for the 50th anniversary of the founding of the American Society of Composers, Authors and Publishers (ASCAP)

1253 5c Homemakers Oct. 26 .12 .05
Designed in the style of an early sampler, this stamp honors U.S. homemakers.

AMERICAN MUSIC

"I hear America singing" wrote Walt Whitman more than a century ago. Today, American voices are still raised in song, whether in the driving sound of Dixieland jazz, the vibrant beat of rock & roll, the lamentations of country or the euphonious strains of Gershwin or Bernstein. All of these styles and composers are uniquely American, and each comprises a segment of the American musical tapestry.

America's music traces the country's development, from Puritan psalms to contemporary twelve-tone compositions. The importation of slaves from Africa influenced American music, and the polyrhythmic concern of their native music nurtured the roots of jazz. In fact, every immigrant group has contributed elements of its own musical heritage to the American sound.

American wars inspired the composition of many marches and ballads. Citizen soldiers were quick to "Rally 'Round the Flag" or to plant a Victory garden to help our boys "Over There." Many a Civil War soldier's heart beat faster as he listened to the inspiring strains of "The Battle Hymn of the Republic."

America's music reflects its history and the diversity of its citizens.

1257 b

1261

1263

1262

1259

1258

1260

1265

1264

REGISTER TO VOTE

With "no taxation without representation" as their rallying cry, the American colonists protested against the British monarch and his subservient ministers. In the long and bitter struggle for independence that followed, the Americans won the right to elect their own officials to govern them.

Today, despite the many sacrifices of the Founding Fathers, many eligible voters rarely, if ever, vote. It is ironical that in a world in which the right to select leaders of their own choosing is still denied to more than half the world's population, a large number of Americans never exercise this valuable privilege.

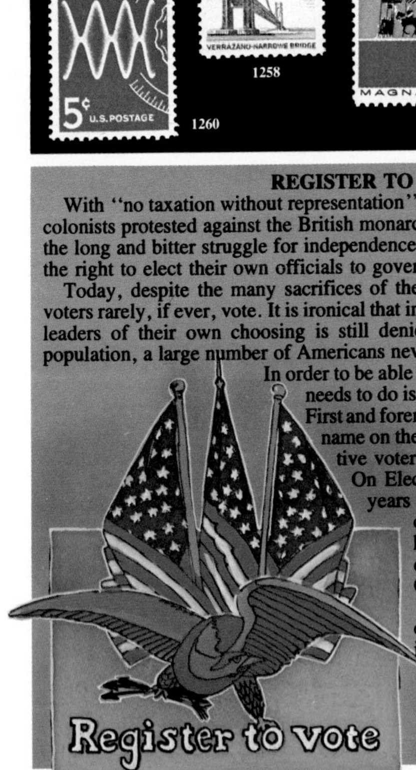

In order to be able to vote, all that any adult American needs to do is to follow a few simple procedures. First and foremost, he must register by placing his name on the list of eligible voters. If a prospective voter does not register, he cannot vote. On Election Day, if a voter is at least 18 years old, a U.S. citizen, and meets the other requirements established by his home state (none of these requirements may violate the U.S. Constitution), he may vote.

It is not only the right of every citizen to cast his or her ballot but it is a responsibility as well.

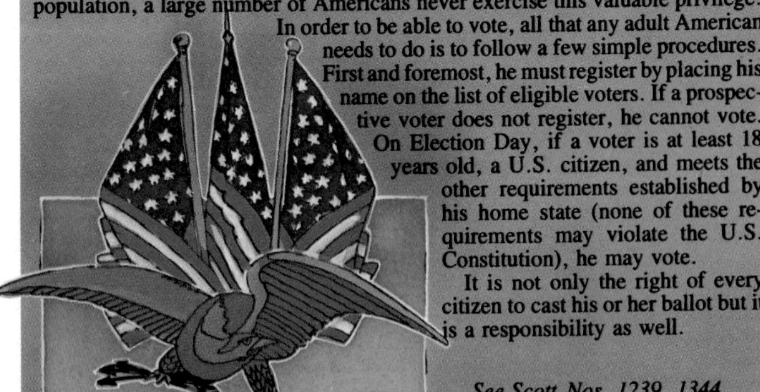

See Scott Nos. 1239, 1344.

1267 1266 1268 1269 1270 1271 1272 1273 1274 1276 1275

Christmas Issue, Nov. 9

1254	5c Holly	1.00	.05
1255	5c Mistletoe	1.00	.05
1256	5c Poinsettia	1.00	.05
1257	5c Sprig of Conifer	1.00	.05
1257b	Block of four	4.50	.40

Perf. 10½x11

1258 5c Verrazano-Narrows Bridge Nov. 21 .12 .05
The world's longest suspension bridge was opened on November 21, 1964. It connects Staten Island and Brooklyn, N.Y.

Perf. 11

1259 5c Fine Arts Dec. 2 .12 .05
Stamp depicts "Abstract Design" by Stuart Davis.

Perf. 10½x11

1260 5c Amateur Radio Dec. 15 .12 .05
The American Radio Relay League for "ham operators" was established in 1914.

Issues of 1965, Perf. 11

1261 5c Battle of New Orleans Jan. 8 .12 .05

1262 5c Physical Fitness-Sokol Feb. 15 .12 .05
The Sokol Athletic Organization was founded in 1915. Issue also promotes physical fitness.

1263 5c Crusade Against Cancer Apr. 1 .12 .05
Issue publicized the fight against cancer; also stressed the importance of early diagnosis.

Perf. 10½x11

1264 5c Churchill Memorial May 13 .12 .05
In memory of the British statesman (1874-1965), Prime Minister and World War II leader.

Perf. 11

1265 5c Magna Carta Jun. 15 .12 .05
This famous document, signed by King John in 1215, is the basis of the common law of England and the U.S.

1266 5c Intl. Cooperation Year Jun. 26 .12 .05
Issued for International Cooperation Year and the 20th anniversary of the United Nations.

1267 5c Salvation Army Jul. 2 .12 .05
William Booth founded the Salvation Army in 1865.

Perf. 10½x11

1268 5c Dante Alighieri Jul.17 .12 .05
The Italian poet, born in 1265, is best known for the *Divine Comedy*.

1269 5c Herbert Hoover Aug. 10 .12 .05
The 31st President of the United States (1929-1933) was born in 1874. He died in 1964.

Perf. 11

1270 5c Robert Fulton Aug. 19 .12 .05

1271 5c Settlement of Florida Aug. 28 .12 .05
Established in 1565, St. Augustine, Florida was the first permanent European settlement in the U.S.

1272 5c Traffic Safety Sep. 3 .12 .05
Issued to help prevent traffic accidents and to publicize highway safety.

1273 5c John Singleton Copley Sep. 17 .18 .05
John Singleton Copley (1738-1815) was an important early U.S. painter. Detail on the stamp is from his oil "The Copley Family" and portrays his daughter.

1274 11c International Telecommunication Union Oct. 6 .45 .16
The International Telecommunication Union, now under the auspices of the United Nations, was established in 1865.

1275 5c Adlai E. Stevenson Oct. 23 .12 .05
Adlai E. Stevenson (1900-1965) was governor of Illinois and U.S. Ambassador to the United Nations.

1276 5c Christmas Issue Nov. 2 .12 .03

1278 1279 1280 1282

1281 1284 1393D 1286A

1283 1283B 1305

1393 1394 1285 1286

1287 1397 1288 1398

1399 1289 1291 1400 1290

1292 1293 1294 1295

ERNIE PYLE

One of the most famous war correspondents of World War II, Ernie Pyle, was born and educated in Indiana. He worked for the Scripps-Howard newspaper chain and his column appeared in as many as 200 newspapers before the war.

At the outbreak of World War II, he went where the fighting was fiercest - North Africa, Sicily, Italy, France, Iwo Jima, Okinawa. Pyle didn't write about military strategy, he wrote instead with touching simplicity about the ordinary young Americans who were performing such extraordinary feats of heroism.

Pyle won the Pulitzer Prize for reporting as well as other awards. His newspaper columns were compiled into popular books: "Ernie Pyle in England," "Here Is Your War," "Brave Men" and, after he was killed by Japanese machine gun fire on an island in the South Pacific, "Last Chapter."

See Scott No. 1398.

Issues of 1965-78, Prominent Americans
Perf. 11x10½, 10½x11

1278	1c	Thomas Jefferson	.03	.03
1278a		Booklet pane of 8	1.00	*.25*
1278b		Booklet pane of 4	.75	*.20*
1279	1½c	Albert Gallatin	.20	.05
1280	2c	Frank Lloyd Wright	.04	.03
1280a		Booklet pane of 5 + label	1.20	*.40*
1280c		Booklet pane of 6	1.00	*.35*
1281	3c	Francis Parkman	.06	.03
1282	4c	Abraham Lincoln	.08	.03
1283	5c	George Washington	.10	.03
1283B	5c	Washington redrawn	.12	.03
1284	6c	Franklin D. Roosevelt	.12	.03
1284b		Booklet pane of 8	1.50	*.50*
1284c		Booklet pane of 5+ label	1.25	*.50*
1285	8c	Albert Einstein	.16	.05
1286	10c	Andrew Jackson	.20	.03
1286A	12c	Henry Ford	.24	.03
1287	13c	John F. Kennedy	.26	.05
1288	15c	Oliver Wendell Holmes	.30	.06
1288B	15c	Dk rose claret Holmes (1288), perf. 10	.30	.05
1288c		Booklet pane of 8	2.40	
1289	20c	George C. Marshall	.40	.06
1290	25c	Frederick Douglass	.50	.03
1291	30c	John Dewey	.60	.08
1292	40c	Thomas Paine	.80	.10
1293	50c	Lucy Stone	1.00	.04
1294	$1	Eugene O'Neill	2.00	.08
1295	$5	John Bassett Moore	10.00	2.00

No. 1288B issued only in booklets.

Coil Stamps, Issues of 1966-78
Perf. 10 Horizontally

1297	3c	violet Parkman (1281)	.06	.03
1298	6c	gray brown F.D.R. (1284)	.40	.05

Perf. 10 Vertically

1299	1c	green Jefferson (1278)	.06	.03
1303	4c	black Lincoln (1282)	.15	.03
1304	5c	blue Washington (1283)	.15	.03
1305	6c	Franklin D. Roosevelt	.20	.03
1305E	15c	rose claret Holmes (1288)	.30	.03
1305C	$1	dull purple Eugene O'Neill (1294)	2.25	.20

FREDERICK DOUGLASS

An escaped slave born in Tuckahoe, Maryland, Frederick Douglass's brilliance and eloquence made him a leader of the abolitionist cause. He was the first black citizen to hold a high position in the U.S. government. And he was one of the 19th century's most famous proponents of human rights.

When his "Autobiography of a Slave" was published, he revealed his former owner's name and had to escape once again to avoid re-enslavement.

He lectured in England and Ireland for two years, returning with enough money to buy his freedom.

Douglass served as a consultant to President Lincoln during the Civil War and helped to enlist blacks in the army. Once the war was over, he fought for full civil rights for the former slaves. He became recorder of deeds in the District of Columbia (1877-86); and U.S. minister and consul general to Haiti (1889-91). In all, he devoted half a century to distinguished public service.

See Scott No. 1290

STAMP SHOWS

The first stamp exhibition in the United States was a display presented by John Walter Scott (originator of the famed Scott Standard Postage Stamp Catalogue) at the Centennial Exposition held in Philadelphia in 1876. The popularity of philatelic exhibitions has grown over the years and is reflected in the large number of international, national and local shows that are held each year. Stamp shows provide philatelists with the opportunity to get together to discuss their hobby, keep up with the latest developments in the stamp world, and to display their collections. At the dealers' bourse held in connection with most shows, a collector is often lucky enough to find a philatelic item he has been searching for that will fill an important gap in his collection.

The biggest stamp show of all—the International Exhibition—is hosted by the United States every ten years. The first U.S. stamp show was held in New York City in 1913. The Centenary International Exhibition (CIPEX) celebrated the 100th anniversary of the first U.S. postage stamps. To coincide with the opening of the Sixth International Exhibition (SIPEX) at Washington, D.C., in 1956 the U.S. Postal Service issued a 5¢ stamp to commemorate the event. Incidentally, the first exhibit ever presented at the New York Coliseum was a stamp show.

See Scott Nos. 730, 778, 948, 1075-1076, 1310-1311

1306

1307

1308

1309

1310

1312

1313

1314

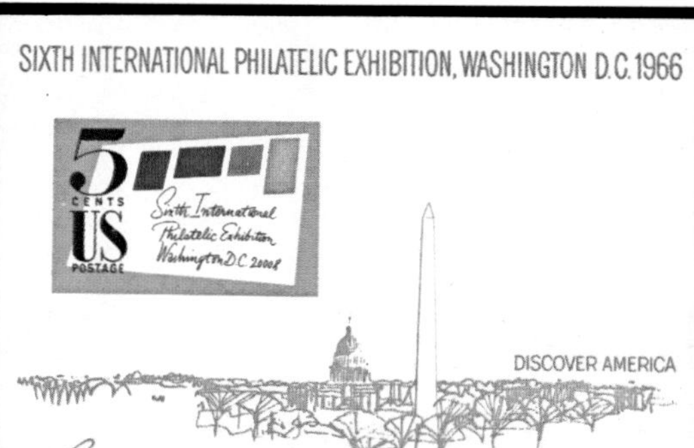

1311

Issues of 1966, Perf. 11

1306 5c Migratory Bird Treaty Mar. 16 .15 .05
In 1916 Canada and the United States ratified this treaty to protect their migratory birds.

1307 5c Humane Treatment of Animals Apr. 9 .15 .05
The American Society for the Prevention of Cruelty to Animals was established in 1866.

1308 5c Indiana Statehood Apr. 16 .12 .05
In 1816, Indiana joined the Union.

1309 5c American Circus May 2 .12 .05
This tribute to the circus also marked the 100th anniversary of the birth of John Ringling, circusmaster.

Sixth International Philatelic Exhibition Issues

1310 5c Stamped Cover May 21 .12 .05

Imperf.

1311 5c Souvenir Sheet May 23 .40 .15
Issued in sheets of one stamp with marginal inscription commemorating the Sixth International Philatelic Exhibition (SIPEX), held in Washington, D.C. from May 21-30.

Perf. 11

1312 5c Bill of Rights Jul. 1 .12 .05
Issued for the 175th anniversary of the Bill of Rights.

Perf. 10½x11

1313 5c Polish Millennium Jul. 30 .15 .05
The people of Poland adopted Christianity in 966 A.D.

Perf. 11

1314 5c National Park Service Aug. 25 .12 .05
Issued for the 50th anniversary of the National Park Service of the Department of the Interior.

HUMANE TREATMENT OF ANIMALS

Cruelty to animals is against the law in the United States. The laws that protect America's animals were the life work of Henry Bergh, U.S. minister to Russia under Abraham Lincoln. One day in St. Petersburg, Bergh watched in stunned horror as a Russian droshky driver beat a horse nearly to death. Since the driver was breaking no law, Bergh was powerless to stop him. But from that moment on, he campaigned for animals in every field from bullfighting to anti-vivisection.

The U.S. wasn't first to make kindness to animals the law of the land, though. England did it in 1822. England became home in 1824 to the first animal welfare society, The Society for the Prevention of Cruelty to Animals (SPCA). In 1866, through Henry Bergh's efforts, the idea crossed the ocean, and the American equivalent—the ASPCA—was formed.

See Scott No. 1307.

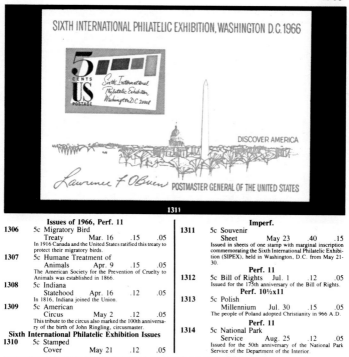

1315 1316 1317 1319

1318 1320 1321 1322

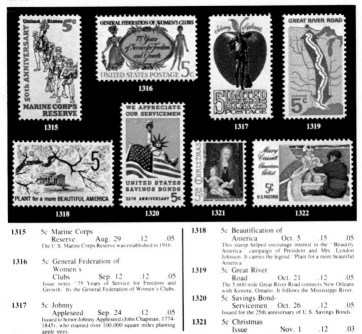

No.	Description	Date	Unused	Used
1315	5c Marine Corps Reserve	Aug. 29	.12	.05
	The U.S. Marine Corps Reserve was established in 1916.			
1316	5c General Federation of Women's Clubs	Sep. 12	.12	.05
	Issue notes "75 Years of Service for Freedom and Growth" by the General Federation of Women's Clubs.			
1317	5c Johnny Appleseed	Sep. 24	.12	.05
	Issued to honor Johnny Appleseed (John Chapman, 1774-1845), who roamed over 100,000 square miles planting apple trees.			
1318	5c Beautification of America	Oct. 5	.15	.05
	This stamp helped encourage interest in the "Beautify America" campaign of President and Mrs. Lyndon Johnson. It carries the legend "Plant for a more beautiful America".			
1319	5c Great River Road	Oct. 21	.12	.05
	The 5,600 mile Great River Road connects New Orleans with Kenora, Ontario. It follows the Mississippi River.			
1320	5c Savings Bond-Servicemen	Oct. 26	.12	.05
	Issued for the 25th anniversary of U.S. Savings Bonds.			
1321	5c Christmas Issue	Nov. 1	.12	.03

JOHNNY APPLESEED

What a sight was Johnny Appleseed, with his long, flowing hair, full grown beard, baggy pants and bare feet. And what a man was he! Cheerful and generous to a fault, he lived in harmony with nature, loving animals, man and God. The Indians were his friends. So were the pioneers who began to settle the Middle West when the 19th century was new. Massachusetts nurseryman Johnny Chapman helped the pioneers by supplying apple tree nursery stock to all who wanted it all along the frontier. And he became an American legend in the process.

Johnny himself planted apple nurseries from the Alleghenies to central Ohio and beyond. And he sold or gave away thousands of seedlings to the pioneers. He was three score and ten when he died of exposure near Ft. Wayne, Indiana. But the thousands of acres of flourishing apple orchards gracing America's newly cultivated lands remained as his living memorial.

See Scott No. 1317.

1323 1324 1327 1329

1325 1326 1328

This stamp shows a detail from the work "Madonna and Child with Angels" by the Flemish artist Hans Memling (c. 1430-1494).

1322 5c Mary Cassatt Nov. 17 .20 .05

Issues of 1967

1323 5c National Grange Apr. 17 .12 .05
The National Grange, a farm organization, was created in 1867.

1324 5c Canada 100th Anniv. May 25 .12 .05
Issued for the 100th anniversary of Canada's Emergence as a nation.

1325 5c Erie Canal Jul. 4 .12 .05

1326 5c "Peace"— Lions Jul. 5 .12 .05
"Search for Peace" was the theme of an essay contest sponsored by Lions International for its 50th anniversary.

1327 5c Henry David Thoreau Jul. 12 .12 .05
A leading author of the nineteenth century. Thoreau is best-known for his book *Walden*.

1328 5c Nebraska Statehood Jul. 29 .12 .05

1329 5c Voice of America Aug. 1 .12 .05
25th anniversary of the Voice of America, the radio branch of the United States Information Agency.

HENRY DAVID THOREAU 1817-1862

New England author, poet and essayist, Thoreau is best remembered for his belief in the rights of the individual to oppose accepted social institutions. Thoreau believed that man is obligated to act according to his own conscience and with no outside interference. In his most famous essay "Civil Disobedience" (1849), he supported a doctrine of passive resistance, urging people to refuse to obey laws they considered unjust.

Ralph Waldo Emerson, his neighbor and friend, encouraged Thoreau in his writing and gave him a parcel of a few acres of land at nearby Walden Pond outside Concord, Mass. Thoreau built a cabin on the land and lived there alone for two years. In his greatest books, *A Week on the Concord and Merrimack Rivers* (1849) and *Walden* (1854), he tells of his experiences in simple living and appeals to people to make their lives less complex and live in closer harmony with nature.

A convinced abolitionist, Thoreau went to jail because he would not pay taxes to a government that condoned and justified human subjugation. He was active in the antislavery movement and helped many slaves in their flight to freedom along the Underground Railroad.

See Scott No. 1327

U.S. SPACE EFFORTS

For hundreds of years, men have dreamed of traveling to the moon, and, on July 20, 1969, that dream came true. As millions of people watched on television, Neil Armstrong climbed down from the Apollo 11 lunar module, saying, ". . . one small step for man, one giant leap for mankind."

The moon landing was the culmination of more than a decade of U.S. space exploration that began in 1957 when the Soviet Union launched the first Sputnik into orbit. When John F. Kennedy became President in 1961, he promised that America would send a man to the moon before the Sixties were over. The race between the Soviet Union and the United States to be first to reach the moon was on. In 1961 Alan Sheppard was the first American to be launched into space in a 15-minute ride, and John Glenn, on February 20, 1962, became the first American to orbit the earth. Projects Gemini and Mercury followed, in which satellites and rockets explored vast areas of space. On June 3, 1965 in Gemini 4, Edward White was the first American to walk in space. The Apollo 8 crew were the first men to orbit the moon. The actual landing on the moon was highlighted by the placing of an American flag on the moon's surface.

See Scott Nos. 1193, 1331-1332, 1371, 1434-1435, 1529, 1556-1557, 1569-1570, 1759, C69, C76

1330	5c Davey Crockett	Aug. 17	.12	.05
	Space Accomplishments Issue, Sep. 29			
1331	5c Space-Walking Astronaut		1.75	.25
1331a	Pair		5.50	2.00
1332	5c Gemini 4 Capsule and Earth		1.75	.25
1333	5c Urban Planning	Oct. 2	.15	.05
1334	5c Finnish Independence	Oct. 6	.15	.05

Issued for the 50th anniversary of Finnish independence, this stamp reproduces Finland's coat of arms.

Perf. 12

1335	5c Thomas Eakins	Nov. 2	.18	.05

Painter Thomas Eakins (1844-1916) is honored on this stamp. Designed from an Eakins oil, "The Biglin Brothers Racing," it was the first U.S. stamp printed by the gravure method.

Perf. 11

1336	5c Christmas Issue	Nov. 6	.12	.04
1337	5c Mississippi Statehood	Dec. 11	.15	.05

In 1817, Mississippi joined the Union. Stamp depicts the Mississippi state flower, the magnolia.

1330 1331a 1333 1334 1335 1336

1337 1339 1338 1341

1340 1342 1343 1344

Issues of 1968-71

1338	6c Flag and White House	.12	.03

Perf. 11x10½

1338D	6c dark blue, red & gr. (1338)	.12	.03
1338F	8c multicolored (1338)	.16	.03

Coil Stamps of 1969-71
Perf. 10 Vertically

1338A	6c dk. blue, red & green (1338)	.12	.03
1338G	8c multicolored (1338)	.16	.03

Issues of 1968, Perf. 11

1339	6c Illinois Statehood	Feb. 12	.18	.05

Illinois entered the Union in 1818.

1340	6c HemisFair '68	Mar. 30	.18	.05

The HemisFair '68 exhibition at San Antonio, Texas, commemorated 250th anniversary of San Antonio.

1341	$1 Airlift	Apr. 4	3.75	2.00

Issued to pay for airlift of parcels to and from servicemen overseas.

1342	6c "Youth"— Elks	May 1	.18	.05

National Youth Week of 1968 was sponsored by the Elks.

1343	6c Law and Order	May 17	.18	.05

To encourage respect for law and order.

1344	6c Register and Vote	Jun. 27	.18	.05

Issued to publicize campaign to get more people to vote.

LAW AND ORDER

No society can advance and flourish unless its citizens respect the laws. A nation's achievements can only be made within a stable and secure structure. Since the dawn of history, civilization has moved forward within the framework of the laws that man has enacted and followed. When man protects the law, he in turn is protected by it. He is freed from fear and allowed to progress.

In America, the citizens themselves have a voice in the laws they are required to obey. Freely elected representatives legislate with the consent of the governed and thus ensure the rights and welfare of the greatest number. The people seek change, the avenues of the democratic process are open to them, and through peaceful and legal means these changes can be effected. The basic liberties guaranteed to every American citizen make it unnecessary to break the law in order to change the law.

Traditionally, the law enforcement officer, with the support of the people he serves, has assumed the role of guardian of the law. Through this partnership, the rights of all citizens are protected and the American way of life is preserved.

See Scott No. 1343

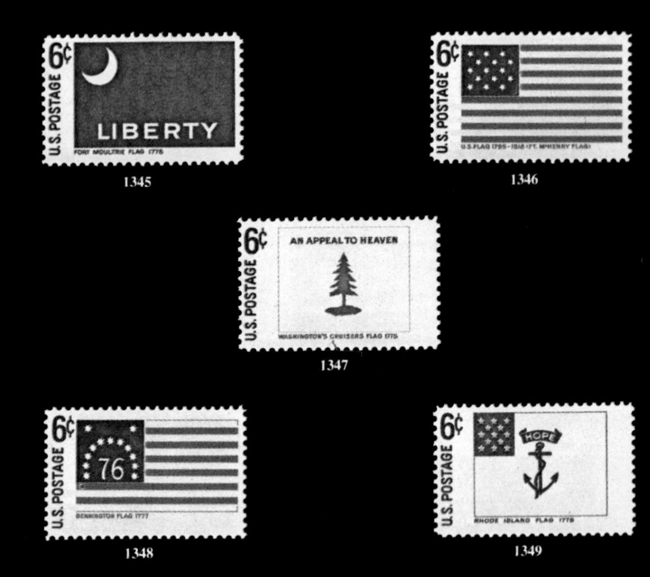

OLD FLAGS

In the early days of the American Revolution, there was no single official American flag. Instead, the colonists made flags and banners with many and various devices, depending upon their native ingenuity. For instance, the colonists' flag at Bunker Hill had a blue ground on which a large red cross and a pine tree were superimposed.

Each of the states adopted a flag of its own. There was no uniformity, though the rattlesnake with 13 rattles was a common decoration, usually accompanied by the inscription, "Don't tread on me." The flags carried by different military regiments differed according to the varied tastes of their commanders.

The first national flag, which also served as the original Navy ensign, was raised by George Washington in 1776. This flag had seven red and six white stripes along with the British insignia.

However, a flag associated with British rule was deemed inappropriate for a nation seeking independence, so the Continental Congress decreed that a new national flag be designed. On June 14, 1777, it was resolved that the flag should be made of "thirteen stripes, alternate red and white, with a union of thirteen stars of white on a blue field, representing a new constellation." Tradition has it that Betsy Ross made the first American flag at George Washington's request.

The first Stars and Stripes flown in battle was the famous '76 flag in the Battle of Bennington on August 16, 1777.

See Scott Nos. 1004, 1345-1354, 1566

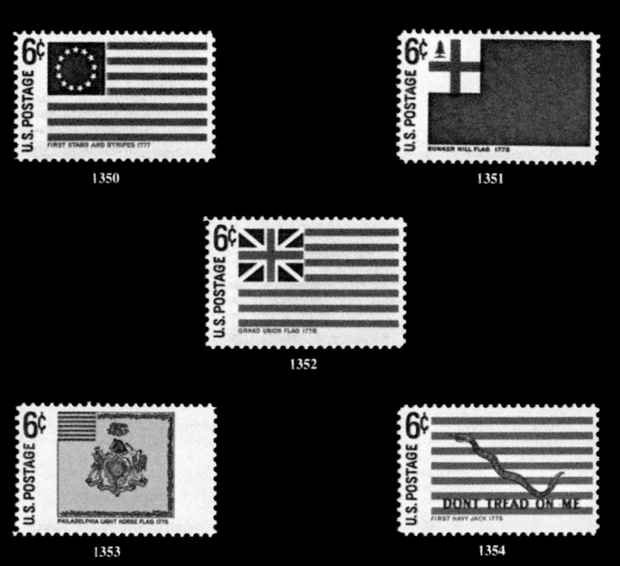

1350 1351

1352

1353 1354

JOHN PAUL JONES 1747-1792

Known as the Father of the American Navy, John Paul Jones was the foremost U.S. Naval officer of the Revolution. At the outbreak of war, he was commissioned a lieutenant on the *Alfred*, the first ship of the Continental Navy. By August 1776, his outstanding military skills were recognized by Congress and he was promoted to captain. In June 1777, he took command of the *Ranger*, the first U.S. Naval vessel to fly the new American flag.

On September 23, 1779, as commander of the *Bonhomme Richard*, Jones fought the battle that earned his lasting place in history. His squadron encountered a large British convoy and his ship attacked the convoy leader, *H.M.S. Serapis*. The British vessel was larger and better equipped than the American ship. Asked to surrender to the superior vessel, Jones' heroism and fighting spirit were expressed in his famous reply, "I have not yet begun to fight."

After more than three hours of raging battle, in which both ships suffered heavy damage, the *Serapis* surrendered. Two days later the *Bonhomme Richard* sank. Jones' victory established the American Navy's fighting tradition.

See Scott Nos. 790, 1789

Historic Flag Series, Jul. 4

1345	6c Ft. Moultrie Flag (1776)	.80	.35
1346	6c Ft. McHenry Flag (1795-1818)	.80	.35
1347	6c Washington's Cruisers Flag (1775)	.80	.35
1348	6c Bennington Flag (1777)	.80	.35
1349	6c Rhode Island Flag (1775)	.80	.35
1350	6c First Stars and Stripes Flag (1777)	.80	.35
1351	6c Bunker Hill Flag (1775)	.80	.35
1352	6c Grand Union Flag (1776)	.80	.35
1353	6c Phila. Light Horse Flag (1775)	.80	.35
1354	6c First Navy Jack (1775)	.80	.35
1354a	Strip of ten	10.00	6.50

Nine of the flags shown in this series were associated with our Revolution. The remaining flag, that of Fort McHenry, was associated with the War of 1812. It inspired Francis Scott Key to compose the "Star-Spangled Banner."

Perf. 12

1355	6c Walt Disney	Sep. 11	.20	.05

Issued in memory of Walt Disney (1901-1966), creator of Mickey Mouse.

Perf. 11

1356	6c Father Marquette	Sep. 20	.20	.05

Father Jacques Marquette (1637-1675) explored the Mississippi River with fur trapper Louis Jolliet.

1357	6c Daniel Boone	Sep. 26	.20	.05

Frontiersman and trapper Daniel Boone (1734-1820) founded Boonesboro, Kentucky.

1358	6c Arkansas River	Oct. 1	.20	.05

Issued for the opening of the Arkansas River to commercial navigation.

1359	6c Leif Erikson	Oct. 9	.20	.05

Leif Erikson, the 11th century Norse explorer, may have been the first European to set foot on the North American continent. This stamp shows a statue of Erikson in Reykjavik, Iceland.

Perf. 11x10½

1360	6c Cherokee Strip	Oct. 15	.20	.05

Issued for the 75th anniversary of the opening of the Cherokee Strip (in the Oklahoma panhandle) to white settlers.

Perf. 11

1361	6c John Trumbull	Oct. 18	.25	.05

John Trumbull (1756-1843) was a noted early U.S. painter. Stamp shows a detail from his work "The Battle of Bunker Hill"

1364 1369 1370 1371 1368 a 1373 1372 1374 1375

1362 6c Waterfowl Conservation Oct. 24 .30 .05
Issued to encourage waterfowl conservation and to honor Ducks Unlimited, an organization which has spent nearly $15 million on conservation.

1363 6c Christmas Issue Nov. 1 .20 .04
This stamp shows the Angel Gabriel, a detail from "The Annunciation" by Flemish painter Jan van Eyck (c. 1390-1441).

1364 6c American Indian Nov. 4 .30 .05
A tribute to the Indian, this stamp shows the great Chief Joseph (c. 1840-1904), leader of the Nez Percé tribe.

Issues of 1969

Beautification of America, Jan. 16

1365 6c Capitol, Azaleas and Tulips 2.00 .15

1366 6c Washington Monument, Potomac River and Daffodils 2.00 .15

1367 6c Poppies and Lupines along Highway 2.00 .15

1368 6c Blooming Crabapples along Street 2.00 .15

1368 a Block of four 8.50 2.50
Nos. 1365-1368 were issued to promote the "Beautification of America" campaign.

1369 6c American Legion Mar. 15 .20 .05
The American Legion was founded in 1919 in Paris.

1370 6c Grandma Moses May 1 .25 .05
Issued to honor Grandma Moses (1860-1961), American primitive painter.

1371 6c Apollo 8 May 5 .30 .06
The Apollo 8 mission of Dec. 21-27, 1968 put the first men into orbit around the moon.

1372 6c W. C. Handy May 17 .20 .05
William Christopher Handy (1873-1958) was a jazz musician and composer ("The St. Louis Blues"). Stamp also notes the 150th anniversary of Memphis, Tennessee.

1373 6c California Settlement Jul. 16 .20 .05
Issued for the 200th anniversary of the settlement of California by Father Junipero Serra and Gaspạr de Portola.

1374 6c John Wesley Powell Aug. 1 .20 .05
Geologist John Wesley Powell (1834-1902) explored the Green and Colorado Rivers.

1375 6c Alabama Statehood Aug. 2 .20 .05
In 1819, Alabama joined the Union. Stamp shows yellow-hammer and camelia—state bird and flower.

1379 a, 1383, 1380, 1384, 1385, 1381, 1386, 1382

Botanical Congress Issue

1376	6c Douglas Fir (Northwest)	2.75	.15
1377	6c Lady's Slipper (Northeast)	2.75	.15
1378	6c Ocotillo (Southwest)	2.75	.15
1379	6c Franklinia (Southeast)	2.75	.15
1379a	Block of four	12.00	2.50

Issued in conjunction with the 11th International Botanical Congress, held in Seattle, Wash., Aug. 23-Sep. 2.

Perf. 10½x11

1380	6c Dartmouth College Case	Sep. 22	.20	.05

The Dartmouth College Case, argued by Daniel Webster before the Supreme Court in 1819, upheld sanctity of contracts.

Perf. 11

1381	6c Professional Baseball	Sep. 24	.25	.05

Issued for the 100th anniversary of professional baseball.

1382	6c Intercollegiate Football	Sep. 26	.25	.05

Issued for the 100th anniversary of intercollegiate football.

1383	6c Dwight D. Eisenhower	Oct. 14	.20	.05

Issued in memory of Dwight D. Eisenhower (1890-1969), General of the Army and 34th President of the United States (1953-1961).

Perf. 11x10½

1384	6c Christmas Issue	Nov. 3	.18	.03
1384a	Precanceled		.30	.06

"A Winter Sunday in Norway, Maine," shown on stamp, was painted around 1870 by an unknown artist.

1385	6c Hope for Crippled	Nov. 20	.18	.05

Issued for the 50th anniversary of the National Society for crippled children and adults, the sponsor of Easter Seals.

1386	6c William M. Harnett	Dec. 3	.18	.05

Artist William M. Harnett (1848-1892) is known for still-life paintings like "Old Models," shown on stamp.

Issues of 1970

Natural History, May 6

1387	6c American Bald Eagle	.30	.12
1388	6c African Elephant Herd	.30	.12
1389	6c Tlingit Chief in Haida Ceremonial Canoe	.30	.12
1390	6c Brontosaurus, Stegosaurus and Allosaurus from Jurassic Period	.30	.12
1390a	Block of four	1.35	.75

These stamps honor the American Museum of Natural History in New York City on its 100th anniversary.

1405 1390a 1391 1392 1406 1407 1396 1408

1391	6c Maine Statehood Jul. 9		.18	.05

Designed from an oil by artist Edward Hopper (1882-1967) this stamp honors Maine on its 150th anniversary.

Perf. 10½x11

1392	6c Wildlife Conservation Jul. 20		.18	.05

This Conservation Issue calls attention to the plight of the American bison, of which about 30,000 remain.

Issues of 1970-74
Perf. 11x10½, 10½x11, 11

1393	6c Dwight D. Eisenhower	.12	.03
1393a	Booklet pane of 8	1.00	*.50*
1393b	Booklet pane of 5 + label	.85	*.35*
1393D	7c Benjamin Franklin	.14	.03
1394	8c Eisenhower	.16	.03
1395	8c Eisenhower	.16	.03
1395a	Booklet pane of 8	1.50	*1.25*
1395b	Booklet pane of 6	1.00	*.75*
1395c	Booklet pane of 4 + 2 labels	1.00	*.50*
1395d	Booklet pane of 7 + label	1.25	*1.00*
1396	8c U.S. Postal Service	.25	.03
1397	14c Fiorello H. LaGuardia	.28	.03
1398	16c Ernie Pyle	.32	.03
1399	18c Dr. Elizabeth Blackwell	.36	.06
1400	21c Amadeo P. Giannini	.42	.06

No. 1395 issued in booklets only.

Coil Stamps, Perf. 10 Vertically

1401	6c dark blue gray Eisenhower (1393)	.20	.03
1402	8c deep claret Eisenhower (1395)	.22	.03

Issues of 1970
Perf. 11

1405	6c Edgar Lee Masters Aug. 22	.18	.05

Edgar Lee Masters (1869-1950), poet, is best known for the *Spoon River Anthology*. This stamp was the first in a series honoring U.S. poets.

1406	6c Woman Suffrage Aug. 26	.18	.05

Issued for the 50th anniversary of the passage of the 19th Amendment, which allowed women to vote.

1407	6c South Carolina Sept. 12	.18	.05

In 1670, South Carolina was settled by the English. Charleston was the state's first permanent settlement.

1408	6c Stone Mountain Mem. Sep. 19	.18	.05

Stone Mountain Memorial, a famous monument to the Confederacy, is carved into the side of Stone Mountain, Georgia.

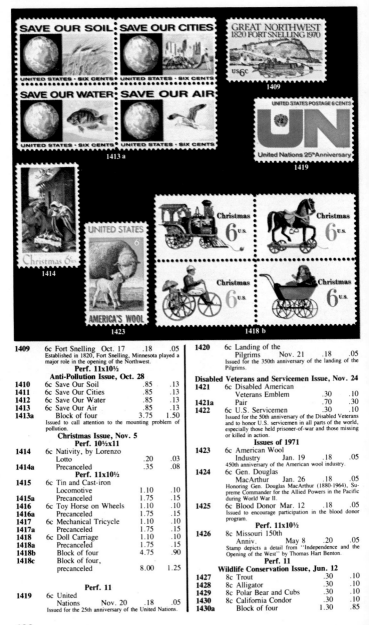

1413 a 1409 1419 1414 1423 1418 b

1409	6c Fort Snelling Oct. 17	.18	.05

Established in 1820, Fort Snelling, Minnesota played a major role in the opening of the Northwest.

Perf. 11x10½

Anti-Pollution Issue, Oct. 28

1410	6c Save Our Soil	.85	.13
1411	6c Save Our Cities	.85	.13
1412	6c Save Our Water	.85	.13
1413	6c Save Our Air	.85	.13
1413a	Block of four	3.75	1.50

Issued to call attention to the mounting problem of pollution.

Christmas Issue, Nov. 5

Perf. 10½x11

1414	6c Nativity, by Lorenzo Lotto	.20	.03
1414a	Precanceled	.35	.08

Perf. 11x10½

1415	6c Tin and Cast-iron Locomotive	1.10	.10
1415a	Precanceled	1.75	.15
1416	6c Toy Horse on Wheels	1.10	.10
1416a	Precanceled	1.75	.15
1417	6c Mechanical Tricycle	1.10	.10
1417a	Precanceled	1.75	.15
1418	6c Doll Carriage	1.10	.10
1418a	Precanceled	1.75	.15
1418b	Block of four	4.75	.90
1418c	Block of four, precanceled	8.00	1.25

Perf. 11

1419	6c United Nations Nov. 20	.18	.05

Issued for the 25th anniversary of the United Nations.

1420	6c Landing of the Pilgrims Nov. 21	.18	.05

Issued for the 350th anniversary of the landing of the Pilgrims.

Disabled Veterans and Servicemen Issue, Nov. 24

1421	6c Disabled American Veterans Emblem	.30	.10
1421a	Pair	.70	.30
1422	6c U.S. Servicemen	.30	.10

Issued for the 50th anniversary of the Disabled Veterans and to honor U.S. servicemen in all parts of the world, especially those held prisoner-of-war and those missing or killed in action.

Issues of 1971

1423	6c American Wool Industry Jan. 19	.18	.05

450th anniversary of the American wool industry.

1424	6c Gen. Douglas MacArthur Jan. 26	.18	.05

Honoring Gen. Douglas MacArthur (1880-1964), Supreme Commander for the Allied Powers in the Pacific during World War II.

1425	6c Blood Donor Mar. 12	.18	.05

Issued to encourage participation in the blood donor program.

Perf. 11x10½

1426	8c Missouri 150th Anniv. May 8	.20	.05

Stamp depicts a detail from "Independence and the Opening of the West" by Thomas Hart Benton.

Perf. 11

Wildlife Conservation Issue, Jun. 12

1427	8c Trout	.30	.10
1428	8c Alligator	.30	.10
1429	8c Polar Bear and Cubs	.30	.10
1430	8c California Condor	.30	.10
1430a	Block of four	1.30	.85

1425

1420

1421 a

1426

1424

1430 a

WILDLIFE CONSERVATION

The greatest danger to wildlife by far is man himself. Although some species have vanished through natural causes, animal life is increasingly threatened as man progresses. Indiscriminating hunters, the spread of industry, and a polluted environment have greatly contributed to fewer varieties of life on earth.

Passenger pigeons, Carolina parakeets, and certain species of elk, grizzly bear and wolf have already become extinct. Others such as the Bengal tiger, the blue whale, and the California condor face the possibility of extinction. The enactment of laws and the establishment of national parks and other protected areas for the preservation of wildlife have helped to save the American buffalo, the bighorn sheep and other endangered species.

The loss of any one of them creates an imbalance in nature and therefore threatens the survival of all remaining life. Wise conservation of the earth and its resources is to the benefit of all.

See Scott Nos. 1077-1079, 1098, 1392, 1427-1430, 1464-1467, 1760-1763

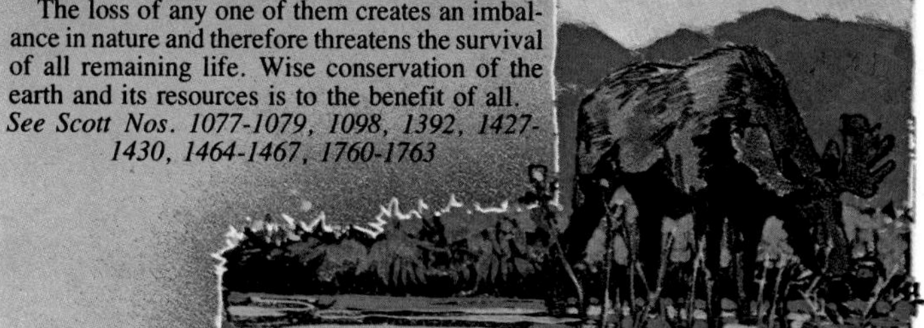

1431

1432

1433

1434 1435

1431	8c Antarctic Treaty	Jun. 23	.25	.05

Tenth anniversary of the Antarctic Treaty pledging peaceful uses of and scientific co-operation in Antarctica.

1432	8c American Revolution 200th Anniv.	Jul. 4	.85	.05

Special issue marks start of U.S. Revolution bicentennial celebration: shows official emblem of Bicentennial Commission.

1433	8c John Sloan	Aug. 2	.22	.05

Issued to honor John Sloan (1871-1951). American painter. Stamp shows his work "The Wake of the Ferry"

Decade of Space Achievements Issue, Aug. 2

1434	8c Earth, Sun, Landing Craft on Moon Pair		.25	.10
1434a	Pair		.60	.35
1435	8c Lunar Rover and Astronauts		.25	.10

Stamps honor a decade of space achievements and the Apollo 15 mission of July 26-August 7.

1436	8c Emily Dickinson	Aug. 28	.18	.05

Emily Dickinson (1830-1886), American poet.

1437	8c San Juan	Sep. 12	.18	.05

450th anniversary of the founding of San Juan, Puerto Rico. Stamp shows the sentry box at Morro Castle.

EMILY DICKINSON

For 25 years she never stepped outside her home in Amherst, Massachusetts. She would not allow her poems to be published. If you'd known her, you might have thought Emily Dickinson was pretty odd. But if you'd read her poetry, you'd have known the truth. Dickinson was one of the greatest lyric poets in the English language.

Like many poets, she concentrated on the great themes: love, death and nature . . . as illustrated by "Hope Is The Thing With Feathers" and "The Lonely House." But the similarity to others ended there. Dickinson was a true original—a boldly experimental poet who used everyday language with power, passion and wit. And even though she would not venture beyond her own front gate, her mind had wings. As she herself wrote, "the brain is wider than the sky."

See Scott No. 1436

"The soul selects its own society,
Then shuts the door."

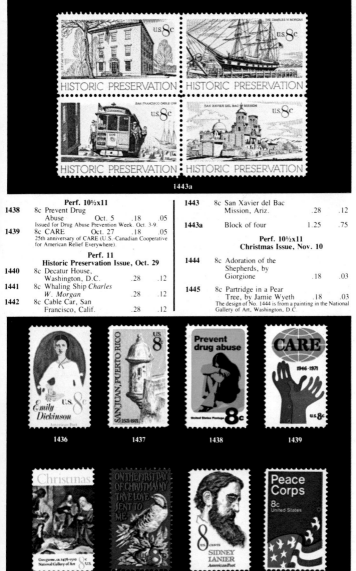

1443a

Perf. 10½x11

1438	8c Prevent Drug Abuse	Oct. 5	.18	.05

Issued for Drug Abuse Prevention Week, Oct. 3-9.

1439	8c CARE	Oct. 27	.18	.05

25th anniversary of CARE (U.S.-Canadian Cooperative for American Relief Everywhere).

Perf. 11
Historic Preservation Issue, Oct. 29

1440	8c Decatur House, Washington, D.C.	.28	.12
1441	8c Whaling Ship *Charles W. Morgan*	.28	.12
1442	8c Cable Car, San Francisco, Calif.	.28	.12
1443	8c San Xavier del Bac Mission, Ariz.	.28	.12
1443a	Block of four	1.25	.75

Perf. 10½x11
Christmas Issue, Nov. 10

1444	8c Adoration of the Shepherds, by Giorgione	.18	.03
1445	8c Partridge in a Pear Tree, by Jamie Wyeth	.18	.03

The design of No. 1444 is from a painting in the National Gallery of Art, Washington, D.C.

1436

1437

1438

1439

1444

1445

1446

1447

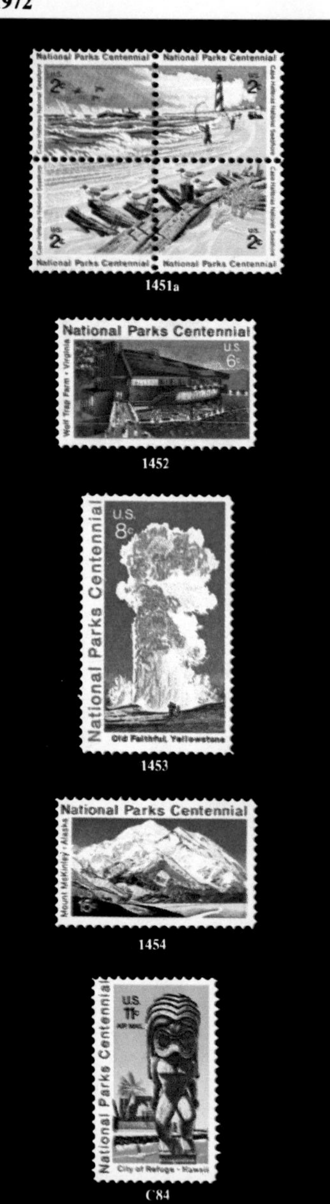

1451a

1452

1453

1454

C84

Issues of 1972

Perf. 11

1446	8c Sidney Lanier	Feb. 3	.18	.05

Sidney Lanier (1842-1881), Southern poet, musician, lawyer, educator.

Perf. 10½x11

1447	8c Peace Corps	Feb. 11	.18	.05

The Act creating the Peace Corps, a volunteer program operating in underdeveloped countries in all parts of the globe, was passed by Congress in 1961.

National Parks 100th Anniversary Issue

Perf. 11

1448	2c Hulk of Ship	Apr. 5	.06	.06
1449	2c Cape Hatteras Lighthouse	Apr. 5	.06	.06
1450	2c Laughing Gulls on Driftwood	Apr. 5	.06	.06
1451	2c Laughing Gulls and Dune	Apr. 5	.06	.06
1451a	Block of four, Cape Hatteras		.25	.30
1452	6c Wolf Trap Farm	Jun. 26	.16	.04
1453	8c Yellowstone	Mar. 1	.18	.05
1454	15c Mt. McKinely	Jul. 28	.35	.22

Yellowstone, created in 1872, was the first national park. Cape Hatteras National Seashore in North Carolina consists of 45 square miles of beach land. Wolf Trap Farm Park, 117 acres, is near Vienna, Virginia. Mt. McKinley National Park in Alaska. 3,020 square miles, was created in 1917.

Note: Beginning with this issue, the U.S.P.S. began to offer stamp collectors first day cancellations affixed to 8x10½ inch souvenir pages. The pages are similar to the stamp announcements that have appeared on post office bulletin boards since Scott No. 1132.

1455	8c Family Planning	Mar. 18	.16	.05

Issue focuses attention on family planning.

Perf. 11 x 10½

American Revolution Bicentennial Issue, Jul. 4

Craftsmen in Colonial America

1456	8c Glassmaker	.30	.08
1457	8c Silversmith	.30	.08
1458	8c Wigmaker	.30	.08
1459	8c Hatter	.30	.08
1459a	Block of four	1.35	.60

Issued in honor of colonial American craftsmen as part of the United States bicentennial celebration.

Olympic Games Issue, Aug. 17

1460	6c Bicycling and Olympic Rings	.12	.04
1461	8c Bobsledding	.16	.05
1462	15c Running	.30	.18

Issued for the 11th Winter Olympic Games, held at Sapporo, Japan, from Feb. 3-13: and for the 20th Summer Olympic Games, held at Munich, Germany from Aug. 26-Sep. 11.

1463	8c P.T.A. 75th Anniv.	Sep. 15	.16	.05

The Parent Teacher Association was founded by Mrs. Phoebe Hearst and Mrs. Alice Birney in 1897. Today, nearly ten million people belong to the organization.

Perf. 11

Wildlife Conservation Issue, Sep. 20

1464	8c Fur Seals	.22	.08
1465	8c Cardinal	.22	.08
1466	8c Brown Pelican	.22	.08
1467	8c Bighorn Sheep	.22	.08
1467a	Block of four	.95	.60

The 1972 wildlife conservation stamps depict birds and animals indigenous to different parts of the United States. The U.S.P.S. has pointed out that these are not necessarily endangered species but that all forms of wildlife should be of public concern.

Note: With this issue the U.S.P.S. introduced the "American Commemorative Series" Stamp Panels. Each panel contains a block of four mint stamps, mounted with text, and background illustrations.

Perf. 11x10½

1468	8c Mail Order 100th Anniv.	Sep. 27	.16	.05

The mail order business was originated in 1872 by Aaron Montgomery Ward of Chicago.

1455

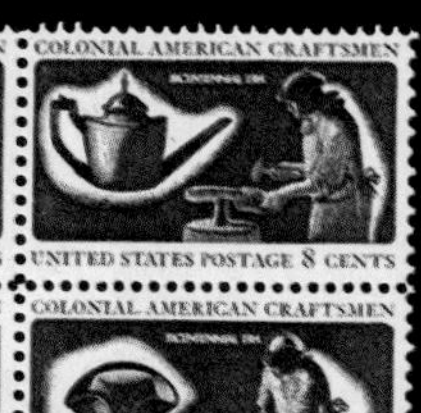

1459a

1460

1461

1463

1462

C85

1468

1467a

1469 1471 1472 1470

1474

1473 1475

1476 1488 1477

1478 1479

1483a

Perf. 10½x11

1469 8c Osteopathic Medicine Oct. 9 .16 .05
Issued for the 75th anniversary of the American Osteopathic Association, founded by Dr. Andrew T. Still.

Perf. 11

1470 8c American Folklore Issue Oct. 13 .16 .05
Created by Mark Twain, Tom Sawyer is one of the most famous characters in American literature.

Perf. 10½x11
Christmas Issue, Nov. 9

1471 8c Angel from "Mary, Queen of Heaven" .16 .03
1472 8c Santa Claus .16 .03
The design of No. 1471 is from a painting by the Master of the St. Lucy Legend in the National Gallery of Art, Washington, D.C.

Perf. 11

1473 8c Pharmacy Nov. 11 .16 .05
Honoring American druggists, this stamp was issued in connection with the 120th anniversary of the American Pharmaceutical Association.

1474 8c Stamp Collecting Nov. 17 .16 .05
Issued to publicize stamp collecting and in honor of the 125th anniversary of U.S. postage stamps. The design reproduces the first U.S. stamp.

Issues of 1973
Perf. 11x10½

1475 8c Love Jan. 26 .16 .05
This "special stamp for someone special" depicts "Love" by contemporary artist Robert Indiana.

Perf. 11
American Revolution Bicentennial Issues
Communications in Colonial America

1476 8c Printer and Patriots Examining Pamphlet Feb. 16 .20 .05
1477 8c Posting a Broadside Apr. 13 .20 .05
478 8c Postrider Jun. 22 .20 .05
479 8c Drummer Sep. 28 .20 .05

Boston Tea Party, Jul. 4

480 8c British Merchantman .22 .10
481 8c British Three-master .22 .10
482 8c Boats and Ship's Hull .22 .10
483 8c Boat and Dock .22 .10
Block of four, Boston Tea Party .95 .70
Nos. 1476-1479 depict the "Rise of the Spirit of Independence" and honor communications in colonial America. Nos. 1480-1483 recall the Boston Tea Party of 1773. These four stamps, printed in a block of four, combine to make a complete design.

American Arts Issue

484 8c George Gershwin Feb. 28 .16 .05
American composer George Gershwin (1899-1937) created *Porgy and Bess*, *Rhapsody in Blue* and *An American in Paris*.

485 8c Robinson Jeffers Aug. 13 .16 .05
American poet Robinson Jeffers (1887-1926) wrote *Tamar and Other Poems*, *The Double Axe* and several plays, including a modern adaptation of *Medea*.

486 8c Henry Ossawa Tanner Sep. 10 .16 .05
American artist Henry Ossawa Tanner (1859-1937) is remembered for oils, drawings and water colors based on themes from the Bible.

487 8c Willa Cather Sep. 20 .16 .05
The works of American novelist Willa Cather (1873-1947) deal with history of life in the Midwest. They include *O Pioneer!*, *My Antonia*, and *Death Comes to the Archbishop*.

488 8c Nicolaus Copernicus Apr. 23 .16 .05
Polish astronomer Nicolaus Copernicus (1473-1543) altered man's conception of the universe by declaring that the earth revolves around the sun.

CHRISTMAS

Did you know that there really was a Santa Claus? Not the fat, jolly fellow in red who rides the sky in a reindeer-drawn sleigh. But a 4th century bishop, Saint Nicholas, who was born in Turkey and whose mortal remains are enshrined to this day in Bari, Italy.

A good many different miracles are attributed to Nicholas, but he was best known for rescuing children from some dread and dire fate. According to one legend, he restored three little boys to life after they'd been chopped up for a meat pie! Stories like that helped him become the patron saint of boys and girls. The children of medieval Europe would put out hay for his horse the night before his Feast Day in hopes of finding a present from a grateful Saint Nicholas the following morning. As you can see, Saint Nicholas was beginning to turn into Santa Claus. The Germans can be thanked for changing him from a normal looking man into a delightful, white-bearded elf. And the finishing touches of the Santa Claus story—the flying reindeer, for example—were added right here in America by the Dutch of 17th century New Amsterdam.

Christmas issues have appeared annually since 1962.

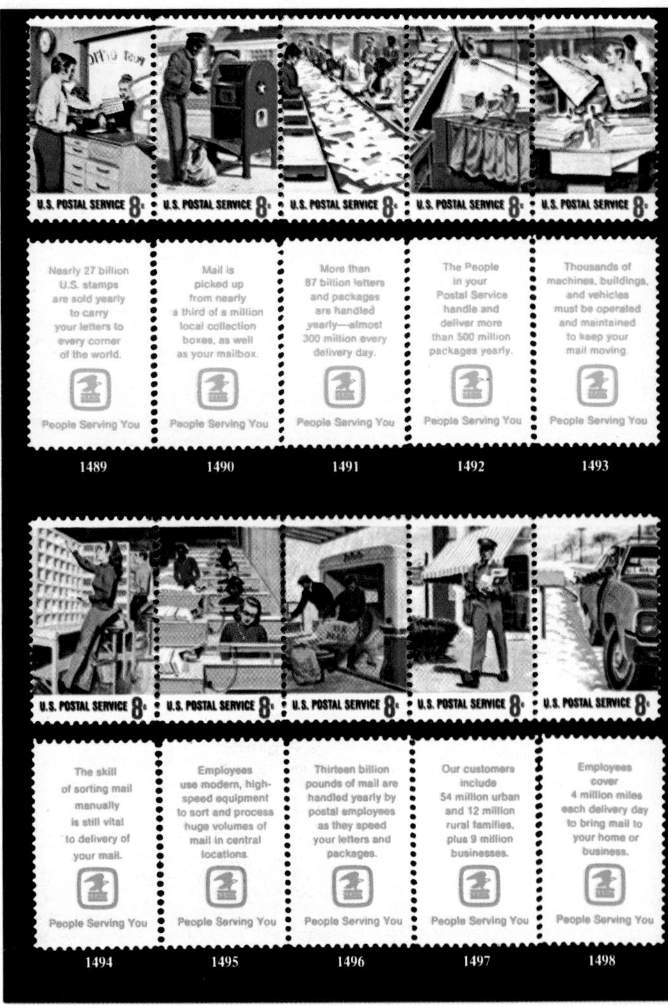

1489 1490 1491 1492 1493

1494 1495 1496 1497 1498

POSTAL PEOPLE ISSUE

This innovative series, inspired by the 1973 observance of Postal Week, is designed to honor the nation's 700,000 postal workers. These men and women are responsible for moving almost half the world's mail, or about 90 billion pieces every year. For the first time in U.S. postal history, the gum (back) side of each stamp bears a printed text relating to the picture on the face.

1484

1485

1486

WILLA CATHER

Willa Cather was born in Virginia, but when she was nine Willa Cather's family pulled up roots and moved to the frontier village of Red Cloud, Nebraska. She grew up among the first farmers to till the soil of the Great Plains. She saw their stolid courage and determination. And years later, she celebrated their simple virtues in story after story.

Cather graduated from the University of Nebraska and obtained a job on a Pittsburgh magazine. For most of the next seventeen years she had a successful career in journalism—as a copy editor first, then a music and drama editor, finally the managing editor of the famous New York magazine, McClure's. And then she quit. Willa Cather didn't want to be an editor any more. She wanted to tell the story of the people she'd grown up among—the strong, struggling, half-articulate immigrants who had fought the soil of Nebraska and won. Her literary style was as plain and simple as the people she wrote about. And her books were all the more powerful because of it. Her first novel, "O Pioneers!", came out in 1913. Next came "My Antonia," an American classic today. She won the Pulitzer Prize for "One of Ours." And she won international fame for "A Lost Lady."

But Cather never glamorized the life she'd observed as a youngster. She wrote of the dreariness of the prairies and the narrow-mindedness of the people as often as she wrote of the rich challenge of frontier life. After she'd written many books on the frontier of her own girlhood, she turned for inspiration to the pioneer spirit of another time and place. "Death Comes for the Archbishop", was about French Catholic missionaries in long-ago New Mexico. "Shadows on the Rock", a story of the French Canadians of Quebec.

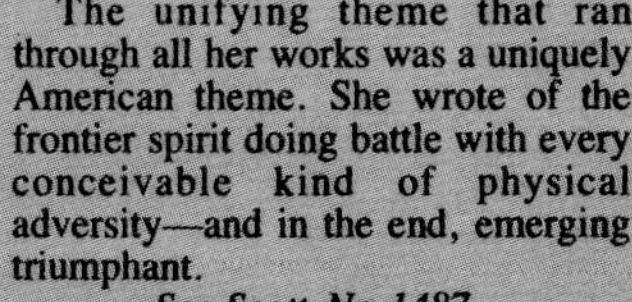

The unifying theme that ran through all her works was a uniquely American theme. She wrote of the frontier spirit doing battle with every conceivable kind of physical adversity—and in the end, emerging triumphant.

See Scott No 1487.

1487

RURAL AMERICA

When tons of American wheat are shipped to Russia or ships filled with American soy beans sail off to China, it makes headlines. But year in and year out, without fuss or fanfare, the products of American agriculture move out in every direction of the compass. So enormous are our nation's agricultural yields that the surplus—above and beyond our own citizens' needs—can nourish people halfway round the world.

Why is American agriculture so remarkably productive? We start out with a lot of advantages. We've got grazing areas vast enough to support tremendous herds of cattle. We've got plains so huge the windswept wheat looks like a golden ocean. We've got topography and climate that's just right for corn in one area, oranges in another, rice in a third. We've got all those things, and what we've done to improve our natural blessings is another matter entirely.

Years ago, immigrants from other lands sometimes brought to America more than a yearning for a better life. Sometimes they brought precious seeds or livestock, too.

In 1874, for example, Mennonite immigrants from Russia arrived in Marion County, Kansas, with a small amount of a wheat that had never been seen in America before. It was a red Turkish strain—hardy, drought-resistant and heavy-yielding. Did it take to American soil? So well that it's the basis of the present-day economy of the entire state of Kansas—and it's extensively grown in Nebraska, Oklahoma and wheat-producing states, too. Have a sandwich for lunch, and you may very well be eating bread made of wheat whose ancestor grains were brought all the way from Russia by the Mennonites!

Today science is constantly on the search for better, stronger, faster growing grains, fruits and vegetables. Livestock is painstakingly bred for greater meatiness, more rapid maturation, increased nutritional value. Today, the government is behind a lot of the scientific and technological advances that are helping America keep pace with the hunger of millions.

See Scott Nos. 1504-1506.

Perf. 10½x11

Postal Service Employees Issue, Apr. 30

1489	8c Stamp Counter	.20	.12
1490	8c Mail Collection	.20	.12
1491	8c Letter Facing Conveyor	.20	.12
1492	8c Parcel Post Sorting	.20	.12
1493	8c Mail Cancelling	.20	.12
1494	8c Manual Letter Routing	.20	.12
1495	8c Electronic Letter Routing	.20	.12
1496	8c Loading Mail on Truck	.20	.12
1497	8c Mailman	.20	.12
1498	8c Rural Mail Delivery	.20	.12
1498a	Strip of ten	2.25	1.75

A tribute to the U.S. Postal Service employees. Printed on the back of each stamp is the Postal Service emblem, "People Serving You," and a brief description of some aspect of the postal service.

Perf. 11

1499	8c Harry S Truman May 8	.16	.05

A memorial to the 33rd President of the United States. Harry S. Truman (1884-1972).

Electronics Progress Issue, July 10

1500	6c Marconi's Spark Coil and Gap	.12	.10
1501	8c Transistor and Printed Circuit Board	.16	.05
1502	15c Microphone, Speaker, Vacuum Tube, TV Camera	.30	.20

This issue traces the progress of electronics from Marconi's turn of the century spark coil to the transistor which set the stage for the space age.

1503	8c Lyndon B. Johnson Aug. 27	.16	.05

A memorial to Lyndon B. Johnson (1908-1972), the 36th President of the United States. This portrait, by Madame Elizabeth Shoumatoff, hangs in the White House and was Mr. Johnson's favorite.

Issues of 1973-74

Rural America Issue

1504	8c Angus and Longhorn Cattle, by F.C. Murphy Oct. 5, 1973	.16	.05
1505	10c Chautauqua centenary Aug. 6, 1974	.20	.05
1506	10c Kansas hard winter wheat centenary Aug. 16, 1974	.20	.05

Perf. 10½x11

Christmas Issue, Nov. 7, 1973

1507	8c Madonna and Child by Raphael	.16	.03
1508	8c Christmas Tree in Needlepoint	.16	.03

LIBERTY BELL

"Proclaim liberty throughout all the land unto all the inhabitants thereof." That's the joyous message—a quotation from the Bible—that's engraved on the symbol of U.S. freedom, the Liberty Bell. Would it surprise you to know that the bell was manufactured in the very country that fought to withhold liberty from the U.S.?

The bell was commissioned in 1751 by the Pennsylvania Provincial Assembly to hang in the new State House in Philadelphia. It was cast in London and delivered in 1752. It seems to have been destined to bear the jagged crack that distinguishes it from all other bells. It cracked initially while being tested, and was recast twice. In June, 1753, it was hung in the steeple of the State House—later, Independence Hall. It became the Liberty Bell at last when it was rung on July 4, 1776, to signal the adoption of the Declaration of Independence by the Continental Congress. The people hid it when British forces entered Philadelphia during the Revolution, for it was already a precious symbol. After the British withdrew, it was rehung in Independence Hall where it remains to this day. But in 1835, while tolling the funeral of Chief Justice John Marshall, the Liberty Bell cracked again. And this time, it was beyond repair. *The Liberty Bell consistently appears on United States stamps.*

1509 1510 1520 1519 1511 1518 1525 1526 1529

Issue of 1973-74
Perf. 11x10½

No.	Description	Unused	Used
1509	10c 50-Star and 13-Star Flags	.20	.03
1510	10c Jefferson Memorial and Signature	.20	.03
1510b	Booklet pane of 5+label	1.00	*.30*
1510c	Booklet pane of 8	1.60	*.30*
1510d	Booklet pane of 6	1.20	*.30*
1511	10c Mail Transport; "Zip"	.20	.03

Coil Stamps, Perf. 10 Vertically

No.	Description	Unused	Used
1518	6.3c Bells Oct. 1	.13	.07
1519	10c red & blue Flags (1509)	.20	.03
1520	10c blue Jefferson Memorial (1510)	.20	.03

Issues of 1974
Perf. 11

No.	Description	Unused	Used
1525	10c V.F.W. Emblem Mar. 11	.20	.05

75th anniversary of Veterans of Spanish-American and other Foreign Wars.

Perf. 10½x11

No.	Description	Unused	Used
1526	10c Robert Frost Mar. 26	.20	.05

Centenary of the birth of Robert Frost (1874-1963), American poet.

Perf. 11

No.	Description	Unused	Used
1527	10c Cosmic Jumper and Smiling Sage, by Peter Max Apr. 18	.20	.05

EXPO '74, Spokane, Wash. May 4-Nov. 4. Theme of the Exposition was "Preserve the Environment."

Perf. 11x10½

No.	Description	Unused	Used
1528	10c Horses Rounding Turn May 4	.20	.05

Centenary of the Kentucky Derby, Churchill Downs.

Perf. 11

No.	Description	Unused	Used
1529	10c Skylab II May 14	.20	.05

First anniversary of the launching of Skylab I, and to honor all who participated in the Skylab projects.

Centenary of UPU Issue, June 6

No.	Description	Unused	Used
1530	10c Michelangelo, by Raphael	.20	.10
1531	10c "Five Feminine Virtues," by Hokusai	.20	.10
1532	10c Old Scraps, by John Fredrick Peto	.20	.10
1533	10c The Lovely Reader, by Jean Liotard	.20	.10
1534	10c Lady Writing Letter, by Gerard Terborch	.20	.10
1535	10c Inkwell and Quill, by Jean Chardin	.20	.10
1536	10c Mrs. John Douglas, by Thomas Gainsborough	.20	.10
1537	10c Don Antonio Noriega, by Francisco de Goya	.20	.10
1537a	Block or strip of 8	1.60	1.75

Centenary of the Universal Postal Union, Nos. 1530-1537 printed in blocks of eight in panes of 32. The designs are details from famous paintings pertaining to letter writing. The quotation "Letters mingle souls" is from a letter by poet John Donne.

Mineral Heritage Issue, June 13

No.	Description	Unused	Used
1538	10c Petrified Wood	.20	.10
1539	10c Tourmaline	.20	.10
1540	10c Amethyst	.20	.10
1541	10c Rhodochrosite	.20	.10
1541a	Block of 4	.80	.60

Nos. 1538-1541 printed in blocks of four in panes of 48.

No.	Description	Unused	Used
1542	10c Fort Harrod June 15	.20	.05

Bicentenary of Fort Harrod, first settlement in Kentucky.

THE TRUMAN ERA

The responsibility of great states is to serve and not dominate the world. Harry S Truman.

Harry S Truman (1884-1972), the son of a poor Missouri farmer, rose to become the 33rd president of the United States. On April 12, 1945, when Franklin Roosevelt died, the presidency passed on to then Vice-President Truman. Shortly afterwards the new president made the difficult decision to drop the atomic bomb on Japan. This decision, the first of many made by Truman, hastened Japan's surrender and the end of World War II.

In 1947 General George C. Marshall, Truman's secretary of state, proposed the Marshall Plan of economic aid to war-devastated Europe. The Marshall Plan was an outgrowth of the "Truman Doctrine", a policy of economic and military aid to countries threatened by aggression. In 1949 the North Atlantic Treaty Organization (NATO) was approved.

During Truman's first full term in office, which began in 1949, postwar international problems continued to overshadow domestic affairs. In 1950 armed hostilities erupted in Korea and U.S. troops were sent to the Orient as part of the U.N. forces supporting the government of South Korea. On March 29, 1952, Truman, who was lauded by Winston Churchill for making "great and valiant decisions," announced that he would not seek another term.

See Scott Nos. 1008, 1127, 1289, 1426, 1499

MINERALS IN U.S.

Have you ever picked up a bright-colored pebble on the beach and stuck it in your pocket just because you liked the way it looked and felt? Maybe a curiously shaped rock from a field or park struck your fancy—a rock dotted and streaked with sparkling stuff. What's it called? Where did it come from? Is it worth anything? Take the trouble to find out, and you may just be bitten by the mineral collecting bug.

Minerals are everywhere. Glass is a mineral. So is water. So is the ink that dried into the print you're reading right now. There are over 3,000 different minerals we know about today, and science discovers another fifty or so every year. The minerals that collectors are interested in, however, are the solid minerals occurring in nature. Quartz and feldspar are the most common rock-forming minerals. Beach sand is full of quartz, and many rocks contain quartz in the form of crystals. Feldspar is usually pink or white, and the color of a rock often depends on the color of the feldspar in it.

Mineral identification can be surprisingly easy. For example, your fingernail can scratch two minerals—talc and gypsum. A penny can scratch those two plus a third mineral—calcite. A pocket knife can scratch two more—fluorite and apatite. Of course, you're not too likely to find the hardest mineral of all in a field. It's the diamond.

How do you start a mineral collection? You start by collecting! Find interesting rocks in the garden, the park, an open field. If there's construction going on nearby, check out the site. The workmen may have dug up something unusual. In the country, check dry creeks and streams. Rock quarries are terrific places to find specimens. You'll need a hammer or pick plus a strong cloth shoulder-strap bag for your collecting expeditions. To identify and display your collection, you'll need a rock and mineral book, boxes and labels. Go ahead. Try it!

See Scott Nos. 1538-1541.

1537a

1527

1541a

1549

1542

1528

1546a
1547
1551
1548
1552
1550

American Revolution Bicentennial
First Continental Congress, July 4

1543	10c Carpenters' Hall		.20	.10
1544	10c "We ask but for Peace, Liberty and Safety"		.20	.10
1545	10c "Deriving their Just Powers."		.20	.10
1546	10c Independence Hall		.20	.10
1546a	Block of four		.80	.60

Nos. 1543-1546 printed in blocks of four in panes of 50.

1547	10c Molecules and Drops of Gasoline and Oil	Sept. 22	.20	.05

Protection and improvement of the environment while dealing with the fuel shortage. Issued during World Energy Conference. Detroit, Sept. 1974.

1548	10c The Headless Horseman	Oct. 10	.20	.05

The Headless Horseman in pursuit of Ichabod Crane from *Legend of Sleepy Hollow* by Washington Irving.

1549	10c Little Girl	Oct. 12	.20	.05

Annual Convention of the National Association of Retarded Children.

Christmas Issues, 1974

1550	10c Angel	Oct. 23	.20	.03
1551	10c Sleigh Ride, by Currier and Ives	Oct. 23	.20	.03

Imperf.
Self-adhesive

1552	10c Weather Vane; precanceled	Nov. 15	.25	.08

The weather vane shown on No. 1552 was designed by George Washington for Mount Vernon.

Issues of 1975
American Art Issue
Perf. 10½x11, 11

1553	10c Benjamin West, Self-portrait	Feb. 10	.20	.05

Benjamin West (1738-1820), painter, who worked in U.S. and England; friend of Sir Joshua Reynolds.

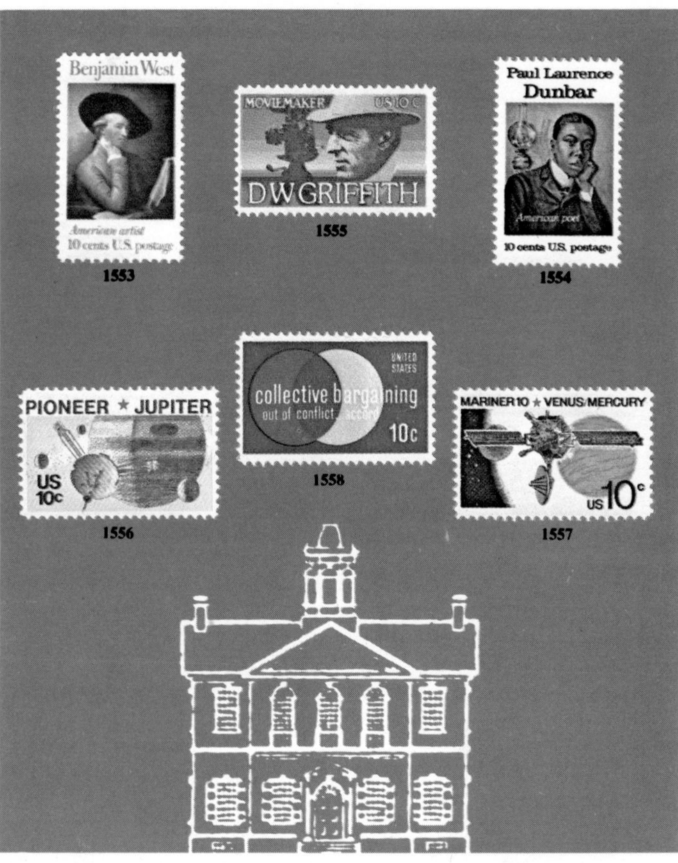

1553 1555 1554 1558 1556 1557

1554 10c Paul Laurence Dunbar May 1 .20 .05
Paul Laurence Dunbar (1872-1906), poet; sone of escaped slave. Volume of poems *Lyrics of Lowly Life*, novel *The Fanatics*, and others.

1555 10c D. W. Griffith May 27 .20 .05
David Lewelyn Wark Griffith (1875-1948), motion picture producer. Pictures include *Birth of a Nation, Orphans of the Storm*.

Space Issue
Perf. 11

1556 10c Pioneer 10 Feb. 28 .20 .05
1557 10c Mariner 10 Apr. 4 .20 .05
U.S. unmanned accomplishments in space. Pioneer 10 passed within 81,000 miles of Jupiter, Dec. 3, 1973. Mariner 10 explored Venus and Mercury in 1974, and Mercury again in March 1975.
1558 10c "Labor and Management" Mar. 13 .20 .05
Collective Bargaining Law, enacted 1935 with Wagner Act.

American Bicentennial Issues
Contributors to the Cause, Mar. 25

Perf. 11x10½

1559 8c Sybil Ludington .16 .13
1560 10c Salem Poor .20 .05
1561 10c Haym Salomon .20 .05
1562 18c Peter Francisco .36 .20
Sybil Ludington, age 16, rallied militia Apr. 26, 1777. Salem Poor, black freeman, fought in Battle of Bunker Hill. Haym Salomon, Jewish immigrant, raised money to finance Revolutionary War. Peter Francisco, Portuguese-French immigrant, joined Continental Army at 15. Emerald inscription on back, printed beneath gum in water-soluble ink, gives thumbnail sketch of portrayed contributor.

Perf. 11

1563 10c "Birth of Liberty," by Henry Sandham Apr. 19 .20 .05
200th anniversary of the Battle of Lexington and Concord.

Contributors To The Cause U.S. 8c
Sybil Ludington Youthful Heroine
1559

YOUTHFUL HEROINE
On the dark night of April 26, 1777, 16-year-old Sybil Ludington rode her horse "Star" alone through the Connecticut countryside rallying her father's militia to repel a raid by the British on Danbury.

Contributors To The Cause... U.S. 10c
Salem Poor Gallant Soldier
1560

GALLANT SOLDIER
The conspicuously courageous actions of black foot soldier Salem Poor at the Battle of Bunker Hill on June 17, 1775, earned him citations for his bravery and leadership ability.

FINANCIAL HERO
Businessman and broker Haym Salomon was responsible for raising most of the money needed to finance the American Revolution and later to save the new nation from collapse.

U.S. 10c Contributors To The Cause
Haym Salomon Financial Hero
1561

FIGHTER EXTRAORDINARY
Peter Francisco's strength and bravery made him a legend around campfires. He fought with distinction at Brandywine, Yorktown and Guilford Court House.

Contributors To The Cause... U.S. 18c
Peter Francisco Fighter Extraordinary
1562

PETER FRANCISCO

As a small boy, speaking no English, a ship set Peter Francisco ashore in the colony of Virginia. Raised on the estate of Patrick Henry's uncle, he learned the trade of blacksmith. Large and incredibly strong, Francisco attained his full growth of 6 feet 6 inches and 260 pounds while still in his teens. When he was only 15 years old, he enlisted in the Continental Army to fight for American Independence.

Serving with Virginia's 10th Regiment, he first engaged in battle at Brandywine in September 1777. As the Revolution progressed, soldiers gathered around campfires to exchange tales of Francisco's herculean strength and daring feats. According to legend, during the Battle of Camden he toted a 1,000 pound cannon by himself and also saved the life of his commanding officer. At the Battle of Guilford Court House, in March 1781, brandishing a broadsword with a five foot blade, Francisco slew eleven British soldiers. A monument commemorating his heroic exploits stands on the site of that battlefield today.

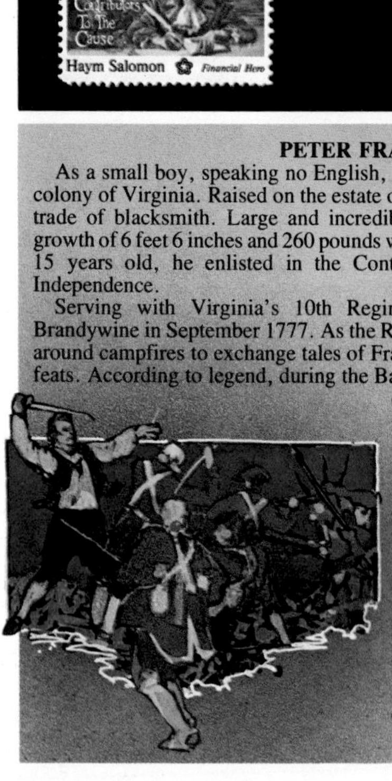

Francisco served with distinction in seven major battles including the one that resulted in the British surrender at Yorktown. This extraordinary fighter made a valuable contribution to the cause of liberty.

See Scott No. 1562

Lexington & Concord 1775 by Sandham
US Bicentennial 10cents

1563

CONTINENTAL ARMY
CONTINENTAL NAVY
CONTINENTAL MARINES
AMERICAN MILITIA
US 10c

Bunker Hill 1775 by Trumbull
US Bicentennial 10c

1564

1568a

SALEM POOR

One of the most famous of the many black soldiers who made a distinctive contribution in the quest for American Independence was Salem Poor. The 28-year-old freeman joined a company of militia headed by Captain Benjamin Ames to fight for his country's freedom. The exceptional bravery and courage Poor displayed at the Battle of Bunker Hill prompted 14 Massachusetts' officers to petition on his behalf to make the state legislature aware of his gallant conduct.

The document, citing Poor's extraordinary battlefield valor, stated that "Salem Poor, of Colonel Frye's regiment, Captain Ames company, in the late battle . . . behaved like an experienced officer, as well as an excellent soldier." A detailed account of Poor's heroism, the citation continued, would prove "tedious." They concluded by noting, "We only beg leave to say, in the person of this said negro centers a brave and gallant soldier . . ." Salem Poor went on to serve the cause of liberty in the Battles of Valley Forge and White Plains.

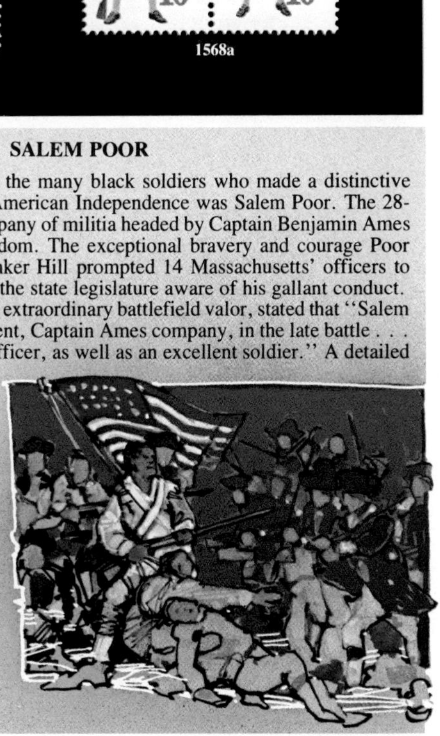

See Scott No. 1560

US 10c
APOLLO SOYUZ 1975
APOLLO SOYUZ SPACE TEST PROJECT
UNITED STATES · 1975
10c
1569a
USA 10c
INTERNATIONAL WOMEN'S YEAR
1571
1975
Ghirlandaio: National Gallery
Christmas US postage
1579
Merry Christmas!
US Postage
1975
Early Card by Louis Prang
1580
World Peace through LAW
USA 10c
1576
US10c 200 Years of Postal Service
US10c 200 Years of Postal Service
US10c 200 Years of Postal Service
US10c 200 Years of Postal Service
1575a
BANKING
COMMERCE
US10c
US10c
1577a

Perf. 11x10½

1564	10c	Battle of Bunker Hill, by John Trumbull Jun. 17	.20	.05

200th anniversary of the Battle of Bunker Hill.

Military Uniforms, Jul. 4
Perf. 11

1565	10c	Soldier with Flintlock Musket, Uniform Button	.20	.08
1566	10c	Sailor with Grappling Hook, First Navy Jack, 1775	.20	.08
1567	10c	Marine with Musket, Full-rigged Ship	.20	.08
1568	10c	Militiaman with Musket, Powder Horn	.20	.08
1568a		Block of 4	.80	.50

200 anniversary of U.S. Military Services.

Apollo-Soyuz Space Issue, Jul. 15
Perf. 11x10½

1569	10c	Apollo and Soyuz after Docking, and Earth	.20	.10
1569a		Pair	.40	.25
1570	10c	Spacecraft before Docking, Earth and Project Emblem	.20	.10
1571	10c	"Worldwide Equality for Women" Aug. 26	.20	.05

International Women's Year 1975.

Postal Service Bicentennial Issue, Sep. 3

1572	10c	Stagecoach and Trailer Truck	.20	.08
1573	10c	Old and New Locomotives	.20	.08
1574	10c	Early Mail Plane and Jet	.20	.08
1575	10c	Satellite for Transmission of Mailgrams	.20	.08
1575a		Block of 4	.80	.50

Perf 11

1576	10c	World Peace Sep. 29	.20	.05

A prelude to 7th World Conference of the World Peace through Law Center at Washington, D.C. Oct. 12-17

Banking and Commerce Issue, Oct. 6

1577	10c	Engine Turning, Indian Head Penny and Morgan Silver Dollar	.20	.05
1577a		Pair	.40	.20
1578	10c	Seated Liberty, Quarter, $20 Gold (Double Eagle), Engine Turning	.20	.05

Banking and Commerce in the U.S. and for the Centennial Convention of the American Bankers' Association.

Christmas Issue, Oct. 14
Perf. 11

1579	(10c)	Madonna, by Domenico Ghirlandaio	.20	.03
1580	(10c)	Christmas Card, by Louis Prang, 1878	.20	.03
1580b		Perf. 10½x11	.25	.05

U.S. POSTAL SERVICE

The United States Postal Service reflects the history of the country; it grew along with a growing America. After the Revolution began, Bemjamin Franklin was appointed by the Continental Congress as Postmaster General for the colonies and served in that office until November 7, 1776. The postal system he planned and put into operation formed the basis for the postal service that has served Americans so well through the years. After independence was secured, the Post Office became a branch of the federal government.

Increasing population and westward expansion in the 1800's placed new demands on the Post Office and additional services were instituted to keep pace with an ever-growing nation. Railway mail cars began operating in 1864 and the first regularly scheduled airmail service in the world was inaugurated in 1918 between New York City and Washington, D.C.

In order to even better serve a modern America, on July 1, 1971 the U.S. Post Office Department became the United States Postal Service, a quasi-independent public utility. Since its beginnings in colonial times, the U.S. Mail has continued to provide an efficient, reliable and inexpensive way to exchange news and conduct business.

See Scott Nos. 1238, 1489-1498, 1572-1575

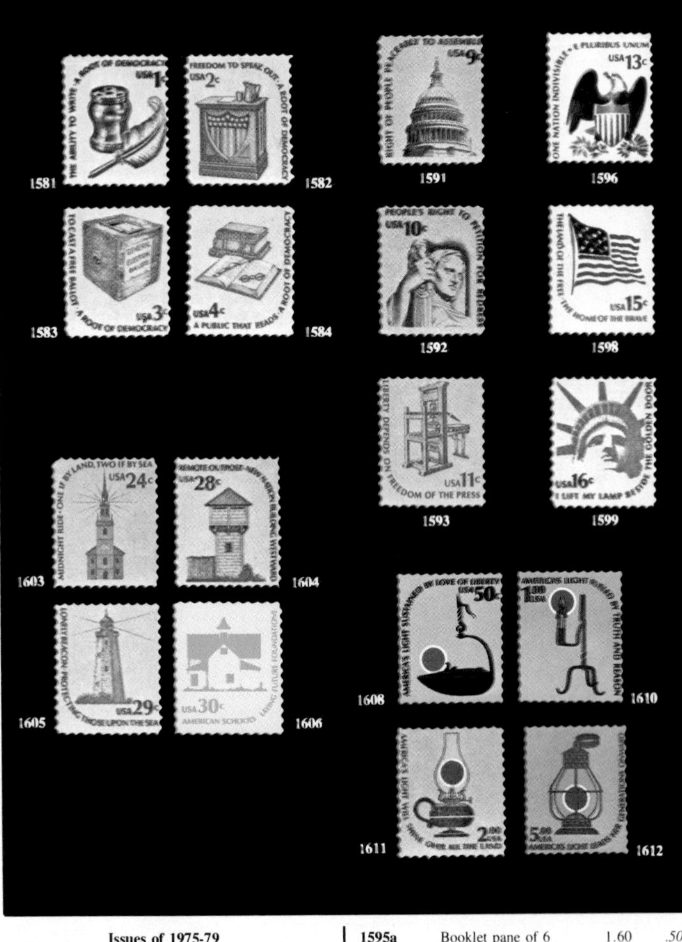

Issues of 1975-79
Americana

Perf. 11x10½

No.	Denom.	Description	Unused	Used
1581	1c	Inkwell & Quill	.03	.03
1582	2c	Speaker's Stand	.04	.03
1584	3c	Early Ballot Box	.06	.03
1585	4c	Books, Bookmark, Eyeglasses	.08	.04
		Size: 17½x20½mm.		
1590	9c	Capitol Dome (1591)	.25	.20
1590a		Perf. 10	15.00	5.00
		Size:18½x22½mm.		
1591	9c	Capitol Dome	.18	.03
1592	10c	Contemplation of Justice	.20	.03
1593	11c	Printing Press	.22	.03
1595	13c	Liberty Bell	.26	.03
1595a		Booklet pane of 6	1.60	*.50*
1595b		Booklet pane of 7 + label	1.80	*.50*
1595c		Booklet pane of 8	2.10	*.50*
1595d		Booklet pane of 5 + label	1.30	*.50*
1596	13c	Eagle and Shield	.26	.03
		Perf. 11		
1597	15c	Fort McHenry Flag	.30	.03
		Perf. 11x10½		
1598	15c	Fort McHenry Flag (1597)	.30	.03
1598a		Booklet pane of 8	2.40	——
1599	16c	Head of Liberty	.32	.03
1603	24c	Old North Church	.48	.06
1604	28c	Fort Nisqually	.56	.08

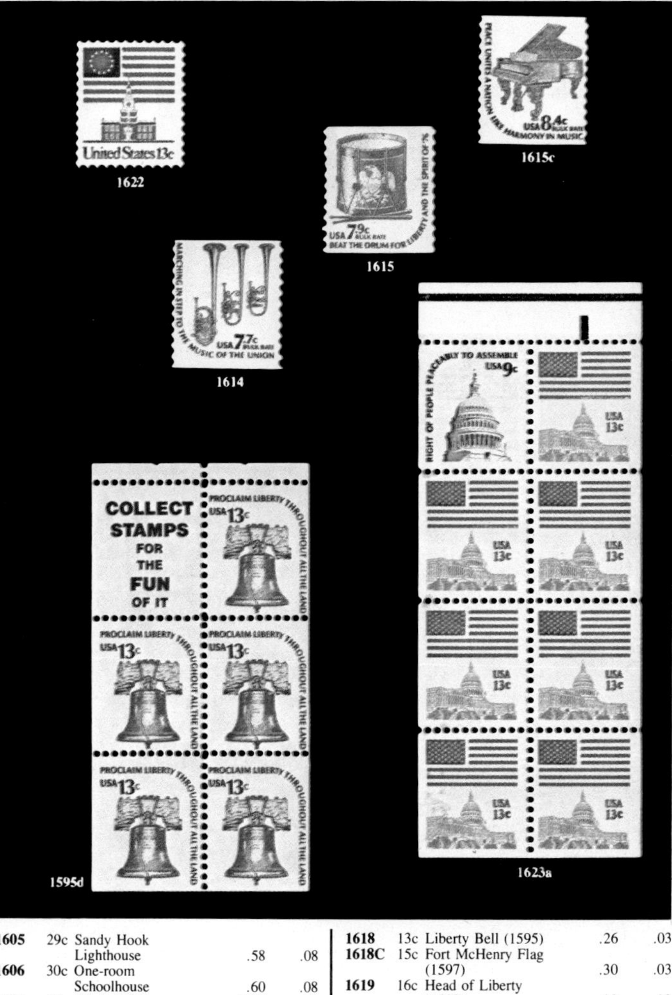
1622 1615c 1615 1614 1595d 1623a

1605	29c	Sandy Hook Lighthouse	.58	.08
1606	30c	One-room Schoolhouse	.60	.08
1608	50c	Whale Oil Lamp	1.00	.10
1610	$1	Candle and Rushlight Holder	2.00	.25
1611	$2	Kerosene Table Lamp	4.00	1.00
1612	$5	Railroad Lantern	10.00	——

No. 1590 is on white paper. No. 1591 on gray paper. Nos. 1590 and 1590a, 1595, 1598 issued only in booklets

Coil Stamps, Perf. 10 Vertically

1614	7.7c	Saxhorns	.16	.08
1615	7.9c	Drum	.16	.08
1615C	8.4c	Piano	.18	.08
1616	9c	Capitol Dome (1591)	.18	.03
1617	10c	Contemplation of Justice (1592)	.20	.03
1618	13c	Liberty Bell (1595)	.26	.03
1618C	15c	Fort McHenry Flag (1597)	.30	.03
1619	16c	Head of Liberty (1599)	.32	.03

Perf. 11x10½

1622	13c	Flag over Independence Hall	.26	.03
1623	13c	Flag over Capitol	.26	.03
1623a		Booklet pane of 8	2.00	——
1623b		Perf. 10	1.00	.50
1623c		Booklet pane of 8, Perf. 10	50.00	——

Nos. 1623, 1623b issued only in booklets

Coil Stamp, Perf. 10 Vertically

1625	13c	Flag over Independence Hall (1622)	.26	.03

1631a

1632

SPIRIT OF '76

The 16-year-old girl who rode all night to warn the Continental Army of a British raid on Danbury; the Jewish banker who helped finance the war; the black militiaman who was cited for heroism at Bunker Hill; the teen-age boy whose military feats became legendary—they all played important roles in American's fight for independence. The young and old, rich and poor, black and white, men and women were all contributors to the cause of liberty.

People of every description and every background joined together to repel the forces of tyranny and create a new nation where free men could govern themselves. In the pursuit of freedom, Americans endured severe hardships and major setbacks. The will and determinatior demonstrated by these brave patriots became known as the "Spirit of '76."

This theme was selected for a painting to be displayed at the Philadelphia Centennial Exposition in 1876. Artist Archibald M. Williard (1837-1918) depicted a young drummer, an older drummer and a fifer with a bandaged head. An American flag appears in the background. In this painting, familiar to almost every American, Williard has captured the indomitable "Spirit of '76."

See Scott Nos. 1629-1631

1633 1634 1635

1636 1637 1638

1639 1640 1641

1642 1643

1644 1645 1646

1647 1648 1649

1650 1651 1652

1653 1654 1655 1656 1657 1658 1659 1660 1661 1662 1663 1664 1665 1666 1667

American Bicentennial State Flags Issue, Feb. 23

1633	13c	Delaware	.45	.30
1634	13c	Pennsylvania	.45	.30
1635	13c	New Jersey	.45	.30
1636	13c	Georgia	.45	.30
1637	13c	Connecticut	.45	.30
1638	13c	Massachusetts	.45	.30
1639	13c	Maryland	.45	.30
1640	13c	South Carolina	.45	.30
1641	13c	New Hampshire	.45	.30
1642	13c	Virgina	.45	.30
1643	13c	New York	.45	.30
1644	13c	North Carolina	.45	.30
1645	13c	Rhode Island	.45	.30
1646	13c	Vermont	.45	.30
1647	13c	Kentucky	.45	.30
1648	13c	Tennessee	.45	.30
1649	13c	Ohio	.45	.30
1650	13c	Louisiana	.45	.30
1651	13c	Indiana	.45	.30
1652	13c	Mississippi	.45	.30
1653	13c	Illinois	.45	.30
1654	13c	Alabama	.45	.30
1655	13c	Maine	.45	.30
1656	13c	Missouri	.45	.30
1657	13c	Arkansas	.45	.30

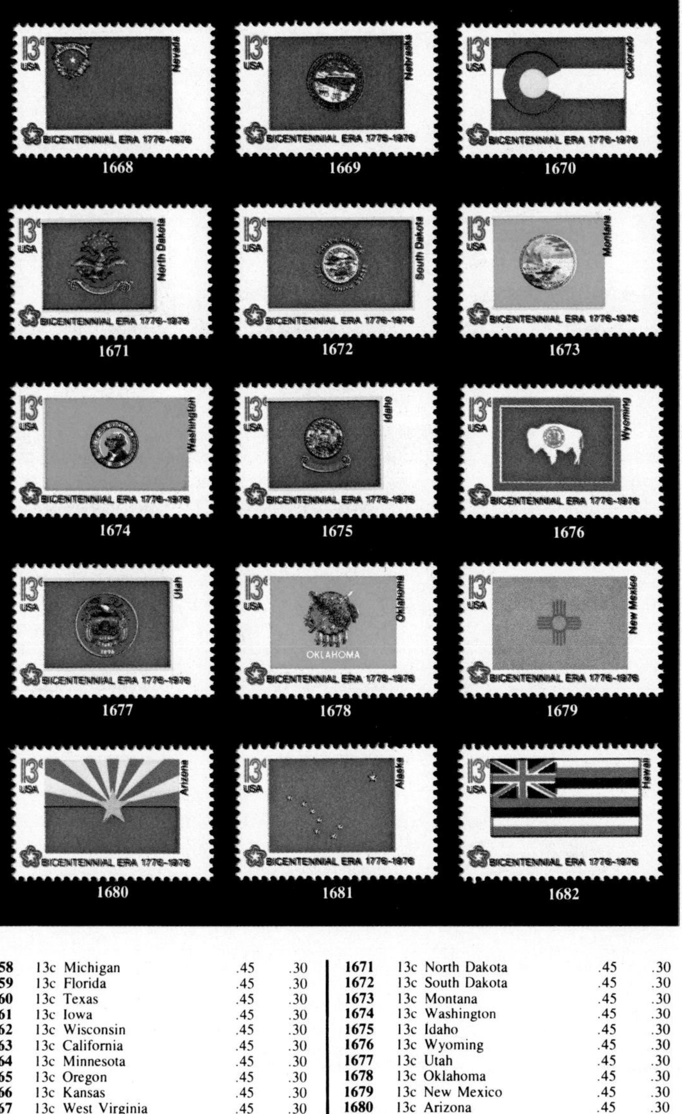

1668 1669 1670
1671 1672 1673
1674 1675 1676
1677 1678 1679
1680 1681 1682

1658	13c	Michigan	.45	.30
1659	13c	Florida	.45	.30
1660	13c	Texas	.45	.30
1661	13c	Iowa	.45	.30
1662	13c	Wisconsin	.45	.30
1663	13c	California	.45	.30
1664	13c	Minnesota	.45	.30
1665	13c	Oregon	.45	.30
1666	13c	Kansas	.45	.30
1667	13c	West Virginia	.45	.30
1668	13c	Nevada	.45	.30
1669	13c	Nebraska	.45	.30
1670	13c	Colorado	.45	.30
1671	13c	North Dakota	.45	.30
1672	13c	South Dakota	.45	.30
1673	13c	Montana	.45	.30
1674	13c	Washington	.45	.30
1675	13c	Idaho	.45	.30
1676	13c	Wyoming	.45	.30
1677	13c	Utah	.45	.30
1678	13c	Oklahoma	.45	.30
1679	13c	New Mexico	.45	.30
1680	13c	Arizona	.45	.30
1681	13c	Alaska	.45	.30
1682	13c	Hawaii	.45	.30
1682a		Sheet of 50	25.00	——

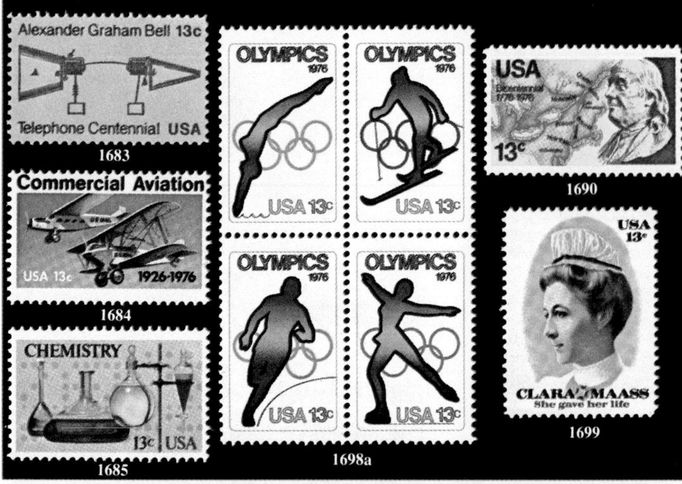

1683 1684 1685 1698a 1690 1699

CHEMISTRY

These laboratory beakers and flasks symbolize the science of chemistry that has uncovered the basic laws of how matter in the universe is put together. Modern technological development due to chemistry is a long way from the primitive understanding of ancient people who thought many chemical changes were caused by magic. It is appropriate to use the distinctive laboratory glassware to represent the science. Today's chemists still use many techniques and procedures developed by 17th century alchemists, who were forerunners in the investigation of matter.

Alchemists devoted their efforts to finding ways to transform ordinary metals into gold. They learned how to take apart some materials and synthesize others, although they never did succeed in solving their initial quest. Modern chemistry began at about the time of the American Revolution when systematic experimentation and measurement began. Progress was marked by the discovery of complex substances that form from these elements.

Technology has put this understanding to good use. New drugs to combat and treat disease, stronger metals for home and industry, and products that help farmers grow better and more abundant crops are some of the applications. The quality of life has been affected with synthetic fabrics and materials. The future promises even greater advances. Researchers are experimenting by weather control, synthetic foods, and more effective drugs. Chemistry has come of age as one of the most important industries in the United States.

See Scott Nos. 1002, 1685

1694a

DECLARATION OF INDEPENDENCE

Even after the Revolutionary War had begun and Americans had fought and died in the Battles of Bunker Hill and Lexington and Concord, the colonists still sought only to secure their rights as Englishmen. But, as the war progressed, the breach between Great Britain and its American colonies widened. The colonists began to realize that a complete break with England was necessary to gain the liberties they desired. The cry for independence mounted throughout the land.

In January 1776, Thomas Paine wrote in "Common Sense" that "'Tis time to part." The idea of separation from the Crown grew and the Continental Congress appointed a committee to prepare a charter of independence. Thomas Jefferson was selected to write a draft of the declaration.

On July 4, 1776, in one of history's most eloquent documents, the thirteen colonies officially declared "these United Colonies are, and of Right ought to be Free and Independent States." To justify these actions, the king of England was charged with a "history of repeated injuries and usurpation." The Declaration of Independence boosted morale and rallied Americans to the cause of liberty by proclaiming "that all men are created equal, that they are endowed by their Creator with certain inalienable Rights, that among these are Life, Liberty and the Pursuit of Happiness." Throughout the years it has continued to serve as a source of pride to Americans and as a source of inspiration to millions of oppressed people everywhere in their quest for freedom.

See Scott Nos. 627, 1687, 1691-1694

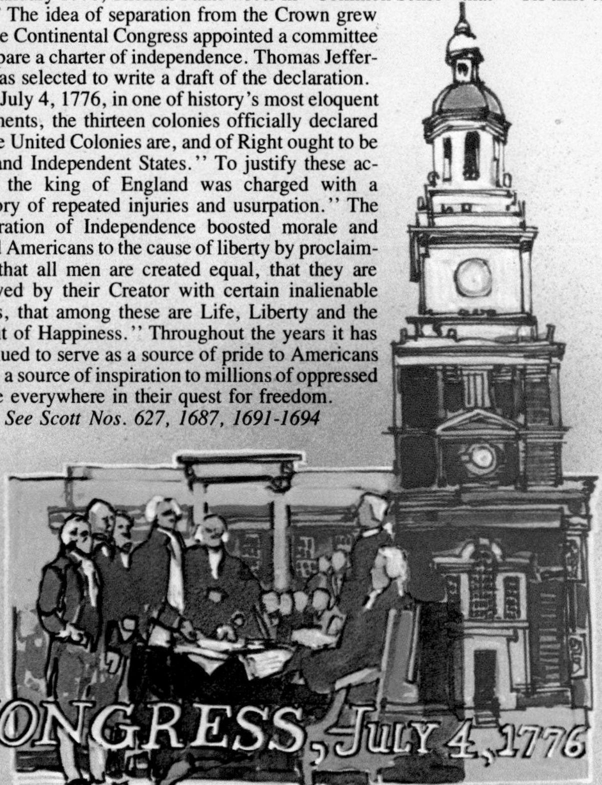

CONGRESS, JULY 4, 1776

The Surrender of Lord Cornwallis at Yorktown
From a Painting by John Trumbull

1686

The Declaration of Independence, 4 July 1776 at Philadelphia
From a Painting by John Trumbull

1687

1683 13c Bell's Telephone Patent Application Mar. 10 .26 .06

1684 13c Ford-Pullman Monoplane and Laird Swallow Biplane Mar. 19 .26 .06

50th anniversary of first contract airmail flights: Dearborn, Mich. to Cleveland, Ohio, Feb. 15, 1926; and Pasco, Wash. to Elko, Nev., Apr. 6, 1926.

1685 13c Various Flasks, Separatory Funnel, Computer Tape Apr. 6 .26 .06

Centenary of American Chemical Society and to honor American Chemists.

American Bicentennial Issues
Souvenir Sheets, May 29
Sheets of 5 Stamps Each

1686 13c Surrender of Cornwallis at Yorktown, by John Trumbull 4.50 ——

1687 18c Declaration of Independence, by John Trumbull 6.00 ——

1688 24c Washington Crossing the Delaware, by Emanuel Leutze/ Eastman Johnson 7.50 ——

1688

USA
31c
Washington Reviewing His Ragged Army at Valley Forge
From a Painting by William T. Trego

1689

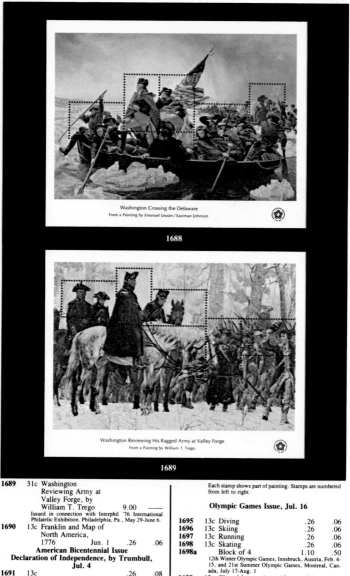

1689	31c	Washington Reviewing Army at Valley Forge, by William T. Trego	9.00	——

Issued in connection with Interphil '76 International Philatelic Exhibition. Philadelphia, Pa., May 29-June 6.

1690	13c	Franklin and Map of North America, 1776	Jun. 1	.26	.06

American Bicentennial Issue
Declaration of Independence, by Trumbull, Jul. 4

1691	13c		.26	.08
1692	13c		.26	.08
1693	13c		.26	.08
1694	13c		.26	.08
1694a		Strip of 4	1.10	.50

Each stamp shows part of painting. Stamps are numbered from left to right.

Olympic Games Issue, Jul. 16

1695	13c	Diving	.26	.06
1696	13c	Skiing	.26	.06
1697	13c	Running	.26	.06
1698	13c	Skating	.26	.06
1698a		Block of 4	1.10	.50

12th Winter Olympic Games, Innsbruck, Austria, Feb. 4-15, and 21st Summer Olympic Games, Montreal, Canada, July 17-Aug. 1

1699	13c	Clara Maass	Aug. 18	.26	.06
1700	13c	Adolph S. Ochs	Sep. 18	.26	.06

Adolph S. Ochs (1858-1935), publisher of the *New York Times*. 1896-1935.

1702

1700

1703

1701

1704

Christmas Issue, Oct. 27

1701	13c	Nativity, by John Singleton Copley	.26	.03
1702	13c	"Winter Pastime," by Nathaniel Currier	.26	.03
1703	13c	as 1702, see footnote	.26	.03

No. 1702 has overall tagging. Lettering at base is black and usually ½mm. below design. As a rule, no "snowflaking" in sky or pond. Pane of 50 has margins on 4 sides with slogans.

No. 1703 has block tagging the size of printed area. Lettering at base is gray black and usually ¾mm. below design. "Snowflaking" generally in sky and pond. Pane of 50 has margin only at right or left, and no slogans.

Issues of 1977
American Bicentennial
Perf. 11

1704	13c	Washington, by Charles Wilson Peale	Jan. 3	.26	.06

200th anniversary of Washington's victory at Princeton over Lord Cornwallis.

ADOLPH S. OCHS 1858-1935

The slogan "All the News That's Fit to Print," which appears on the masthead of *The New York Times*, reflects the journalistic philosophy of Adolph Ochs. As its longtime publisher, Ochs devoted his energies to creating a newspaper that presented an unbiased, complete, and accurate account of the news.

The son of immigrants, Ochs began his lengthy newspaper career as a newsboy at the age of 14. He worked as a copyboy and compositor, and in 1878, when he was 20, Ochs bought a half interest in the *Chatanooga Times* for $250. Under his supervision, the paper became one of the foremost publications of the South.

Ochs became manager of *The New York Times* in 1896. Four years later he acquired controlling ownership. In his 38-year association with the *Times*, it grew from a financially faltering paper that had a daily circulation of 9,000 to a flourishing journal with 460,000 copies sold daily. As publisher, Ochs transformed the *Times* into one of the world's most trusted and reliable sources of news. Until his death in 1935, Adolph Ochs exerted a strong influence on responsible newspaper publishing in the United States.

See Scott No. 1700

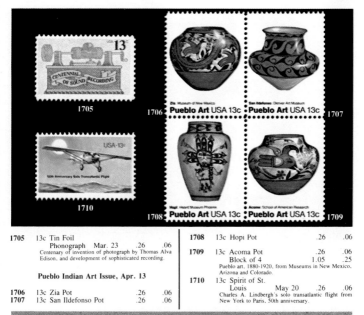

1705 1706 1707

1710 1708 1709

1705 13c Tin Foil Phonograph Mar. 23 .26 .06
Centenary of invention of photograph by Thomas Alva Edison, and development of sophisticated recording.

Pueblo Indian Art Issue, Apr. 13

1706 13c Zia Pot .26 .06
1707 13c San Ildefonso Pot .26 .06
1708 13c Hopi Pot .26 .06
1709 13c Acoma Pot .26 .06
Block of 4 1.05 .25
Pueblo art, 1880-1920, from Museums in New Mexico, Arizona and Colorado.

1710 13c Spirit of St. Louis May 20 .26 .06
Charles A. Lindbergh's solo transatlantic flight from New York to Paris, 50th anniversary.

SPIRIT OF ST. LOUIS

Many had tried, and failed, to win the $25,000 prize, offered since 1919, for the first non-stop flight between New York and Paris. Early in 1927, a determined Charles Lindbergh set out to be the first pilot to successfully make the crossing. With funds provided by a group of St. Louis businessmen, he purchased a Ryan monoplane. The plane was not built for long distance flying; its fuel tanks were too small. Lindbergh supervised the necessary changes of the craft, the *Spirit of St. Louis*. He put it to the test in a record-setting coast-to-coast flight on May 12, 1927.

When he took off for Paris on May 20, 1927, Lindbergh had to omit both a radio and his parachute in order to carry extra fuel. The heavily laden plane almost failed to clear the trees at the end of the runway. Alone, he began his long, arduous 3,600 mile journey. Battling sleep, fog and rain Lindbergh flew for 33½ hours from New York to Paris. When he stepped out of the *Spirit of St. Louis* in France, the "Lone Eagle" was an international hero.

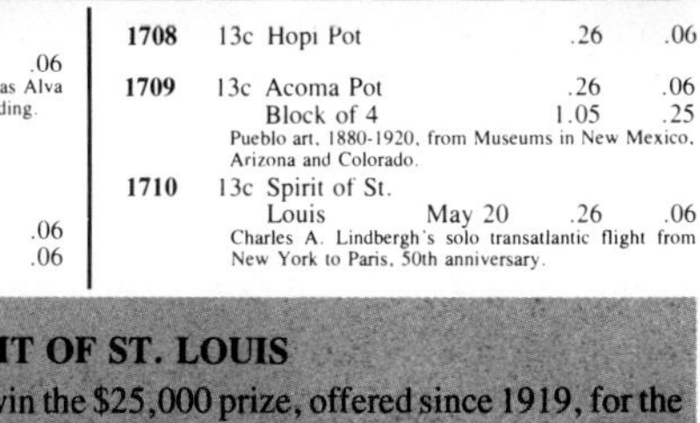

Scott No. 1710, C10

1711

1715a

1721

1716

1711	13c Columbine and Rocky Mountains	May 21	.26	.06
	Butterfly Issue, Jun. 6			
1712	13c Swallowtail		.26	.06
1713	13c Checkerspot		.26	.06
1714	13c Dogface		.26	.06
1715	13c Orange Tip		.26	.06
1715a	Block of 4		1.05	.25

American Bicentennial Issues

1716	13c Marquis de Lafayette	Jun. 13	.26	.06
	200th anniversary of Lafayette's landing on the coast of South Carolina, north of Charleston.			
	Skilled Hands for Independence, Jul. 4			
1717	13c Seamstress		.26	.06
1718	13c Blacksmith		.26	.06
1719	13c Wheelwright		.26	.06

ENERGY CONSERVATION

Through the years Americans became accustomed to a seemingly limitless supply of energy. We bought bigger, more powerful cars and surrounded ourselves with an ever-increasing number of electric appliances. With the onset of the seventies, however, the days of indiscriminate energy consumption had vanished forever. Energy supplies dwindled and America, which had always been the land of plenty, had suddenly become America, the land of shortages. In 1973, gasoline was in such critically short supply that it was not uncommon to see long lines of cars at gas stations. By the end of the year, gasoline prices had almost doubled. Nor was the crisis limited to the automobile. By 1979, the energy crunch

1723 a

1720a

1722

1720	13c Leatherworker		.26	.06
1720a	Block of 4		1.05	.25

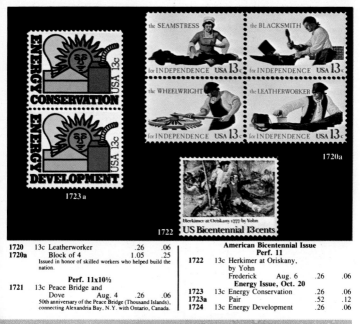

Issued in honor of skilled workers who helped build the nation.

Perf. 11x10½

1721	13c Peace Bridge and Dove	Aug. 4	.26	.06

50th anniversary of the Peace Bridge (Thousand Islands), connecting Alexandria Bay, N.Y. with Ontario, Canada.

American Bicentennial Issue
Perf. 11

1722	13c Herkimer at Oriskany, by Yohn Frederick	Aug. 6	.26	.06

Energy Issue, Oct. 20

1723	13c Energy Conservation	.26	.06
1723a	Pair	.52	.12
1724	13c Energy Development	.26	.06

has affected nearly every facet of American life.

Energy is used to provide heat, operate machines in both home and industry, and in countless other ways. Since 1900, the amount of energy consumed by man has doubled every 20 years. How long can this go on until we overstretch our sources of energy supply? This grim outlook means that in the 1980's man will be challenged to conserve his sources of energy more than ever. But the United States has overcome major crises in the past, and there is every reason to believe that American ingenuity and know-how will come through again to provide alternative sources of energy in the years to come.

See Scott Nos. 1547, 1723-1724

1725 1726 1727

1729 1728 1730

American Bicentennial Issues

1725 13c Farm House Sep. 9 .26 .06
First civil settlement in Alta California, 200th anniversary.

1726 13c Articles of Confederation Sep. 30 .26 .06
200th anniversary of the Drafting of the Articles of Confederation, York Town, Pa.

1727 13c Movie Projector and Phonograph Oct. 6 .26 .06
50th anniversary of talking pictures.

American Bicentennial Issue

1728 13c Surrender of Saratoga, by John Trumbull Oct. 7 .26 .06
200th anniversary of Gen. Burgoyne's surrender to Gen. Gates.

Christmas Issue, Oct. 21

1729 13c Washington at Valley Forge .26 .03

1730 13c Rural Mailbox .26 .03

TALKING PICTURES

When Al Jolson delivered a few dramatic lines of dialogue in *The Jazz Singer* (in 1927) the entertainment industry was changed forever. The synchronization of dialogue and film captured the public's fancy and, almost overnight, the era of silent films was a thing of the past. Within a year every major Hollywood production included at least some sound.

In response to public enthusiasm, theater owners hastily installed sound projection systems and by 1929, movie attendance almost doubled. Early "talkies" were generally undistinguished and of poor artistic quality; actors were inhibited and self-conscious. The popularity of many silent film stars declined because their unpleasant voices were unsuitable for sound movies. By the mid-thirties, a new group of stars emerged to replace those who fell victim to "talkies."

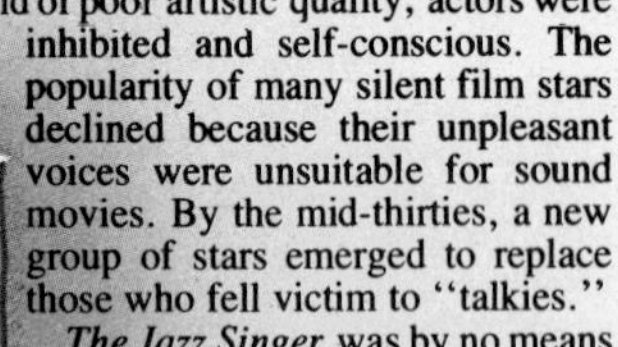

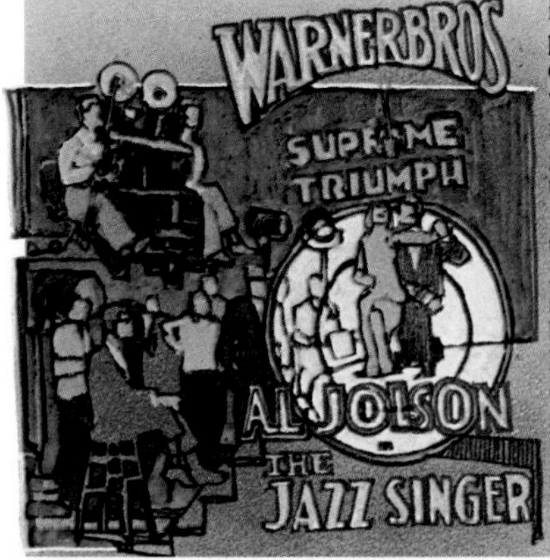

The Jazz Singer was by no means the first attempt at sound movies. As far back as 1889, Thomas Edison had demonstrated the practicability of making talking pictures. But it was *The Jazz Singer*, which combined the charisma of Jolson and a dramatic story with sound, that revolutionized American film-making.

See Scott Nos. 926, 1555, 1727

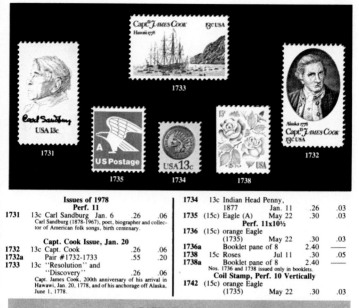

Issues of 1978
Perf. 11

1731	13c	Carl Sandburg	Jan. 6	.26	.06

Carl Sandburg (1878-1967), poet, biographer and collector of American folk songs, birth centenary.

Capt. Cook Issue, Jan. 20

1732	13c	Capt. Cook	.26	.06
1732a		Pair #1732-1733	.55	.20
1733	13c	"Resolution" and "Discovery"	.26	.06

Capt. James Cook, 200th anniversary of his arrival in Hawawi, Jan. 20, 1778, and of his anchorage off Alaska, June 1, 1778.

1734	13c	Indian Head Penny, 1877	Jan. 11	.26	.03
1735	(15c)	Eagle (A)	May 22	.30	.03

Perf. 11x10½

1736	(15c)	orange Eagle (1735)	May 22	.30	.03
1736a		Booklet pane of 8		2.40	——
1738	15c	Roses	Jul 11	.30	.05
1738a		Booklet pane of 8		2.40	——

Nos. 1736 and 1738 issued only in booklets.

Coil Stamp, Perf. 10 Vertically

1742	(15c)	orange Eagle (1735)	May 22	.30	.03

CAPTAIN COOK

James Cook son of a migrant farmhand, was born in England and joined the Royal Navy. In 1768 he was appointed commander of the first scientific sea voyage to the Pacific. He discovered and charted New Zealand, navigated the Great Barrier Reef, and surveyed 2,000 miles of Australian coast. But Cook was more than a great explorer, navigator and mapmaker. He was a self-taught dietician! Because he imposed strict rules of diet on his crew, not a single one of his sailors contracted scurvy, the crippling disease of seamen.

On his second expedition in 1772, Cook circumnavigated the Antarctic Ocean. He set sail once more in 1776, sailed east past Europe, Asia and New Zealand, and discovered the Hawaiian Islands. In search of a northern passage between the Atlantic and the Pacific, Cook sailed ever northward, charting the Alaskan coast and traversing the fearsome Bering Straits to the northwest tip of Alaska. While he was retracing the long route home, Captain Cook was slain by Polynesian natives on a beach in Hawaii. He was dead at 50. But he had done more to change the map of the world than any other man who ever lived.

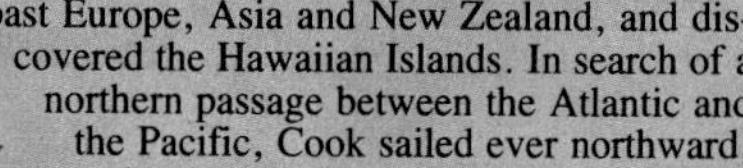

See Scott Nos. 1732, 1733

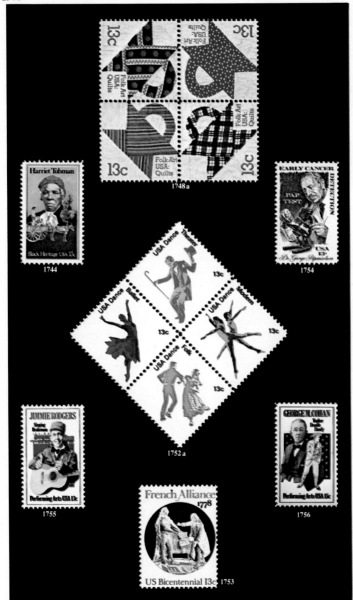

1748 a

Harriet Tubman

Black Heritage USA 13c

1744

EARLY CANCER DETECTION

PAP TEST

USA 13c

1754

1752 a

JIMMIE RODGERS

Singing Brakeman

Performing Arts USA 13c

1755

GEORGE M. COHAN

Yankee Doodle Dandy

Performing Arts USA 15c

1756

French Alliance 1778

US Bicentennial 13c

1753

Perf. 11

1744	13c	Harriet Tubman Feb. 1	.26	.06

Harriet Tubman (1820-1913), born a slave, helped more than 300 slaves escape to freedom.

American Folk Art Issue
American Quilts, Mar. 8

1745	13c	Basket design, red & orange	.26	.06
1746	13c	Basket design, red	.26	.06
1747	13c	Basket design, orange	.26	.06
1748	13c	Basket design, black	.26	.06
1748a		Block of 4	1.05	——

American Dance Issue, Apr. 26

1749	13c	Ballet	.26	.06
1750	13c	Theater	.26	.06
1751	13c	Folk Dance	.26	.06
1752	13c	Modern Dance	.26	.06
1752a		Block of 4	1.05	——
1753	13c	French Alliance May 4	.26	.06

Bicentenary of the French Alliance, signed in Paris, February 1778, and ratified by Continental Congress, May 4, 1778.

Perf 10½x11

1754	13c	Dr. Papanicolaou with Microscope May 13	.26	.06

Dr. George Papanicolaou (1883-1962), developer of Pap Test for early cancer detection in women.

Performing Arts Issue
Perf. 11

1755	13c	Jimmie Rodgers May 24	.26	.06
1756	15c	George M. Cohan July 3	.30	.06

Jimmie Rodgers (1897-1933), country singer, and George M. Cohan (1878-1942), actor and playwright.

1757	13c	Souvenir sheet of 8 June 10	2.25	——

CAPEX 78, Canadian International Philatelic Exhibition, Toronto, June 9-18.

1758	15c	Photographic Equipment June 26	.30	.06
1759	15c	Viking I Landing on Mars July 20	.30	.06

Successful conclusion of Viking Space Program.

American Owls, Aug. 26

1760	15c	Great Gray Owl	.30	.06
1761	15c	Saw-whet Owl	.30	.06
1762	15c	Barred Owl	.30	.06
1763	15c	Great Horned Owl	.30	.06
1763a		Block of 4	1.25	.30

American Trees, Oct. 9

1764	15c	Giant Sequoia	.30	.06
1765	15c	White Pine	.30	.06
1766	15c	White Oak	.30	.06
1767	15c	Gray Birch	.30	.06
1767a		Block of 4	1.25	.30

Christmas Issue, Oct. 18

1768	15c	Madonna and Child	.30	.03
1769	15c	Hobby Horse	.30	.03

HARRIET TUBMAN

The Underground Railroad was an elaborate pre-Civil War network of individuals and groups that helped escaped slaves move in secret to the safety of the north. In 1849 a slave named Harriet Tubman escaped from a plantation in Maryland and passed along the route of the Underground Railroad. A year later she was back in Maryland, not because she'd been re-enslaved but because she wanted others to share the gift of freedom.

In 1850, at great personal risk, Tubman guided members of her family along the same path to freedom she'd taken herself. It was only the beginning. Again and again she returned to the South. By then, huge rewards were being offered for her capture. But in her dedication to the cause of freedom for the slaves, Harriet Tubman was fearless. All in all, "the Moses of her people" led more than 300 slaves out of bondage.

See Scott No. 1744

1757

JIMMIE RODGERS

The "Father of Country Music" was born in Mississippi. He went to work on the railroad at 14, and rose to the position of brakeman. But from 1924 on, Jimmie Rodgers was riding a death train called tuberculosis. Turning to music for a living, he was discovered by the record industry in 1927. It was only a matter of months before he was America's number one recording star and a celebrated performer worldwide. But dogged by ill health, Rodgers died at the age of 35. He left behind over 100 records including such Country Music classics as "Jimmie the Kid", "T.B. Blues", "Treasures Untold" and "Sleep Baby Sleep". Fittingly, he was the first artist honored by the Country Music Hall of Fame.

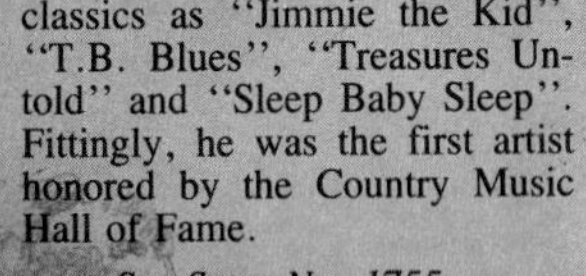

See Scott No. 1755

Photography USA 15c

1758

Viking missions to Mars

Expanding human knowledge USA 15c

1759

GREAT GRAY OWL 15c WILDLIFE CONSERVATION-USA

SAW-WHET OWL 15c WILDLIFE CONSERVATION-USA

BARRED OWL 15c WILDLIFE CONSERVATION-USA

GREAT HORNED OWL 15c WILDLIFE CONSERVATION-USA

1763a

OWLS

Did you think the only word in an owl's vocabulary is "Hooo"? In the mating season, North American screech owls sing back and forth for 15 minutes and then switch to a duet! There's a note the mother owl sings when she's looking for her young, a note the nestlings sing when they're hungry, a barking call that indicates territorial boundaries. Many kinds of owls can puff themselves up to twice their normal size when they're defending the nest. And they can compress themselves into what looks like a broken branch when they want to escape notice.

Owls are birds of prey, living on insects, mice and other tiny creatures of field and forest. They hunt by night, flying on silent wings. Because their eyes don't move, they can look only straight ahead. They make up for it, though, with heads that effortlessly turn clear around and even upside down!

See Scott Nos. 1760-63

1767a

1768 1769

VIKING SPACE MISSIONS

In August and September of 1975, two unmanned U.S. spacecraft, Viking 1 and 2, blasted off. The following July, having traveled 212 million miles and photographed several possible landing sites. Viking 1's lander detached from its orbiter and touched down gently on the surface of Mars. Within four minutes it had raised its antenna for contact with Earth and begun transmitting color photographs. (Mars is bright red under a pink sky!)

It was joined by Viking 2 in September, 1976. Experiments by the two craft produced a wealth of information that will take years to assess. Vast sections of the surface of Mars were mapped. Seasonal climate patterns were observed and recorded. Rocks, surface particles and atmosphere were analyzed. Temperatures were measured, and the presence of water vapor was confirmed. In November a Marsquake was registered.

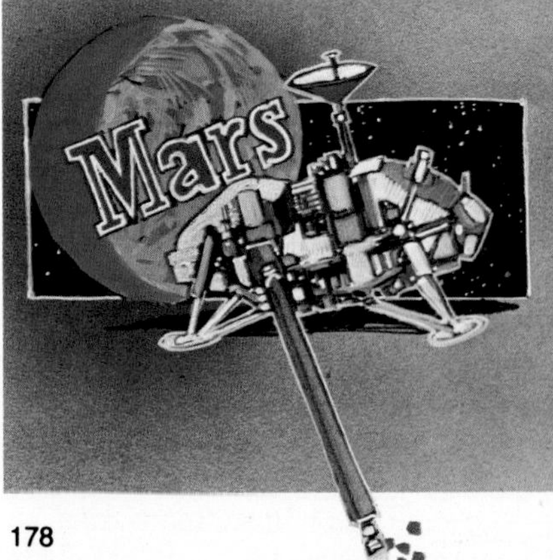

But the big question—whether or not life exists or ever existed on Mars—remains unanswered. Three separate experiments produced only inconclusive results. And no little green men showed up to have their pictures taken!

See Scott No. 1759

1770

1772

1771

1773

1778a

1774

Issues of 1979
Perf. 11

1770 15c Robert F. Kennedy Jan. 12 .30 .06
Robert F. Kennedy (1925-1968), U.S. Attorney General.

1771 15c Martin Luther King, Jr. Jan. 13 .30 .06
Dr. Martin Luther King, Jr. (1929-1968), civil rights leader.

1772 15c Internat'l Year of the Child Feb. 15 .30 .06

Perf. 10½x11

1773 15c John Steinbeck Feb. 27 .30 .06
John Steinbeck (1902-1968), novelist.

1774 15c Albert Einstein Mar. 4 .30 .06
Albert Einstein (1879-1955), theoretical physicist.

American Folk Art Issue, Apr. 19
Pennsylvania Toleware

1775	15c Coffeepot	.30	.06
1776	15c Tea Caddy	.30	.06
1777	15c Sugar Bowl	.30	.06
1778	15c Coffeepot	.30	.06
1778a	Block of 4	1.20	

American Architecture Issue, June 4

1779	15c Virginia Rotunda	.30	.06
1780	15c Baltimore Cathedral	.30	.06
1781	15c Boston State House	.30	.06
1782	15c Philadelphia Exchange	.30	.06
1782a	Block of 4	1.20	

ROBERT F. KENNEDY 1925-1968

Born to great wealth, and the seventh of nine children, Robert Kennedy believed he had an obligation to make a contribution to society. He became the champion of the oppressed and dispossessed. He had a deep commitment to Martin Luther King's struggle for racial justice and to the improvement of the quality of life for all disadvantaged people. Soon after he entered President Kennedy's cabinet as Attorney General, he declared, "My fundamental belief is that all people are created equal."

The Kennedy brothers were very close political partners. Robert successfully managed all of his brother's campaigns, including the 1960 Presidential election. He was also deeply involved in the major events of the Kennedy administration.

Although he was grief-stricken at John F. Kennedy's death in 1963, he said, "My brother barely had a chance to get started—and there is so much to be done." Robert Kennedy went on to serve as U.S. Senator from New York and later to seek the Presidency of the United States.

He appeared destined to be heir to his brother's political office; instead, on June 6, 1968, he fell victim to John F. Kennedy's tragic fate; death at the hands of an assassin. Seeking the Presidential nomination, he was killed just after celebrating his victory in the California primary.

See Scott No. 1770

MARTIN LUTHER KING 1929-1968

The highlight of the 1963 Civil Rights "March on Washington," the largest protest demonstration ever in the United States, was Martin Luther King's moving eloquence. In his stirring plea for racial equality and justice for all, he told the crowd of more than 200,000 people gathered at the Lincoln Memorial and countless millions who watched the event on TV, "I have a dream that someday all men will be brothers . . . and the evils of prejudice and segregation will vanish."

Throughout his life, Martin Luther King worked to bring about social, political and economic advancement for blacks through non-violent means. He began his civil rights crusade in 1955 with a successful boycott of bus lines that discriminated against black passengers. Although he was often arrested and imprisoned, King continued to lead protests against injustice. He convinced people that civil rights could be obtained by peaceful actions. In recognition of the contribution he made to the enactment of civil rights legislation, King was awarded the 1964 Nobel Peace Prize.

But his work was not yet done. The "Poor People's Campaign," a crusade for the rights of the downtrodden of all races, was in the planning stage when, on April 4, 1968, King was assassinated. Inscribed on this great leader's tombstone are the words, "Free at Last."

See Scott No. 1771

1787

1782a

1788

1789

1799

1800

1786a

Endangered Flora Issue, June 7

1783	15c Persistent Trillium	.30	.06
1784	15c Hawaiian Wild Broadbean	.30	.06
1785	15c Contra Costa Wallflower	.30	.06
1786	15c Antioch Dunes Evening Primrose	.30	.06
1786a	Block of 4	1.20	
1787	15c Seeing Eye Dogs June 15	.30	.06
1788	15c Special Olympics Aug. 9	.30	.06
1789	15c John Paul Jones, by Charles Willson Peale Sept. 23	.30	.06

John Paul Jones (1747-1792), Naval Commander, American Revolution.

Olympic Games Issue, Oct.

1790	10c Javelin	.20	.06
1791	15c Running	.30	.06
1792	15c Swimming	.30	.06
1793	15c Canoeing	.30	.06
1794	15c Equestrian	.30	.06
1794a	Block of 4, #1791-1974	1.20	

22nd Summer Olympic Games, Moscow, July 19–Aug. 3, 1980.

Christmas Issue, Oct. 18

1799	15c Virgin and Child, by Gerard David	.30	.03
1800	15c Santa Claus	.30	.03
1801	15c Will Rogers Nov. 4	.30	.06

Will Rogers (1879-1935), actor and humorist.

1802	15c Viet Nam Veterans Nov. 11	.30	.06

ALBERT EINSTEIN 1879-1955

The year Albert Einstein was 26 and working as a clerk in a patent office, he published five papers that profoundly altered our concept of time and space. Einstein's theories were only dimly understood because they were very much against the common sense approach laid down in classical physics. To Einstein all motion is relative, time can be slowed down, space is warped, and mass and energy are the same thing. This last concept, expressed by his famous formula $E=mc^2$, says that a small amount of mass is equal to a vast amount of energy. The practical application of this equation began the atomic age.

As a boy in Germany, Einstein displayed little evidence of genius. He was rebellious and did poorly at school. One teacher said he would "never amount to anything." Despite this apparent lack of promise, Einstein went on to graduate from the Swiss Polytechnic Institute and become a professor at the University of Berlin in 1914.

Einstein was a guest lecturer in the U.S. when Hitler came to power in the early 1930's. As a Jew, he realized there was no point in returning to Germany. Instead, he accepted a post at Princeton University. He became a U.S. citizen in 1940.

Einstein remained a simple, unassuming man throughout his life. His disregard for his personal appearance and apparent unawareness of commonplace events made him the stereotype of the absent-minded professor. Yet he played an important role in history. In 1939, Einstein warned President Roosevelt of the possibilty of a German nuclear weapon and urged the administration to take "quick action." The resulting Manhattan Project that built the A-bomb led to Einstein's informal title as "father of the atomic age." But he always regretted the role he played. He said, "Had I known that the Germans would not succeed . . . . I would have done nothing for the bomb."

See Scott Nos. 1285, 1774

ARCHITECTURE

When Thomas Jefferson designed Virginia's new Capitol (1780) he selected the architecture of Rome and Greece as his models. He believed a structure derived from the classical style found in ancient republics was best suited for the buildings of a new democratic nation. The neo-classic design Jefferson used for the Virginia Capitol exerted great influence on American architecture during the 18th and 19th centuries.

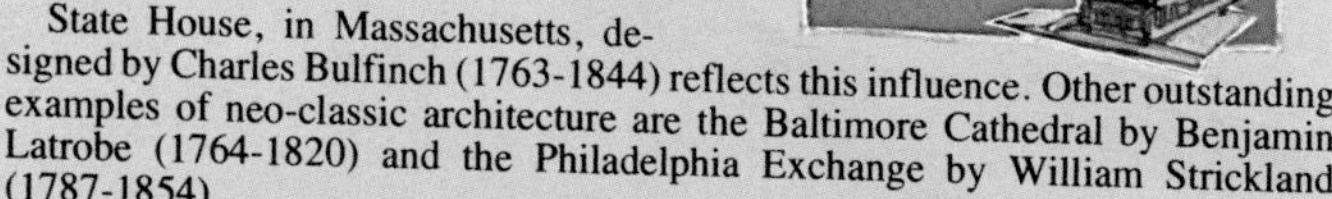

State House, in Massachusetts, designed by Charles Bulfinch (1763-1844) reflects this influence. Other outstanding examples of neo-classic architecture are the Baltimore Cathedral by Benjamin Latrobe (1764-1820) and the Philadelphia Exchange by William Strickland (1787-1854).

The 1800's saw a new series of revivals in American architecture. In addition to the classical revival, Gothic and baroque styles became fashionable. With the Industrial Revolution and the growth of cities, a new type of structure appeared on the scene: the skyscraper. The first, the ten-story Home Insurance Building in Chicago, was constructed in 1884.

The "Chicago school" of architects who followed the completion of the first skyscraper tried to break away from traditional design. Many of their structures are historic landmarks today.

By the 1920's, the foundations for contemporary architecture were established. An American, Frank Lloyd Wright (1867-1959), was a major contributor to the growth of this new form, featuring functional design and uncluttered surfaces.

See Scott Nos. 1779-1782

1794a

1790

C97

1801

1802

OLYMPICS—1980

Because athletics played such an important role in the lives of the ancient Greeks, Olympic Games were made part of their religious ceremonies. Although authorities believe the Olympics date as far back as 3,000 years, the games held at the Stadium of Olympia in 776 B.C. were the first to be recorded by historians. Early contests consisted only of footraces but soon wrestling, the pentathlon, chariot races, and other tests of physical skill were added.

After the Roman conquest of Greece, the Olympics began to lose both its religious significance and its general fine quality of sportsmanship. The games were ended in the year 394, and were not held again for more than 1,500 years.

As a result of the efforts of a determined Frenchman, Baron Pierre de Coubertin (1863-1937), who believed athletic competition was a necessary factor in developing character, the modern Olympic games began in Athens in 1896. Winter games, as a separate entity, were added in 1924.

Except for wartime, the Olympics have been held every four years and each Olympiad is hosted by a different country. In 1932 the United States hosted the Summer Games at Los Angeles and the Winter Games at Lake Placid. The 1960 winter contests were held in Squaw Valley. In 1980 the Summer Olympics will be in Moscow and Lake Placid will again be the scene of the Winter Games.

From its inception the modern Olympics have been marked by exceptional individual performances by its amateur athletes. In 1912, an American Indian, Jim Thorpe, who many consider one of the finest athletes of all time, won both the decathlon and pentathlon. However, when it was discovered that he once received payment for playing semi-professional baseball, he was stripped of his amateur standing. His records were cancelled and his medals returned. The youngest person to ever win a gold medal was a 12-year-old American girl, Aileen Riggin, who took the diving honors in 1920. A young black man, Cassius Clay, earned a gold medal for boxing in 1960; he later changed his name to Muhammed Ali and went on to become the heavyweight champion of the world.

Another group of our best amateur athletes will represent the United States at the 1980 Olympics in Moscow. Americans hope that among them there will be a runner that can match Jesse Owens' spectacular track and field feats or a swimmer who can better Mark Spitz's record of seven gold medals.

See Scott Nos. 716, 718-719, 1146, 1460-1462, 1695-1698, 1790-1794, C85, C97

AIRMAIL STAMPS SPECIAL DELIVERY STAMPS

THE HISTORY OF AIRMAIL

The very first airmail service took place in 1911, only eight years after the very first flight at Kitty Hawk. The mail was flown between Windsor and Hendon in England to celebrate the coronation of King George V. But once the celebration was over, so was airmail, and regular airmail service didn't come along for another seven years.

In 1918, the U.S. Army established regular airmail service between Washington, D.C., and New York, a distance of 216 miles. A few months later the British Army initiated the first international airmail, between Folkestone, England and Cologne, Germany. So there was airmail service on two continents by 1918, but it was strictly a military operation.

Up to that point, only letters were flown. Heavier mail was still earthbound. Then, in 1921, the first regular airmail parcel service began between London and Paris. Meanwhile, back on this side of the Atlantic, the U.S. Post Office Department decided that airmail was the wave of the future, and the Post Office's interest in putting wings on the mail made a giant contribution to America's later supremacy in the air.

In the early days of aviation, European countries were investing large sums of money in their passenger-carrying air systems. At the same time, the United States was expanding its airways for the benefit of the airmail system. The U.S. Post Office Department had its own fleet of mail-carrying planes and its own pilots. (One of those pilots was a young fellow named Charles A. Lindbergh.) It wasn't until 1925 that the U.S. contracted with private airlines to carry the mail. The origins of today's vast and complex U.S. airline system go back to a law passed in 1925 that connected a large number of U.S. cities and towns to the transcontinental mail routes operated by the Post Office.

Transatlantic airmail service started in 1939, from New York to Marseilles, France, with stops in Bermuda and Portugal. Later the route was extended all the way to Singapore and Hong Kong. And by the early 1970's low-cost airmail service blanketed the world. The Post Office is no longer in the air transportation business, of course, but it pioneered flight in America and played a major role in the development of air travel.

C1 C2 C3 C4 C5 C6 C3a C7 C10 C11

Air Post Stamps

For prepayment of postage on all mailable matter sent by airmail. All unwatermarked.

No.	Denom.	Description	Unused	Used
		Issue of 1918, Perf. 11		
C1	6c	Curtiss Jenny	125.00	25.00
C2	16c	Curtiss Jenny	175.00	35.00
C3	24c	Curtiss Jenny	160.00	35.00
C3a		Center Inverted	*100,000.00*	
		Issue of 1923		
C4	8c	Wooden Propeller and Engine Nose	50.00	15.00
C5	15c	Air Service Emblem	175.00	32.50
C6	24c	De Havilland Biplane	200.00	25.00
		Issue of 1926-27		
C7	10c	Map of U.S. and Two Mail Planes	4.50	.50
C8	15c	olive brown (C7)	5.00	2.75
C9	20c	yellow green (C7)	15.00	2.25
		Issue of 1927		
C10	10c	Lindbergh's "Spirit of St. Louis" Jun. 18	12.50	3.50
C10a		Booklet pane of 3	100.00	*50.00*

Nos. C1-C10 inclusive were also available for ordinary postage.

No.	Denom.	Description	Unused	Used
		Issue of 1928		
C11	5c	Beacon on Rocky Mountains Jul. 25	5.25	.65
		Issues of 1930		
C12	5c	Winged Globe Feb. 10	16.50	.65

STORY OF C3a—THE INVERTED AIRMAIL

William T. Robey, a stockbroker in Washington, D.C. had a most fortunate day at his local post office in 1918. On line in front of him was an irate customer who had turned down a sheet of 100 twenty-four cent airmails. The stamps were, by error, printed with the Curtiss "Jenny" airplane upside down. Robey quickly offered his $24 and purchased the sheet, the only one known to have escaped the normally careful scrutiny of the postal inspectors. It is believed the error went unnoticed because the Bureau of Printing and Engraving, operating at peak World War I production, was working day and night printing Liberty Bonds and new currency, in addition to stamps.

Word of the error spread quickly. Robey quickly sold the sheet to a Philadelphia dealer who immediately resold it for $20,000. The purchaser broke the sheet into blocks and singles and sold the singles for $250 each. Before he broke up the sheet, the dealer numbered each of the stamps lightly in pencil on the gum side to show

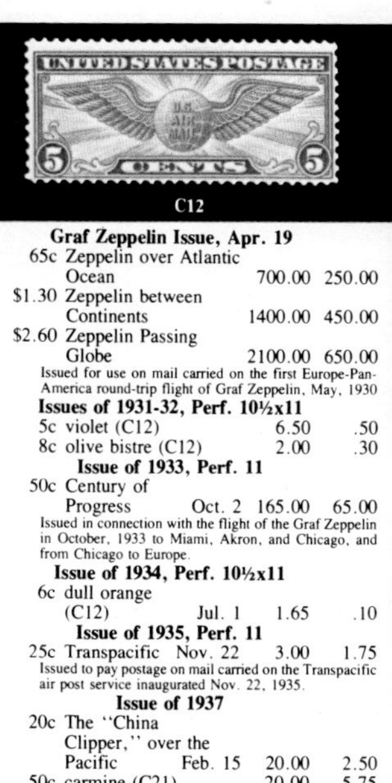

C12

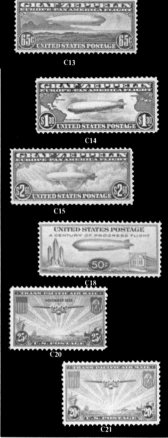

C13

Graf Zeppelin Issue, Apr. 19

C13	65c	Zeppelin over Atlantic Ocean	700.00	250.00
C14	$1.30	Zeppelin between Continents	1400.00	450.00
C15	$2.60	Zeppelin Passing Globe	2100.00	650.00

Issued for use on mail carried on the first Europe-Pan-America round-trip flight of Graf Zeppelin, May, 1930

Issues of 1931-32, Perf. 10½x11

C16	5c	violet (C12)	6.50	.50
C17	8c	olive bistre (C12)	2.00	.30

Issue of 1933, Perf. 11

C18	50c	Century of Progress Oct. 2	165.00	65.00

Issued in connection with the flight of the Graf Zeppelin in October, 1933 to Miami, Akron, and Chicago, and from Chicago to Europe.

Issue of 1934, Perf. 10½x11

C19	6c	dull orange (C12) Jul. 1	1.65	.10

Issue of 1935, Perf. 11

C20	25c	Transpacific Nov. 22	3.00	1.75

Issued to pay postage on mail carried on the Transpacific air post service inaugurated Nov. 22, 1935.

Issue of 1937

C21	20c	The "China Clipper," over the Pacific Feb. 15	20.00	2.50
C22	50c	carmine (C21)	20.00	5.75

C14

C15

C18

C20

C21

their original position. Although some copies no longer have their number because they have been handled so frequently through the years, the foresight of the Philadelphia dealer allows philatelists to keep track of the original sheet.

The fame of the "Inverted Airmail" mounted steadily and copies began to change hands at increasingly higher prices. Princeton University owned a block of four of this philatelic rarity. It was recently sold for over $200,000 and the proceeds went to furthering higher education.

This famous stamp has been the subject of numerous stories and articles and continues to be a popular topic of conversation among philatelists whenever and wherever they gather. The inverted airmail was the object of a police investigation when, in 1955, a block of four, while on exhibition at the American Philatelic Society in Norfolk, Virginia, was stolen. There are even counterfeit "copies" of this famous error in circulation.

The stamp itself marked the inauguration of a new era in America: air mail service. The 24¢ stamp was issued by the United States Post Office for use on the first regularly scheduled air mail service between Washington, Philadelphia and New York in May 1918.

Currently, leading philatelic experts place a value of $80,000 on an ordinary copy and much more for extra fine. Although few can ever hope to own this famous stamp, it has achieved worldwide notoriety among collectors and non-collectors.

C23 C25 C32

C33 C24 C38

C34 C35 C36

C42 C43 C44

C40 C45 C46

C47 C49 C53

C48 C51 C54 C55

Issue of 1938

No.	Description	Date	Unused	Used
C23	6c Eagle Holding Shield, Olive Branch, and Arrows	May 14	.50	.06

Issue of 1939

No.	Description	Date	Unused	Used
C24	30c Transatlantic	May 16	11.00	1.50

Issues of 1941-44, Perf. 11x10½

No.	Description	Date	Unused	Used
C25	6c Twin-motor Transport Plane		.18	.03
C25a	Booklet pane of 3		6.50	*1.00*
C26	8c olive green (C25)		.25	.05
C27	10c violet (C25)		1.25	.20
C28	15c brown carmine (C25)		2.75	.35
C29	20c bright green (C25)		2.25	.30
C30	30c blue (C25)		3.00	.30
C31	50c orange (C25)		21.00	4.00

Singles from No. C25a are imperf. at sides or imperf. at sides and bottom.

Issue of 1946

No.	Description	Date	Unused	Used
C32	5c DC-4 Skymaster	Sep. 25	.15	.04

Issues of 1947, Perf. 10½x11

No.	Description	Date	Unused	Used
C33	5c DC-4 Skymaster	Mar. 26	.15	.04

Perf. 11x10½

No.	Description	Date	Unused	Used
C34	10c Pan American Union Building, Washington, D.C.		.40	.06
C35	15c Statue of Liberty and New York Skyline		.55	.05
C36	25c Plane over San Francisco-Oakland Bay Bridge		1.25	.12

Issues of 1948
Coil Stamp, Perf. 10 Horizontally

No.	Description	Date	Unused	Used
C37	5c carmine (C33)	Jan. 15	1.75	.50

Perf. 11x10½

No.	Description	Date	Unused	Used
C38	5c New York City	Jul. 31	.22	.20

Issued for the 50th anniversary of the consolidation of the five boroughs of New York City.

Issues of 1949
Perf. 10½x11

No.	Description	Date	Unused	Used
C39	6c carmine (C33)	Jan. 18	.18	.03
C39a	Booklet pane of 6		13.50	*5.00*

Perf. 11x10½

No.	Description	Date	Unused	Used
C40	6c Alexandria 200th Anniv.	May 11	.18	.10

Issued for the 200th anniversary of the founding of Alexandria, Virginia.

Coil Stamp, Perf. 10 Horizontally

No.	Description	Date	Unused	Used
C41	6c carmine (C33)	Aug. 25	4.25	.05

Univerdal Postal Union Issue
Perf. 11x10½

No.	Description	Date	Unused	Used
C42	10c Post Office Department Bldg.		.55	.30
C43	15c Globe and Doves Carrying Messages		.70	.40
C44	25c Boeing Stratocruiser and Globe		1.10	.75

The Universal Postal Union was established in 1874.

No.	Description	Date	Unused	Used
C45	6c Wright Brothers	Dec. 17	.16	.10

Issued for the 46th anniversary of the first flight of the Wright brothers, December 17, 1903.

Issue of 1952

No.	Description	Date	Unused	Used
C46	80c Diamond Head, Honolulu, Hawaii	Mar. 26	8.50	1.20

Issue of 1953

No.	Description	Date	Unused	Used
C47	6c Powered Flight	May 29	.16	.10

Issued for the 50th anniversary of powered flight.

Issue of 1954

No.	Description	Date	Unused	Used
C48	4c Eagle in Flight	Sep. 3	.12	.08

Issue of 1957

No.	Description	Date	Unused	Used
C49	6c Air Force	Aug. 1	.20	.10

Issued for the 50th anniversary of the U.S. Air Force.

BALLOONS AND DIRIGIBLES

Balloons were the first aircraft of man. In 1783 in France, to the amazement of observers, the Montgolfier brothers launched a large paper-lined cloth bag. Filled with hot smoke, it rose 6,000 feet up into the sky. Within the next 50 years, scientists had worked out many of the principles and devices balloonists still use today.

Because early balloons were at the mercy of the winds, they were not considered a practical means of transportation. However, by 1859, the balloon *Jupiter* carried mail from Lafayette to Crawfordsville, Indiana. A balloon traveled 1,897 miles in 1914, and, in 1935, before airplanes could ascend that high, a balloon reached an altitude of 72,000 feet.

Balloons developed into the more sophisticated dirigible with propeller engines and rudders for steering. The *Graf Zeppelin*, which like the balloon was a lighter-than-air craft, flew around the world in 1929. Eight hundred feet long and 135 feet wide at the center, it made ten round trips between the United States and Germany during the 1930's. The building of dirigibles was discontinued after the *Hindenburg* mysteriously burst into flames and within minutes was reduced to a pile of molten metal on May 6, 1937.

See Scott Nos. C13-C15, C18, C54

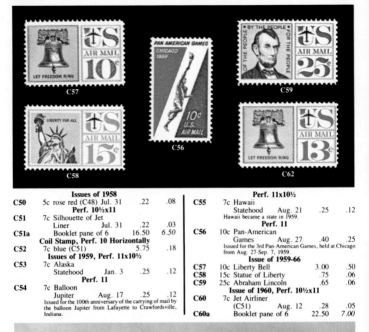

C57 C56 C59 C58 C62

Issues of 1958

C50	5c rose red (C48) Jul. 31	.22	.08
	Perf. 10½x11		
C51	7c Silhouette of Jet Liner Jul. 31	.22	.03
C51a	Booklet pane of 6	16.50	*6.50*
	Coil Stamp, Perf. 10 Horizontally		
C52	7c blue (C51)	5.75	.18
	Issues of 1959, Perf. 11x10½		
C53	7c Alaska Statehood Jan. 3	.25	.12
	Perf. 11		
C54	7c Balloon Jupiter Aug. 17	.25	.12

Issued for the 100th anniversary of the carrying of mail by the balloon Jupiter from Lafayette to Crawfordsville, Indiana.

Perf. 11x10½

C55	7c Hawaii Statehood Aug. 21	.25	.12

Hawaii became a state in 1959.

Perf. 11

C56	10c Pan-American Games Aug. 27	.40	.25

Issued for the 3rd Pan-American Games, held at Chicago from Aug. 27-Sep. 7, 1959.

Issue of 1959-66

C57	10c Liberty Bell	3.00	.50
C58	15c Statue of Liberty	.75	.06
C59	25c Abraham Lincoln	.65	.06
	Issue of 1960, Perf. 10½x11		
C60	7c Jet Airliner (C51) Aug. 12	.28	.05
C60a	Booklet pane of 6	22.50	*7.00*

AMELIA EARHART

Amelia Earhart was five years old when the Wright Brothers made their historic flight at Kitty Hawk. The little girl from Kansas grew up during the years when aviation was young and the idea of flight was wildly glamorous. She was a nurse during World War I and later a social worker. But what she wanted to be was a pilot.

In 1932 Amelia Earhart flew alone across the Atlantic. An instant celebrity, she then crisscrossed the U.S. in a series of highly publicized flights. In 1935 she was the first pilot—male or female—to make the long and arduous solo flight from Hawaii to California. One of America's most famous and admired women, Earhart set out in 1937 with a crew of one on a round-the-world flight in a small, two-engine plane. She completed more than two-thirds of the distance. Then, over the waters of the South Pacific, her plane vanished. The world waited for news. No trace of Amelia Earhart was ever found.

See Scott No. C68.

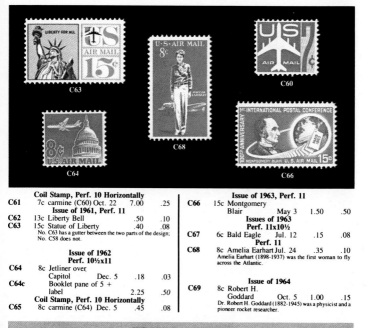

C63 C68 C60 C64 C66

Coil Stamp, Perf. 10 Horizontally

C61	7c carmine (C60)	Oct. 22	7.00	.25

Issue of 1961, Perf. 11

C62	13c Liberty Bell		.50	.10
C63	15c Statue of Liberty		.40	.08

No. C63 has a gutter between the two parts of the design; No. C58 does not.

Issue of 1962
Perf. 10½x11

C64	8c Jetliner over Capitol	Dec. 5	.18	.03
C64c	Booklet pane of 5 + label		2.25	*.50*

Coil Stamp, Perf. 10 Horizontally

C65	8c carmine (C64)	Dec. 5	.45	.08

Issue of 1963, Perf. 11

C66	15c Montgomery Blair	May 3	1.50	.50

Issues of 1963
Perf. 11x10½

C67	6c Bald Eagle	Jul. 12	.15	.08

Perf. 11

C68	8c Amelia Earhart	Jul. 24	.35	.10

Amelia Earhart (1898-1937) was the first woman to fly across the Atlantic.

Issue of 1964

C69	8c Robert H. Goddard	Oct. 5	1.00	.15

Dr. Robert H. Goddard (1882-1945) was a physicist and a pioneer rocket researcher.

WRIGHT BROTHERS
WILBUR 1867-1912
ORVILLE 1871-1948

Although the plane only flew a distance of 120 feet, and remained airborne for just twelve seconds, it made history. The world's first flight in a power-driven, heavier-than-air flying machine marked the beginning of the Air Age. On that cold winter day, December 17, 1903, in Kitty Hawk, North Carolina, the Wright brothers could not possibly foresee the great impact their successful flight would have on civilization.

The Wright brothers made three additional flights that historic day; the longest lasted 59 seconds and achieved a distance of 852 feet.

The first successful flight was the result of painstaking years of hard work and experimentation. Wind tunnel tests, on more than 200 wing models were required before they found one that met their specifications. Additional experiments with gliders solved many of their problems with balance in flight. In 1902, they began to plan the construction of a powered craft. They had to build their own lightweight four-cylinder engine and the propeller for their revolutionary machine. It is said that the Wrights had such great confidence in their new machine that they displayed no surprise when it actually flew.

ORVILLE WILBUR

See Scott Nos. C45, C91-C92

C70 C67 C69 C71 C74 C72 C78 C76 C79 C75 C77 C80 C85 C84 C86 C87 C88 C89 C90 CE2

Issues of 1967

C70	8c Alaska Purchase	Mar. 30	.75	.12

Issued for the 100th anniversary of the Alaska Purchase, this stamp shows a Tlingit totem from southern Alaska.

C71	20c "Columbia Jays" by Audubon	Apr. 26	1.10	.15

See note after No. 1241.

Issues of 1968, Perf. 11x10½

C72	10c 50-Star Runway	Jan. 5	.25	.03
C72b	Booklet pane of 8		2.25	*.75*
C72c	Booklet pane of 5 + label		2.50	*.75*

Coil Stamp, Perf. 10 Vertically

C73	10c carmine (C72)		.50	.04

The $1 Air Lift stamp is listed as No. 1341.

Air Mail Service Issue
Perf. 11

C74	10c Curtiss Jenny	May 15	.75	.10

Issued for the 50th anniversary of regularly scheduled U.S. air mail service.

C75	20c U.S.A. and Jet	Nov. 22	.85	.06

Issue of 1969

C76	10c Moon Landing	Sep. 9	.25	.10

Issues of 1971-73
Perf. 10½x11, 11x10½

C77	9c Plane	May 15, 1971	.18	.06
C78	11c Silhouette of Jet	May 7, 1971	.22	.03
C78a	Booklet pane of 4 + 2 labels		1.50	*.40*
C79	13c Winged Airmail Envelope	Nov. 16, 1973	.25	.10
C79a	Booklet pane of 5 + label	Dec. 27, 1973	1.35	*.70*

Perf. 11

C80	17c Statue of Liberty	Jul. 13, 1971	.40	.15

Perf. 11x10½

C81	21c red, blue and black (C75)	May 21, 1971	.42	.21

Coil Stamps, Perf. 10 Vertically

C82	11c Silhouette of Jet	May 7, 1971	.27	.06
C83	13c red (C79)	Dec. 27, 1973	.30	.10

Issues of 1972, Perf. 11

C84	11c City of Refuge	May 3	.30	.11

The City of Refuge National Park, 180 acres on island of Hawaii, preserves Polynesian temples, royal tombs.

Perf. 11x10½

C85	11c Skiing and Olympic Rings	Aug. 17	.25	.11

Issued in honor of the 1972 Olympic Games.

Issue of 1973

C86	11c De Forest Audions	Jul. 10	.30	.11

Issued to note the progress of electronics from Marconi to the space age.

Issues of 1974, Perf. 11

C87	18c Statue of Liberty	Jan. 11	.45	.18
C88	26c Mt. Rushmore National Memorial	Jan. 2	.60	.26

Issue of 1976

C89	25c Plane & Globes	Jan. 2	.50	.25
C90	31c Plane, Globes & Flag	Jan. 2	.62	.30

Issues of 1978
Wright Brothers Issue, Sept. 23

C91	31c Orville & Wilbur Wright	.62	.30
C92	31c Orville & Wilbur Wright	.62	.30
C92a	Pair	1.25	.65

75th anniversary of first powered flight.

C92a

C94a

C96a

C97

Issues of 1979
Octave Chanute Issue, March 29

C93	21c Octave Chanute	.42	.20
C94	21c Octave Chanute	.42	.20
C94a	Pair	.85	—

Octave Chanute (1832-1910), civil engineer and aviation pioneer.

Wiley Post Issue, Nov. 20

C95	25c Wiley Post	.50	.25
C96	25c Wiley Post	.50	.25
C96a	Pair	1.00	—

Wiley Post (1900-1935), aviation pioneer

Olympic Games Issue

C97	31c High Jump	.62	.30

22nd Olympic Games, Moscow, July 19-Aug. 3, 1980.

Air Post Special Delivery Stamps

To provide for the payment of both the postage and the special delivery with one stamp.

Issue of 1934, Perf. 11

CE1	16c dark blue (CE2)	.80	.70

For imperforate variety, see No. 771.

Issue of 1936

CE2	16c Great Seal of United States	.50	.18

E1 E3 E4 E6 E7 E12 E13 E14 E15 E17 E18 E20 E21 E22 E23

Special Delivery Stamps
When affixed to any letter or mailable article, ordinarily secure separate and after hours delivery.

Unwmkd.

Issue of 1885, Perf. 12

E1	10c Messenger Running	175.00	22.50

Issue of 1888

E2	10c blue (E3)	175.00	6.50

Issue of 1893

E3	10c Messenger Running	100.00	10.00

Issue of 1894, Line under "Ten Cents"

E4	10c Messenger Running	400.00	15.00

Issue of 1895
Wmkd. (191)

E5	10c blue (E4)	75.00	2.50

Issue of 1902

E6	10c Messenger on Bicycle	45.00	2.50

Issue of 1908

E7	10c Mercury Helmet and Olive Branch	50.00	20.00

Issue of 1911
Wmkd. (190)

E8	10c ultramarine (E6)	55.00	3.00

Issue of 1914, Perf. 10

E9	10c ultramarine (E6)	150.00	4.00

Unwmkd.
Issue of 1916

E10	10c ultramarine (E6)	250.00	15.00

Issue of 1917, Perf. 11

E11	10c ultramarine (E6)	12.00	.18

Issue of 1922

E12	10c Postman and Motorcycle	25.00	.10

Issue of 1925

E13	15c Postman and Motorcycle	15.00	.30
E14	20c Post Office Truck	3.00	1.00

Issue of 1927, Perf. 11x10½

E15	10c Postman and Motorcycle	.60	.04

Issue of 1931

E16	15c orange (E12)	.65	.08

Issue of 1944

E17	13c Postman and Motorcycle	.50	.06
E18	17c Postman and Motorcycle	5.00	1.35

Issue of 1951

E19	20c black (E14)	1.50	.12

Issue of 1954-57

E20	20c Delivery of Letter	.70	.08
E21	30c Delivery of Letter	1.00	.04

Issue of 1969-71, Perf. 11

E22	45c Arrows	2.25	.12
E23	60c Arrows	1.20	.12

REGISTRATION AND CERTIFIED MAIL STAMPS POSTAGE DUE STAMPS

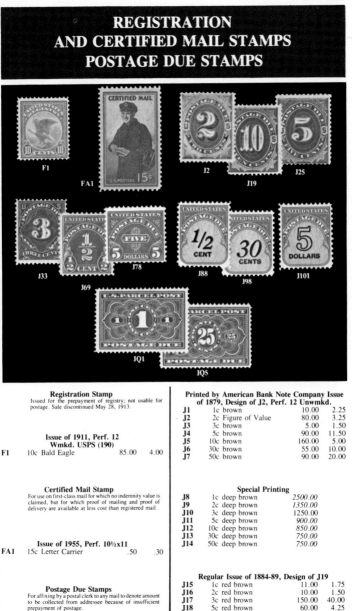

Registration Stamp

Issued for the prepayment of registry; not usable for postage. Sale discontinued May 28, 1913.

Issue of 1911, Perf. 12 Wmkd. USPS (190)

F1	10c Bald Eagle	85.00	4.00

Certified Mail Stamp

For use on first-class mail for which no indemnity value is claimed, but for which proof of mailing and proof of delivery are available at less cost than registered mail.

Issue of 1955, Perf. 10½x11

FA1	15c Letter Carrier	.50	.30

Postage Due Stamps

For affixing by a postal clerk to any mail to denote amount to be collected from addressee because of insufficient prepayment of postage.

Printed by American Bank Note Company Issue of 1879, Design of J2, Perf. 12 Unwmkd.

J1	1c brown	10.00	2.25
J2	2c Figure of Value	80.00	3.25
J3	3c brown	5.00	1.50
J4	5c brown	90.00	11.50
J5	10c brown	160.00	5.00
J6	30c brown	55.00	10.00
J7	50c brown	90.00	20.00

Special Printing

J8	1c deep brown	*2500.00*
J9	2c deep brown	*1350.00*
J10	3c deep brown	1250.00
J11	5c deep brown	*900.00*
J12	10c deep brown	*850.00*
J13	30c deep brown	*750.00*
J14	50c deep brown	*750.00*

Regular Issue of 1884-89, Design of J19

J15	1c red brown	11.00	1.75
J16	2c red brown	10.00	1.50
J17	3c red brown	150.00	40.00
J18	5c red brown	60.00	4.25

J19	10c Figure of Value	50.00	2.50
J20	30c red brown	45.00	12.00
J21	50c red brown	450.00	70.00

Issue of 1891-93, Design of J25

J22	1c bright claret	2.50	.50
J23	2c bright claret	3.00	.45
J24	3c bright claret	4.00	2.25
J25	5c Figure of Value	7.50	2.25
J26	10c bright claret	15.00	4.00
J27	30c bright claret	100.00	40.00
J28	50c bright claret	110.00	47.50

Printed by the Bureau of Engraving and Printing
Issue of 1894, Design of J33, Perf. 12

J29	1c vermilion	175.00	30.00
J30	2c vermilion	55.00	15.00
J31	1c deep claret	5.50	2.00
J32	2c deep claret	4.50	1.00
J33	3c Figure of Value	17.50	10.00
J34	5c deep claret	25.00	11.00
J35	10c deep rose	15.00	6.00
J36	30c deep claret	60.00	22.50
J37	50c	150.00	55.00

Issue of 1895, Design of J33, Wmkd. (191)

J38	1c deep claret	1.50	.20
J39	2c deep claret	1.25	.12
J40	3c deep claret	6.00	1.00
J41	5c deep claret	6.00	.50
J42	10c deep claret	7.00	1.00
J43	30c deep claret	100.00	12.00
J44	50c deep claret	25.00	12.00

Issue of 1910-12 Design of J33, Wmkd. (190)

J45	1c deep claret	5.50	2.00
J46	2c deep claret	4.50	.15
J47	3c deep claret	110.00	10.00
J48	5c deep claret	15.00	2.00
J49	10c deep claret	17.50	4.50
J50	50c deep claret	250.00	42.50

Issue of 1914-15, Design of J33, Perf. 10

J52	1c carmine lake	15.00	6.00
J53	2c carmine lake	5.00	.15
J54	3c carmine lake	125.00	8.50
J55	5c carmine lake	5.00	1.00
J56	10c carmine lake	10.00	.60
J57	30c carmine lake	45.00	12.00
J58	50c carmine lake	*1750.00*	200.00

Issue of 1916, Design of J33, Unwmkd.

J59	1c rose	400.00	100.00
J60	2c rose	20.00	1.25

Issue of 1917, Design of J33, Perf. 11

J61	1c carmine rose	.50	.05
J62	2c carmine rose	.50	.04
J63	3c carmine rose	2.00	.08
J64	5c carmine	2.00	.08
J65	10c carmine rose	2.50	.20
J66	30c carmine rose	10.00	.20
J67	50c carmine rose	12.50	.08

Issue of 1925, Design of J33

J68	½c dull red	.25	.06

Issue of 1930-31, Design of J69

J69	½c Figure of Value	1.50	.18
J70	1c carmine	1.00	.10
J71	2c carmine	2.00	.10
J72	3c carmine	7.50	.40
J73	5c carmine	6.00	.50
J74	10c carmine	7.50	.30
J75	30c carmine	30.00	.50
J76	50c carmine	35.00	.12

Design of J78

J77	$1 carmine	12.00	.12
J78	$5 "FIVE" on $	20.00	.18

Issue of 1931-56, Design of J69
Perf. 11x10½

J79	½c dull carmine	.50	.08
J80	1c dull carmine	.08	.03
J81	2c dull carmine	.10	.03
J82	3c dull carmine	.15	.03
J83	5c dull carmine	.20	.03
J84	10c dull carmine	.60	.03
J85	30c dull carmine	3.25	.08
J86	50c dull carmine	4.25	.06

Perf. 10½x11

J87	$1 scarlet, same design as J78	15.00	.20

Issue of 1959, Perf. 11x10½
Design of J88 and J98

J88	½c Figure of Value	.60	.30
J89	1c carmine rose	.04	.04
J90	2c carmine rose	.06	.05
J91	3c carmine rose	.07	.04
J92	4c carmine rose	.08	.04
J93	5c carmine rose	.10	.04
J94	6c carmine rose	.12	.05
J95	7c carmine rose	.14	.05
J96	8c carmine rose	.16	.05
J97	10c carmine rose	.20	.04
J98	30c Figure of Value	.70	.05
J99	50c carmine rose	1.10	.06

Design of J101

J100	$1 carmine rose	2.00	.06
J101	$5 Outline Figure of Value	8.00	.15

Design of J88

J102	11c carmine rose	.22	.04
J103	13c carmine rose	.26	.04

Parcel Post Postage Due Stamps

For affixing by a postal clerk to any parcel post package to denote the amount to be collected from the addresee because of insufficient prepayment of postage.

Beginning July 1, 1913, these stamps were valid for use as regular postage due stamps.

Issue of 1912
Design of JQ1 and JQ5
Perf. 12

JQ1	1c Figure of Value	6.00	2.00
JQ2	2c dark green	60.00	15.00
JQ3	5c dark green	6.50	2.50
JQ4	10c dark green	100.00	32.50
JQ5	25c Figure of Value	40.00	2.00

OFFICIAL POSTAGE STAMPS

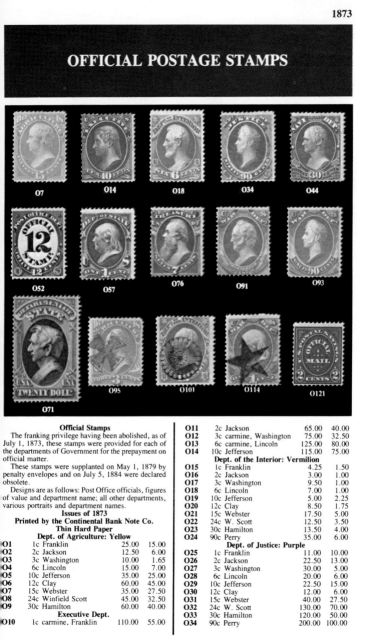

O7 O14 O18 O34 O44 O52 O57 O76 O91 O93 O71 O95 O101 O114 O121

Official Stamps

The franking privilege having been abolished, as of July 1, 1873, these stamps were provided for each of the departments of Government for the prepayment on official matter.

These stamps were supplanted on May 1, 1879 by penalty envelopes and on July 5, 1884 were declared obsolete.

Designs are as follows: Post Office officials, figures of value and department name; all other departments, various portraits and department names.

Issues of 1873
Printed by the Continental Bank Note Co.
Thin Hard Paper

	Dept. of Agriculture: Yellow		
O1	1c Franklin	25.00	15.00
O2	2c Jackson	12.50	6.00
O3	3c Washington	10.00	1.65
O4	6c Lincoln	15.00	7.00
O5	10c Jefferson	35.00	25.00
O6	12c Clay	60.00	45.00
O7	15c Webster	35.00	27.50
O8	24c Winfield Scott	45.00	32.50
O9	30c Hamilton	60.00	40.00
	Executive Dept.		
O10	1c carmine, Franklin	110.00	55.00
O11	2c Jackson	65.00	40.00
O12	3c carmine, Washington	75.00	32.50
O13	6c carmine, Lincoln	125.00	80.00
O14	10c Jefferson	115.00	75.00
	Dept. of the Interior: Vermilion		
O15	1c Franklin	4.25	1.50
O16	2c Jackson	3.00	1.00
O17	3c Washington	9.50	1.00
O18	6c Lincoln	7.00	1.00
O19	10c Jefferson	5.00	2.25
O20	12c Clay	8.50	1.75
O21	15c Webster	17.50	5.00
O22	24c W. Scott	12.50	3.50
O23	30c Hamilton	13.50	4.00
O24	90c Perry	35.00	6.00
	Dept. of Justice: Purple		
O25	1c Franklin	11.00	10.00
O26	2c Jackson	22.50	13.00
O27	3c Washington	30.00	5.00
O28	6c Lincoln	20.00	6.00
O29	10c Jefferson	22.50	15.00
O30	12c Clay	12.00	6.00
O31	15c Webster	40.00	27.50
O32	24c W. Scott	130.00	70.00
O33	30c Hamilton	120.00	50.00
O34	90c Perry	200.00	100.00

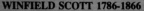

WINFIELD SCOTT 1786-1866

General Winfield Scott is remembered for his patriotic devotion to his country and for his uprightness and moral principles. As an officer in the U.S. Army for over fifty years, he served his country in three wars.

Scott gave up his law studies in 1808 in order to join the Army. As a young lieutenant colonel in the War of 1812, he led a successful attack on Fort George on the Canada-U.S. border. He became a brigadier general in March of 1814 and in the same year he fought at the Battle of Lundy's Lane, showing outstanding heroism by fighting while badly wounded and after his horse was shot from under him. For this, Scott was decorated by Congress and by his native state of Virginia.

Scott was an expert tactician and in 1825 he prepared the first complete Army manual on military tactics. He demonstrated his outstanding leadership in the Mexican War in 1847, where his successful campaigns and capture of Mexico City led to the U.S. victory in the war. In politics, Scott was not so successful, however. In his only run for the presidency he was beaten by Franklin Pierce in 1852.

Although he was a native Virginian, Scott refused to follow his state into the Confederacy, but instead went to Washington to become invaluable to President Lincoln as his military adviser in the early days of the Civil War.

"Old Fuss and Feathers," as Scott was fondly known by his soldiers, retired from military service in 1861.

See Scott Nos. 142, 153, 175, 200, 786

		Navy Dept.: Ultramarine		
O35	1c	Franklin	12.50	6.00
O36	2c	Jackson	9.00	5.00
O37	3c	Washington	10.00	2.25
O38	6c	Lincoln	6.50	3.25
O39	7c	Stanton	70.00	30.00
O40	10c	Jefferson	11.50	6.50
O41	12c	Clay	16.50	5.00
O42	15c	Webster	32.50	13.00
O43	24c	W. Scott	32.50	20.00
O44	30c	Hamilton	25.00	9.00
O45	90c	Perry	120.00	50.00
		Post Office Dept.: Black		
O47	1c	Figure of Value	3.75	2.00
O48	2c	Figure of Value	3.25	1.65
O49	3c	Figure of Value	1.00	.50
O50	6c	Figure of Value	3.00	1.20
O51	10c	Figure of Value	15.00	10.00
O52	12c	Figure of Value	7.00	2.00
O53	15c	Figure of Value	8.00	4.25
O54	24c	Figure of Value	11.50	4.00
O55	30c	Figure of Value	11.00	4.00
O56	90c	Figure of Value	15.00	5.00
		Dept. of State		
O57	1c	dark green Franklin	12.50	6.50
O58	2c	dark green Jackson	32.50	15.00
O59	3c	bright green Washington	9.00	5.00
O60	6c	bright green Lincoln	7.00	5.00
O61	7c	dark green Stanton	21.00	10.00
O62	10c	dark green Jefferson	12.50	8.50
O63	12c	dark green Clay	27.50	20.00
O64	15c	dark green Webster	16.00	10.00
O65	24c	dark green W. Scott	67.50	50.00
O66	30c	Hamilton	52.50	30.00
O67	90c	dark green Perry	135.00	70.00
O68	$2	green and black Seward	250.00	135.00
O69	$5	green and black Seward	2000.00	1200.00
O70	$10	green and black Seward	1150.00	800.00
O71	$20	Seward	1000.00	650.00
		Treasury Dept.: Brown		
O72	1c	Franklin	5.00	1.10
O73	2c	Jackson	7.00	1.10
O74	3c	Washington	3.25	.50
O75	6c	Lincoln	7.00	.50
O76	7c	Stanton	11.00	7.00
O77	10c	Jefferson	11.00	1.50
O78	12c	Clay	11.00	.75
O79	15c	Webster	12.50	1.50
O80	24c	W. Scott	65.00	25.00
O81	30c	Hamilton	20.00	1.50
O82	90c	Perry	20.00	1.25
		War Dept.: Rose		
O83	1c	Franklin	22.50	1.25
O84	2c	Jackson	22.50	2.50
O85	3c	Washington	20.00	.65
O86	6c	Lincoln	75.00	1.10
O87	7c	Stanton	16.50	11.00
O88	10c	Jefferson	5.00	1.50
O89	12c	Clay	18.50	1.00

OLIVER HAZARD PERRY

1785-1819

The great courage and seamanship demonstrated by Admiral Perry at the Battle of Lake Erie during the War of 1812 made him a national hero. On September 10, 1813, from his headquarters on the Ohio shore, Perry led his fleet of nine small ships into battle against the British. The flagship of the fleet, the *Lawrence*, commanded by Perry, bore the motto "Don't give up the ship." The crew of the *Lawrence* suffered heavy casualties and finally the ship itself was disabled. Perry transferred by rowboat to a sister ship, the *Niagara*, and through his able command the *Niagara* prevented the British from capturing the *Lawrence*. By sailing along the British line and firing broadsides, the Americans forced the enemy ships to surrender.

With control of Lake Erie once again in U.S. hands, Perry sent his famous message to General William Henry Harrison, the military commander of the West: "We have met the enemy and they are ours . . ." Perry's victory enabled American troops, under General Harrison, to cross the lake and capture a large portion of Upper Canada.

See Scott Nos. 144, 155, 166, 177, 191, 202, 218, 229, 261, 261A, 276, 276A, O24, O34, O45, O67, O82, O93, O113

O90	15c Webster	2.25	.65
O91	24c W. Scott	3.25	1.10
O92	30c Hamilton	3.00	.90
O93	90c Perry	10.00	6.00

Issues of 1879
Printed by the American Bank Note Co.
Soft, Porous Paper
Dept. of Agriculture: Yellow

O94	1c Franklin, issued without gum	750.00	
O95	3c Washington	75.00	12.50

Dept. of the Interior: Vermilion

O96	1c Franklin	45.00	30.00
O97	2c Jackson	.75	.55
O98	3c Washington	.60	.35
O99	6c Lincoln	.75	.55
O100	10c Jefferson	11.00	10.00
O101	12c Clay	20.00	15.00
O102	15c Webster	47.50	35.00
O103	24c W. Scott	700.00	

Dept. of Justice: Bluish Purple

O106	3c Washington	15.00	10.00
O107	6c Lincoln	45.00	35.00

Post Office Dept.: Black

O108	3c Figure of Value	2.00	.90

Treasury Dept.: Brown

O109	3c Washington	6.50	2.00
O110	6c Lincoln	15.00	10.00
O111	10c Jefferson	25.00	6.00
O112	30c Hamilton	400.00	100.00
O113	90c Perry	400.00	100.00

War Dept.: Rose Red

O114	1c Franklin	.45	.45
O115	2c Jackson	.70	.65
O116	3c Washington	.55	.35
O117	6c Lincoln	.45	.40
O118	10c Jefferson	5.00	5.00
O119	12c Clay	3.50	1.00
O120	30c Hamilton	15.00	15.00

Official Postal Savings Mail
Perf. 12

These stamps were used to prepay postage on official correspondence of the Postal Savings Division of the Post Office Department.
Discontinued Sept. 23, 1914

Issues of 1911
Wmkd.
(191)

O121	2c Official Postal Savings	5.00	.60
O122	50c Official Postal Savings	55.00	20.00
O123	$1 Official Postal Savings	35.00	6.50

Wmkd.
(190)

O124	1c Official Postal Savings	2.00	.50
O125	2c Official Postal Savings	12.50	2.25
O126	10c Official Postal Savings	5.00	.60

NEWSPAPER STAMPS
PARCEL POST STAMPS

NEWSPAPERS, PARCEL POST AND SPECIAL HANDLING

Some types of mail required special kinds of postage. Newspaper stamps were first issued in 1865 for prepayment of postage on bulk shipments of newspapers. Because many of these stamps were not circulated, used copies are quite rare and very valuable. Newspaper issues include the highest denomination ($100) and the largest size of postage stamp printed by the United States. Discontinued in 1898, and no longer valid for postage, copies were sold to collectors for $5 a set—the only time the post office has ever offered reduced prices.

In 1912 the Post Office Department prepared a set of 12 parcel post stamps and five parcel post postage due stamps for exclusive use on parcel post. The 20¢ issue, depicting a biplane, was the first postage stamp in the world to picture an airplane. The following year regular postage stamps and parcel post stamps were made interchangeable and further printing of these distinctive issues was discontinued.

The Postal Service Act of February 28, 1925 authorized a 25¢ special handling stamp that would provide 4th class mail the same kind of handling first class mail received.

PR1 PR2 PR3

PR15

PR18

PR24

PR25

PR26

Newspaper Stamps

Perf. 12
Issues of 1865
Printed by the National Bank Note Co.
Thin, Hard Paper, No Gum, Unwmkd.
Colored Borders

PR1	5c Washington	80.00	
PR2	10c Franklin	35.00	
PR3	25c Lincoln	25.00	

White Border, Yellowish Paper

PR4	5c light blue (PR1)	16.50	15.00

Reprints of 1875
Printed by the Continental Bank Note Co.
Hard, White Paper, No Gum

PR5	5c dull blue (PR1), white border	30.00	
PR6	10c dark bluish green, (PR2), colored border	20.00	
PR7	25c dark carmine (PR3), colored border	35.00	

Issue of 1880
Printed by the American Bank Note Co.
Soft, Porous Paper, White Border

PR8	5c dark blue (PR1)	60.00	

Issue of 1875
Printed by the Continental Bank Note Co.
Thin, Hard Paper

PR9-PR15; "Statue of Freedom" (PR15)

PR9	2c black	3.00	2.50
PR10	3c black	5.00	3.50
PR11	4c black	4.00	3.25
PR12	6c black	5.50	5.00
PR13	8c black	8.50	5.50
PR14	9c black	15.00	10.00
PR15	10c Statue of Freedom	8.00	4.00

PR16-PR23: "Justice" (PR18)

PR16	12c rose	15.00	6.00
PR17	24c rose	22.50	12.50

PR22	84c rose	70.00	40.00
PR23	96c rose	50.00	30.00
PR24	$1.92 Ceres	55.00	25.00
PR25	$3 "Victory"	70.00	35.00
PR26	$6 Clio	140.00	65.00
PR27	$9 Minerva	175.00	70.00
PR28	$12 Vesta	185.00	75.00
PR29	$24 "Peace"	185.00	85.00
PR30	$36 "Commerce"	250.00	125.00
PR31	$48 red brown Hebe (PR78)	325.00	200.00
PR32	$60 violet Indian Maiden (PR79)	325.00	150.00

Special Printing, Hard, White Paper, Without Gum

PR33-PR39: Statue of Freedom (PR15)

PR33	2c gray black	35.00
PR34	3c gray black	35.00
PR35	4c gray black	35.00
PR36	6c gray black	45.00
PR37	8c gray black	50.00
PR38	9c gray black	55.00
PR39	10c gray black	60.00

PR40-PR47: "Justice" (PR18)

PR40	12c pale rose	80.00
PR41	24c pale rose	125.00
PR42	36c pale rose	150.00
PR43	48c pale rose	200.00
PR44	60c pale rose	275.00
PR45	72c pale rose	350.00
PR46	84c pale rose	375.00
PR47	96c pale rose	450.00
PR48	$1.92 dark brown Ceres (PR24)	*1250.00*
PR49	$3 vermilion "Victory" (PR25)	*2000.00*
PR50	$6 ultra. Clio (PR26)	*2750.00*
PR51	$9 yel. Minerva (PR27)	—
PR52	$12 bl. grn. Vesta (PR28)	—
PR53	$24 dark gray violet "Peace" (PR29)	—
PR54	$36 brown rose "Commerce" (PR30)	—
PR55	$48 red brown Hebe (PR78)	—
PR56	$60 violet Indian Maiden (PR79)	—

All values of this issue Nos. PR33 to PR56 exist imperforate but were not regularly issued.

Issue of 1879
Printed by the American Bank Note Co.
Soft, Porous Paper

PR57-PR62: Statue of Freedom (PR15)

PR57	2c black	1.75	1.50
PR58	3c black	2.25	1.75
PR59	4c black	2.25	2.00
PR60	6c black	5.25	5.00
PR61	8c black	5.25	5.00
PR62	10c black	5.00	3.75

PR63-PR70: "Justice" (PR18)

PR63	12c red	16.00	10.00
PR64	24c red	16.00	8.50
PR65	36c red	65.00	37.50
PR66	48c red	45.00	25.00
PR67	60c red	35.00	25.00
PR68	72c red	85.00	50.00
PR69	84c red	62.50	42.50
PR70	96c red	45.00	30.00
PR71	$1.92 pale brown Ceres (PR24)	35.00	25.00
PR72	$3 red vermilion "Victory" (PR25)	35.00	25.00
PR73	$6 blue Clio (PR26)	60.00	35.00
PR74	$9 org. Minerva (PR27)	37.50	20.00
PR75	$12 yellow green Vesta (PR28)	55.00	30.00
PR76	$24 dark violet "Peace" (PR29)	77.50	40.00
PR77	$36 Indian red, "Commerce" (PR30)	100.00	50.00
PR78	$48 Hebe	125.00	60.00
PR79	$60 Indian Maiden	140.00	60.00

All values of the 1879 issue except Nos. PR63 to PR66 and PR68 to PR70 exist imperforate but were not regularly issued.

Issue of 1883
Special Printing

PR80	2c intense black Statue of Freedom (PR15)	85.00

Regular Issue of 1885

PR81	1c black Statue of Freedom (PR15)	1.50	1.10

PR82-PR89: "Justice" (PR18)

PR82	12c carmine	6.00	3.50
PR83	24c carmine	7.00	5.00
PR84	36c carmine	10.00	6.00
PR85	48c carmine	15.00	10.00
PR86	60c carmine	22.00	14.00
PR87	72c carmine	30.00	17.50
PR88	84c carmine	55.00	32.50
PR89	96c carmine	37.50	25.00

All values of the 1885 issue exist imperforate but were not regularly issued.

Issue of 1894
Printed by the Bureau of Engraving and Printing
Soft Wove Paper

PR90-PR94: Statue of Freedom (PR90)

PR90	1c Statue of Freedom	8.50
PR91	2c intense black	8.50
PR92	4c intense black	10.00
PR93	6c intense black	400.00
PR94	10c intense black	16.00

PR95-PR99: "Justice" (PR18)

PR95	12c pink	100.00
PR96	24c pink	85.00
PR97	36c pink	*600.00*
PR98	60c pink	*600.00*
PR99	96c pink	*1000.00*
PR100	$3 scarlet "Victory" (PR25)	*1750.00*
PR101	$6 pale blue Clio (PR26)	*2500.00*

Issue of 1895, Unwmkd.
PR102-PR105: Statue of Freedom (PR116)

PR102	1c	black	6.00	1.35
PR103	2c	black	7.00	1.75
PR104	5c	black	8.50	2.25
PR105	10c	black	20.00	7.50
PR106	25c	carmine "Justice" (PR118)	25.00	8.50
PR107	50c	carmine "Justice" (PR119)	60.00	25.00
PR108	$2	scarlet "Victory" (PR120)	70.00	10.00
PR109	$5	ultra Clio (PR121)	100.00	40.00
PR110	$10	green Vesta (PR122)	90.00	40.00
PR111	$20	slate "Peace" (PR123)	175.00	85.00
PR112	$50	dull rose "Commerce" (PR124)	175.00	75.00
PR113	$100	purple Indian Maiden (PR125)	200.00	100.00

Issue of 1895-97
Wmkd.
(191)
Yellowish Gum

PR114-PR117: Statue of Freedom (PR116)

PR114	1c	black	.80	.70
PR115	2c	black	.75	.60
PR116	5c	black	1.60	1.40
PR117	10c	black	.85	.65
PR118	25c	"Justice"	1.50	1.20
PR119	50c	"Justice"	1.75	1.10
PR120	$2	"Victory"	3.50	3.00
PR121	$5	Clio	7.50	7.50
PR122	$10	Vesta	5.50	6.00
PR123	$20	"Peace"	5.50	8.50
PR124	$50	"Commerce"	6.50	8.50
PR125	$100	Indian Maiden	8.50	10.00

In 1899 the Government sold 26,989 sets of these stamps, but, as the stock of the high values was not sufficient to make up the required number, the $5, $10, $20, $50 and $100 were reprinted. These are virtually indistinguishable from earlier printings.

Q1 Q2 Q3 Q4 Q5 Q6 Q7 Q8 Q9 Q10 Q11 Q12 QE1 QE2 QE3 QE4

PARCEL POST STAMPS

Issued for the prepayment of postage on parcel post packages only.
Beginning July 1, 1913, these stamps were valid for all postal purposes.

Issue of 1912-13, Perf. 12

Q1	1c	Post Office Clerk	2.50	.55
Q2	2c	City Carrier	3.00	.40
Q3	3c	Railway Postal Clerk	6.00	3.00
Q4	4c	Rural Carrier	15.00	1.10
Q5	5c	Mail Train	12.50	.60
Q6	10c	Steamship and Mail Tender	22.50	1.25
Q7	15c	Automobile Service	30.00	6.50
Q8	20c	Airplane Carrying Mail	75.00	10.00
Q9	25c	Manufacturing	25.00	3.50
Q10	50c	Dairying	100.00	25.00
Q11	75c	Harvesting	30.00	20.00
Q12	$1	Fruit Growing	200.00	12.00

SPECIAL HANDLING STAMPS

For use on parcel post packages to secure the same expeditious handling accorded to first class mail matter.

Issue of 1925-29, Design of QE3, Perf. 11

QE1	10c	Special Handling	1.25	.75
QE2	15c	Special Handling	1.50	.75
QE3	20c	Special Handling	1.75	1.25
QE4	25c	Special Handling	22.50	5.75

CONFEDERATE STATES OF AMERICA

JEFFERSON DAVIS (1808-1889)

He might have become President of the United States. But when his home state of Mississippi followed South Carolina in seceding from the Union, Jefferson Davis renounced the nation he might have led.

Born in 1808, Davis graduated from West Point and served on the frontier during the Mexican War. He saved the day at Buena Vista and came home a hero. He was elected first to the House of Representatives, then to the U.S. Senate. He was named Secretary of War in 1853, earning an unsurpassed reputation in office. As America's foremost Southerner, Davis was nominated for the U.S. Presidency at the 1860 Democratic convention. Then came secession.

Davis was unanimously chosen president of the newly formed Confederate States. It was not an office he wanted, but no other man was so well qualified for the post. Despite tremendous odds, he managed to keep the South together for four long years.

Following the Confederacy's collapse, he was imprisoned on treason charges for two years but was released after the amnesty proclamation of 1868. But both sides later acknowledged that no other Southerner could have done as well as Jefferson Davis.

See Confederate States Scott Nos. 1, 6, 9, 10, 11, 12

General issues, All Imperf.

Issue of 1861: Lithographed, Unwatermarked

1	5c Jefferson Davis	65.00	25.00
2	10c Thomas Jefferson	70.00	35.00
	Issue of 1862		
3	2c Andrew Jackson	250.00	300.00
4	5c blue J. Davis (6)	35.00	25.00
5	10c Thomas Jefferson	425.00	225.00
	Typographed		
6	5c J. Davis (London print)	3.50	4.50
7	5c blue (6) (local print)	7.00	7.50
	Issues of 1863, Engraved		
8	2c Andrew Jackson	15.00	*75.00*
	Thick or Thin Paper		
9	10c Jefferson Davis	225.00	150.00
10	10c blue (9), (with rectangular frame)	1350.00	700.00
	Prices of No. 10 are for copies showing parts of lines on at least two sides of frame.		
11	10c Jefferson Davis, die A	3.50	4.00
12	10c blue J. Davis, die B (11)	4.00	4.50
	Dies A and B differ in that B has an extra line outside its corner ornaments.		
13	20c George Washington	12.00	*65.00*
	Issue of 1862, Typographed		
14	1c John C. Calhoun (This stamp was never put in use.)	40.00	

MAJOR U.S. PHILATELIC PUBLICATIONS AND SOCIETIES

Catalogues

First Day Cover Catalogue (U.S.-U.N.) Washington Press, Maplewood, New Jersey 07040.

Minkus New World Wide Stamp Catalogue 1978-79 New York,

Scott Standard Postage Stamp Catalogue, 1980, New York

Magazines and Newspapers

Canadian Stamp News
1567 Sedlescomb Drive,
Mississauga, Ont. L4X 1M5

Linn's Stamp News
Box 29
Sidney, Ohio 45365

Mekeel's Weekly Stamp News
Box 1660
Portland, Maine 04104

Minkus Stamp Journal
116 West 32nd Street
New York, New York 10001

Scott's Monthly Stamp Journal
3 East 57th St.
New York, New York 10022

Stamps
153 Waverly Place
New York, New York 10014

Stamp Collector
Box 10
Albany, Oregon 97321

Philatelic Literature

Brookman, Lester G. *The 19th Century Postage Stamps of the United States.* (3 volumes). New York, 1968.

Chase, Carroll C. *The 3c Stamps of the United States.* Springfield, Massachusetts, 1942.

Johl, Max G. *The United States Commemorative Stamps of the Twentieth Century.* New York, 1947.

Linn's World Stamp Almanac, Sidney, Ohio, 1978.

Mueller, Barbara R. *United States Postage Stamps.* Princeton, 1958.

Patrick, Douglas and Mary. *The Musson Stamp Dictionary.* Toronto, 1972.

D. G. Phillips Publ. Co. *The American Stampless Cover Catalog.* No. Miami, Fla., 1978.

Scheele, Carl H. *A Short History of the Mail Service.* Washington, D.C. 1970.

Scott's New Handbook for Philatelists. New York, 1967.

Thorp, Prescott H. *Stamped Envelopes and Wrappers of the United States.* Netcong, N.J., 1954.

United Postal Stationery Society. *United States Postal Card Catalog.* Albany, Oregon, 1975.

United States Postal Service. *United States Postage Stamps.* Washington, D.C., 1970 as revised.

Many of the books listed above, while not currently in print, are available at public libraries.

Philatelic Societies

American First Day Cover Society
Box 23
Elberton, N.J. 07740

American Philatelic Society
Box 800
State College, Pennsylvania 16801

American Stamp Dealers' Association
840 Willis Ave.
Albertson, NY 11507

American Topical Association
3308-W North 50th St.
Milwaukee, Wisconsin 53216

Bureau Issues Association
19 Maple Street
Arlington, Massachusetts 02174

Society of Philatelic Americans
Box 9041
Wilmington, Delaware 19809

For the name of the stamp dealer nearest you, consult your Yellow Pages under the listing "Stamps" or "Stamps for Collectors."

SPECIALTY COLLECTING

Specialty collecting hasn't anything to do with the subject matter of the stamps you collect. It refers strictly to the form in which you collect them.

Most new collectors start off by buying new issues. After a time, many specialize in one of the following areas. Consider it yourself.

BLOCKS OF FOUR

A block of four, with two mint stamps above and two below, can come from anywhere on a sheet of stamps. That makes it the most plentiful form of block and the easiest to come by.

That's not to say that collecting plate blocks, ZIP blocks, copyright blocks or booklet panes presents any insurmountable difficulty. On the contrary, these collector's items are extremely easy to acquire. All are available at face value, within the sales policies of the United States Postal Service at most local post offices at the time they're issued.

BOOKLET PANES

Stamp booklets were first issued in 1898. On the average, two new booklet panes are issued per year. Most philatelists collect entire panes or entire booklets, just as they came from the post office. The first combination pane, consisting of one 9¢ Freedom to Assemble stamp and seven 13¢ Flag stamps was issued March 11, 1977.

The entire booklet program was fully automated following the rate change on May 29, 1978. Due to the automation of the booklet program, individual panes are no longer available. The entire booklet must be purchased to get one specific pane.

COVERS

Covers (or envelopes) canceled on a postage stamp's first day of issue are collected with tremendous enthusiasm by a large philatelic audience. You could further refine this specialty by collecting covers that relate to subject matter of particular interest to you—anniversaries, dedications, flight, space, whatever. On pages 207 and 208 you'll find a more detailed discussion of first day covers.

PLATE BLOCKS

Plates used in the production of postage stamps carry serial numbers for identification. The number appears at all four corners of a sheet of stamps. After the sheet is cut into four panes for distribution, the plate number indicates which portion of the original sheet the pane occupied and identifies the plate that printed it. The plate number blocks may include as few as four stamps where a single number appears, or as many as twenty where multiple floating numbers and other markings such as Mr. ZIP and notice of copyright appear. Plate block collecting is one of the oldest areas of philatelic interest in the United States. Since some plates wear out faster than others, plate block collectors seek most avidly those blocks with scarce serial numbers produced by the least durable plates.

"COPYRIGHT" BLOCKS

The U.S. Postal Service now copyrights all new stamp designs. The copyright "C" in a circle, followed by "United States Postal Service" or "USPS" and the year, appears in the selvage of each pane. The first copyright inscription appeared January 6, 1978, in the margin of sheets of the Carl Sandburg stamp. Most philatelists collect copyrights in blocks of four.

"MR. ZIP" BLOCKS

The Zoning Improvement Plan—better known as ZIP Code—was devised to increase postal efficiency. And it succeeded dramatically. This geographically keyed number system enables postal clerks to speed the routing of an ever-increasing volume of mail. A "Mr. ZIP" cartoon and slogan were inaugurated January 10, 1964, with the Sam Houston issue. The cartoon and slogan with adjoining block of four immediately became a popular collectible.

SOUVENIR CARDS

In 1938 and 1939, the Post Office Department Philatelic Truck toured the country distributing souvenir sheets that pictured the White House. They were the forerunners of the modern souvenir card. Now issued at philatelic exhibitions in which the government participates, souvenir cards bear reproductions of U.S. stamps which are made postally invalid by enlargement or by alteration to remove denomination, country name and reference to postage. Souvenir card collecting, a new wrinkle in philately, is attracting enthusiasts by the thousands.

THINK IT OVER!

As you can see, there's more to stamp collecting than just collecting stamps. Would you enjoy collecting blocks, plain or fancy? Booklet panes, covers or souvenir cards? Stamp collecting is such a personal hobby that no two collections are ever quite the same. Perhaps a form of specialty collecting is right for you. Think it over.

NO POSTAGE
NECESSARY
IF MAILED
IN THE
UNITED STATES

BUSINESS REPLY CARD

FIRST CLASS PERMIT NO. 73026 WASHINGTON, DC

POSTAGE WILL BE PAID BY ADDRESSEE

Philatelic Sales Branch
United States Postal Service
Washington, DC 20265

Please send me the up-to-date list of all stamps and stamp products, Philatelic Order List, Form 3300.

____

Name

____

Address

__________________________ __________ __________

City State ZIP Code

PLATE NUMBER BLOCK, SHEET AND FIRST DAY COVER PRICES

The Plate Block and First Day Cover prices have been derived from the 1979 edition of Scott's Specialized Catalogue of United States Stamps. The sheet prices were developed by the Editorial Staff of Scott Publishing Co. exclusively for this edition of Stamps & Stories. Sheet prices start with the 1957 Flag Issue (Scott 1094), the beginning of contemporary multicolor and multiple plate number printing.
All plate blocks are blocks of four, unless otherwise indicated in parenthesis.

Scott No.	Pl. Blk.	FDC
	1893	
230	(6) 400.00	*1,200.00*
231	(6) 375.00	*850.00*
232	(6) 675.00	*3,000.00*
233	(6) 850.00	*3,000.00*
234	(6) 1,000.00	*3,250.00*
235	(6) 900.00	*4,000.00*
236	(6) 675.00	
237	(6) 1,500.00	*4,000.00*
238	(6) *2,500.00*	
239	(6) *3,500.00*	
240	(6) *5,000.00*	
241	(6) *11,500.00*	
242	(6) *12,500.00*	*7,500.00*
243	(6) *20,000.00*	
244	(6) *35,000.00*	
245	(6) *28,500.00*	
	1894 With Triangles Unwatermarked	
246	(6) 165.00	
247	(6) 300.00	
248	(6) 95.00	
249	(6) 525.00	
250	(6) 150.00	
251	(6) 1,150.00	
252	(6) 500.00	
253	(6) 450.00	
254	(6) 450.00	
255	(6) 325.00	
256	(6) 575.00	
257	(6) 425.00	
258	(6) 1,000.00	
259	(6) 1,750.00	
260	(6) 2,350.00	
261	(6) *6,000.00*	
262	(6) *9,500.00*	
263	(6) *12,000.00*	
	1895 With Triangles Watermarked	
264	(6) 75.00	
265	(6) 200.00	
266	(6) 250.00	
267	(6) 55.00	
268	(6) 300.00	
269	(6) 300.00	
270	(6) 275.00	
271	(6) 475.00	
272	(6) 225.00	
273	(6) 400.00	
274	(6) 1,400.00	
275	(6) 2,100.00	
276	(6) *5,000.00*	
276A	(6) *8,000.00*	
277	(6) *7,500.00*	
278	(6) *20,000.00*	
	1898	
279	(6) 90.00	
279B	(6) 80.00	
280	(6) 250.00	
281	(6) 275.00	
282	(6) 375.00	
282C	(6) 1,100.00	
283	(6) 800.00	
284	(6) 1,000.00	
	1898	
285	200.00	*2,500.00*
286	200.00	*2,300.00*

Scott No.	Pl. Blk.	FDC
287	1,100.00	
288	900.00	*3,250.00*
289	1,300.00	*5,000.00*
290	1,500.00	
291	*7,250.00*	*6,000.00*
292	*19,000.00*	
293	*37,500.00*	
	1901	
294	75.00	*1,650.00*
295	75.00	*1,500.00*
296	350.00	*2,500.00*
297	350.00	*2,600.00*
298	450.00	
299	625.00	
	1902-03	
300	(6) 100.00	*2,000.00*
301	(6) 115.00	*2,000.00*
302	(6) 425.00	*2,000.00*
303	(6) 425.00	*2,000.00*
304	(6) 425.00	*2,200.00*
305	(6) 550.00	*2,200.00*
306	(6) 350.00	*2,400.00*
307	(6) 600.00	*2,400.00*
308	(6) 325.00	
309	(6) 2,000.00	
310	(6) 4,250.00	
311	(6) *8,000.00*	
312	(6) *12,000.00*	
313	(6) *35,000.00*	
	1906-08 Imperforate	
314	(6) 185.00	
315	(6) 3,250.00	
	1903	
319	(6) 75.00	
	1906 Imperforate	
320	(6) 165.00	
	1904	
323	165.00	*1,750.00*
324	185.00	*1,750.00*
325	500.00	*2,100.00*
326	650.00	*2,250.00*
327	1,850.00	*4,500.00*
	1907	
328	(6) 225.00	—
329	(6) 300.00	
330	(6) 2,000.00	
	1908-09	
331	(6) 50.00	*750.00*
332	(6) 35.00	*750.00*
333	(6) 160.00	*1,200.00*
334	(6) 185.00	
335	(6) 275.00	*1,000.00*
336	(6) 400.00	*1,000.00*
337	(6) 250.00	*1,000.00*
338	(6) 450.00	*1,200.00*
339	(6) 300.00	*1,200.00*
340	(6) 400.00	*1,200.00*
341	(6) *3,000.00*	
342	(6) *4,500.00*	
	1908-09 Imperforate	
343	(6) 55.00	*750.00*
344	(6) 95.00	
345	(6) 150.00	
346	(6) 285.00	
347	(6) 500.00	
	1909 Bluish Paper	
357	(6) 700.00	
358	(6) 675.00	
359	(6) *8,500.00*	
361	(6) —	
362	(6) *6,500.00*	
363	(6) —	
364	(6) *7,000.00*	
365	(6) *12,500.00*	
366	(6) *5,750.00*	
	1909	
367	(6) 160.00	*325.00*
368	(6) 325.00	*1,450.00*
369	(6) *2,750.00*	
370	(6) 275.00	*1,450.00*
371	(6) 375.00	*1,750.00*
372	(6) 265.00	*700.00*
373	(6) 400.00	*1,500.00*
	1910-11 Watermarked Single-Line USPS	
374	(6) 52.50	
375	(6) 45.00	
376	(6) 100.00	
377	(6) 140.00	
378	(6) 165.00	
379	(6) 325.00	
380	(6) 575.00	
381	(6) 525.00	
382	(6) 950.00	
	1911 Imperforate	
383	(6) 50.00	
384	(6) 135.00	
	1913	
397	(6) 165.00	*2,150.00*
398	(6) 285.00	*2,350.00*
399	(6) 2,000.00	*2,850.00*
400	(6) 2,500.00	*4,250.00*
400A	(6) *8,000.00*	
	1914-15 Perforated 10	
401	(6) 285.00	*1,000.00*
402	(6) 1,200.00	
403	(6) 3,500.00	*2,400.00*
404	(6) *10,000.00*	
	1912-14 Perforated 12	
405	(6) 40.00	*1,000.00*
406	(6) 50.00	*750.00*
407	(6) 600.00	*900.00*
	1914 Imperforate	
408	(6) 15.00	*650.00*
409	(6) 30.00	*650.00*
	1912-14 Perforated 12	
414	(6) 250.00	*1,110.00*
415	(6) 325.00	*800.00*
416	(6) 250.00	*1,100.00*
417	(6) 185.00	*1,000.00*
418	(6) 400.00	*1,200.00*
419	(6) 900.00	*1,000.00*
420	(6) 825.00	*1,100.00*
421	(6) 3,750.00	

Scott No.		Pl. Blk.	FDC
		1914	
		Watermarked	
		Double-Line USPS	
422	(6)	2,100.00	
423	(6)	5,000.00	
		1914-15	
		Perforated 10	
424	(6)	35.00	
425	(6)	21.00	
426	(6)	70.00	
427	(6)	275.00	
428	(6)	185.00	
429	(6)	200.00	
430	(6)	450.00	
431	(6)	225.00	
432	(6)	275.00	
433	(6)	210.00	
434	(6)	110.00	
435	(6)	120.00	
437	(6)	500.00	
438	(6)	1,300.00	
439	(6)	2,250.00	
440	(6)	4,500.00	
		1915	
460	(6)	5,500.00	
		1915	
		Perforated 11	
461	(6)	550.00	
		1916-17	
		Perforated 10	
		Unwatermarked	
462	(6)	65.00	
463	(6)	45.00	
464	(6)	625.00	
465	(6)	400.00	
466	(6)	525.00	
468	(6)	525.00	
469	(6)	575.00	
470	(6)	350.00	
471	(6)	300.00	
472	(6)	750.00	
473	(6)	140.00	
474	(6)	250.00	
475	(6)	1,100.00	
476	(6)	1,600.00	
476A	(6)	——	
477	(6)	9,500.00	
478	(6)	5,500.00	
479	(6)	3,000.00	
480	(6)	2,250.00	
		1916-17	
		Imperforate	
481	(6)	10.00	*700.00*
482	(6)	22.50	
483	(6)	120.00	
484	(6)	85.00	
		1917-19	
		Perforated 11	
498	(6)	10.00	*750.00*
499	(6)	9.00	*750.00*
500	(6)	1,750.00	
501	(6)	85.00	*750.00*
502	(6)	110.00	
503	(6)	100.00	*800.00*
504	(6)	80.00	*800.00*
506	(6)	95.00	*800.00*
507	(6)	200.00	*850.00*
508	(6)	120.00	*850.00*
509	(6)	160.00	*900.00*
510	(6)	140.00	*900.00*
511	(6)	80.00	*900.00*
512	(6)	67.50	*900.00*
513	(6)	100.00	
514	(6)	350.00	*900.00*
515	(6)	350.00	*1,000.00*
516	(6)	375.00	*1,100.00*
517	(6)	675.00	*1,300.00*
518	(6)	625.00	*2,500.00*
		1917	
		Type of 1908-09	
		Perforated 11	
519	(6)	1,000.00	
		1918	
523	(8)	*11,000.00*	
524	(8)	4,000.00	*4,500.00*
		1918-20	
		Offset Printing	
525	(6)	22.50	*500.00*
526	(6)	150.00	*450.00*
527	(6)	90.00	
528	(6)	37.50	
528A	(6)	185.00	
528B	(6)	110.00	
529	(6)	30.00	*350.00*
530	(6)	10.00	*350.00*
		1918-20	
		Offset, Imperforate	
531	(6)	75.00	*450.00*
532	(6)	250.00	*550.00*
533	(6)	1,300.00	
534	(6)	75.00	
534A	(6)	275.00	
534B	(6)	9,500.00	
535	(6)	60.00	*500.00*
		1919	
		Offset, Perf. 12½	
536	(6)	115.00	*400.00*
		1919	
537	(6)	160.00	*475.00*
		1919	
		Perforated 11X10	
538		65.00	*450.00*
539		*8,500.00*	
540		70.00	
541		350.00	*550.00*
		1920	
		Perforated 10X11	
542	(6)	75.00	*300.00*
		1921	
		Rotary	
543		12.00	
545		625.00	
546		400.00	
		1920	
547	(8)	4,000.00	
548	(6)	75.00	*425.00*
549	(6)	100.00	*350.00*
550	(6)	750.00	
		1922-25	
		Perforated 11	
551	(6)	4.00	10.00
552	(6)	20.00	22.50
553	(6)	32.50	25.00
554	(6)	21.00	30.00
555	(6)	175.00	25.00
556	(6)	170.00	30.00

Scott No.		Pl. Blk.	FDC
557	(6)	200.00	65.00
558	(6)	325.00	125.00
559	(6)	50.00	65.00
560	(6)	600.00	60.00
561	(6)	125.00	60.00
562	(6)	225.00	70.00
563	(6)	32.50	350.00
564	(6)	55.00	85.00
565	(6)	45.00	200.00
566	(6)	175.00	200.00
567	(6)	210.00	200.00
568	(6)	185.00	400.00
569	(6)	300.00	500.00
570	(6)	700.00	550.00
571	(6)	300.00	2,000.00
572	(6)	1,100.00	*6,000.00*
573	(8)	5,250.00	*9,500.00*
		1923-25 Imperforate	
575	(6)	80.00	
576	(6)	30.00	25.00
577	(6)	35.00	
		1923-26 Perforated 11X10	
578		475.00	
579		275.00	
		Perforated 10	
581		50.00	1,500.00
582		30.00	35.00
583		20.00	
584		185.00	35.00
585		125.00	35.00
586		120.00	35.00
587		45.00	45.00
588		70.00	40.00
589		210.00	45.00
590		35.00	55.00
591		450.00	60.00
		Perforated 11 Rotary	
595		900.00	
		1923	
610	(6)	27.50	40.00
611	(6)	130.00	65.00
612	(6)	350.00	80.00
		1924	
614	(6)	55.00	30.00
615	(6)	90.00	45.00
616	(6)	425.00	70.00
		1925	
617	(6)	50.00	25.00
618	(6)	110.00	35.00
619	(6)	350.00	55.00
620	(6)	325.00	25.00
621	(6)	1,000.00	55.00
		1925-26	
622	(6)	115.00	22.50
623	(6)	125.00	22.50
		1926	
627	(6)	65.00	15.00
628	(6)	110.00	22.50
629	(6)	65.00	5.00
631		65.00	10.00
		1926-34 Perforated 11X10½	
632		2.00	35.00

Scott No.		Pl. Blk.	FDC
633		65.00	35.00
634		.75	37.50
634A		1,500.00	
635		3.00	
636		80.00	35.00
637		10.00	35.00
638		10.00	40.00
639		11.00	45.00
640		12.00	40.00
641		12.50	55.00
642		16.50	55.00
		1927	
643	(6)	55.00	4.50
644	(6)	65.00	15.00
		1928	
645	(6)	42.50	5.00
646		50.00	10.00
647		185.00	12.00
648		400.00	25.00
649		17.50	6.50
650	(6)	77.50	9.00
		1929	
651	(6)	13.50	4.00
653		1.00	13.00
654	(6)	45.00	6.00
655		75.00	45.00
657	(6)	40.00	2.50
		"Kansas"	
658		21.00	15.00
659		32.50	15.00
660		35.00	15.00
661		135.00	20.00
662		130.00	20.00
663		110.00	22.50
664		225.00	27.50
665		267.50	30.00
666		525.00	55.00
667		115.00	45.00
668		235.00	45.00
		"Nebraska"	
669		21.00	15.00
670		30.00	15.00
671		22.50	15.00
672		120.00	20.00
673		135.00	22.50
674		125.00	22.50
675		250.00	35.00
676		150.00	35.00
677		225.00	35.00
678		260.00	40.00
679		575.00	45.00
		1929	
680	(6)	42.50	2.25
681	(6)	35.00	2.25
		1930	
682	(6)	42.50	2.25
683	(6)	70.00	2.75
684	(6)	1.50	2.25
685	(6)	6.50	3.50
688	(6)	55.00	3.50
689	(6)	35.00	3.50
		1931	
690	(6)	23.50	2.25
		Regular Issue	
692		16.50	55.00
693		21.00	55.00
694		15.00	55.00
695		20.00	55.00

Scott No.		Pl. Blk.	FDC
696		42.50	55.00
697		23.50	200.00
698		57.50	75.00
699		40.00	210.00
700		90.00	150.00
701		250.00	200.00
		1931	
702		2.50	1.50
703		4.00	1.75
		1932	
704		4.50	2.25
705		5.50	3.00
706		25.00	3.00
707		1.75	3.00
708		22.50	3.50
709		7.00	3.50
710		25.00	4.00
711		90.00	4.50
712		8.50	4.50
713		115.00	4.50
714		75.00	5.00
715		190.00	6.50
		1932	
716	(6)	18.50	2.50
717		11.50	1.75
718		27.50	2.50
719		37.50	5.00
720		1.50	4.50
724	(6)	20.00	2.00
725	(6)	35.00	2.00
		1933	
726	(6)	22.50	2.00
727		7.00	1.00
728		3.00	1.00
729		4.00	1.00
732		2.00	1.75
733	(6)	27.50	2.50
734	(6)	55.00	3.75
		1934	
736	(6)	13.50	.70
737	(6)	1.50	1.00
738	(6)	6.75	1.25
739	(6)	6.50	.75
740	(6)	1.50	1.00
741	(6)	2.00	1.00
742	(6)	3.50	1.00
743	(6)	10.00	1.20
744	(6)	12.00	1.35
745	(6)	24.00	1.75
746	(6)	14.50	1.75
747	(6)	28.50	1.75
748	(6)	22.50	2.00
749	(6)	47.50	3.50
		1935	
752	(6)	16.50	6.00
753	(6)	22.50	7.00
754	(6)	35.00	7.00
755	(6)	35.00	7.00
756	(6)	6.00	7.00
757	(6)	8.00	7.00
758	(6)	20.00	7.00
759	(6)	27.50	7.50
760	(6)	32.50	7.50
761	(6)	40.00	7.50
762	(6)	40.00	8.00
763	(6)	50.00	8.00
764	(6)	50.00	9.00
765	(6)	65.00	10.00
771	(6)	125.00	17.50
772		2.00	2.50
773		2.00	2.50
774	(6)	2.25	3.00
775		2.00	2.50
		1936	
776		1.75	2.50
777		2.00	2.50
782		1.85	2.50
783		1.75	2.50
784		.75	2.00
		1936-37	
785		1.00	2.00
786		1.10	2.00
787		1.50	2.00
788		12.00	2.00
789		12.50	2.50
790		1.00	2.00
791		1.10	2.00
792		1.50	2.00
793		12.00	2.00
794		12.50	2.50
		1937	
795		1.75	2.00
796	(6)	10.00	2.25
798		1.65	2.00
799		1.75	2.00
800		1.75	2.25
801		1.75	2.25
802		1.75	2.25
		1938	
803		.50	.80
804		.30	1.10
805		.35	1.00
806		.35	1.00
807		.50	1.00
808		1.75	1.00
809		2.00	1.60
810		1.50	1.60
811		1.50	1.60
812		2.00	1.60
813		2.25	1.60
814		2.25	1.60
815		2.25	1.70
816		3.00	1.70
817		4.25	1.70
818		4.75	1.70
819		5.00	2.25
820		3.25	2.25
821		6.50	2.50
822		6.00	2.50
823		8.75	2.75
824		8.00	2.75
825		4.25	2.75
826		8.50	3.00
827		10.00	3.75
828		12.50	3.75
829		6.50	3.75
830		35.00	4.00
831		52.50	7.50
832		80.00	32.50
833		225.00	45.00
834		850.00	80.00
		1938	
835		6.00	2.75
836	(6)	6.00	2.75
837		16.50	2.75
838		8.00	2.75

Scott No.		Pl. Blk.	FDC
		1939	
852		1.65	2.50
853		2.00	2.50
854	(6)	4.25	3.00
855		3.50	4.00
856	(6)	6.00	2.50
857		1.65	2.50
858		1.65	2.50
		1940	
859		1.25	1.10
860		1.50	1.10
861		2.00	1.25
862		14.00	2.00
863		60.00	4.50
864		1.85	1.10
865		2.25	1.10
866		4.00	1.10
867		14.00	2.00
868		60.00	5.50
869		1.85	1.10
870		1.65	1.10
871		3.75	1.10
872		15.00	2.00
873		40.00	4.50
874		1.50	1.10
875		1.30	1.10
876		1.75	1.10
877		11.00	2.00
878		37.50	4.50
879		1.50	1.10
880		1.50	1.10
881		2.00	1.25
882		15.00	2.00
883		57.50	4.50
884		1.10	1.10
885		1.10	1.10
886		1.25	1.10
887		12.50	2.00
888		47.50	4.50
889		3.00	1.10
890		1.75	1.10
891		2.75	1.10
892		25.00	2.00
893		120.00	9.00
		1940	
894		7.50	2.00
895		7.00	2.00
896		3.25	2.00
897		3.25	2.00
898		3.25	2.00
899		.60	1.50
900		.70	1.50
901		1.40	1.50
902		7.75	2.00
		1941-43	
903		2.75	1.75
904		1.75	1.75
905		.60	1.50
906		18.50	3.00
907		.50	1.25
908		1.00	1.10
909		13.50	4.00
910		4.75	3.00
911		3.50	2.75
912		3.50	2.75
913		3.50	2.75
914		3.50	2.00
915		3.50	2.00
916		20.00	2.00

Scott No.	Pl. Blk.	FDC
917	9.00	2.00
918	7.50	2.00
919	7.50	2.00
920	8.00	2.00
921	12.50	3.25
	1944	
922	1.75	1.25
923	2.00	1.25
924	1.60	1.25
925	2.75	1.25
926	1.50	1.25
	1945	
927	.80	1.25
928	.70	1.00
929	.60	1.00
	1945-46	
930	.30	.90
931	.50	.90
932	.55	.90
933	.65	.90
	1945	
934	.50	.70
935	.50	.70
936	.50	.70
937	.55	.70
938	.50	.70
	1946	
939	.50	.70
940	.55	.70
941	.50	.70
942	.50	.70
943	.50	.70
944	.50	.70
	1947	
945	.50	.70
946	.50	.70
947	.50	.70
949	.50	.70
950	.50	.70
951	.50	.70
952	.50	.70
	1948	
953	.50	.60
954	.50	.60
955	.50	.60
956	.50	.60
957	.50	.60
958	.85	.70
959	.50	.60
960	.60	.60
961	.50	.60
962	.50	.60
963	.50	.60
964	1.00	.60
965	2.50	.60
966	4.25	1.00
967	.60	.60
968	.80	.60
969	.65	.60
970	.65	.60
971	.75	.60
972	.75	.60
973	1.00	.60
974	.65	.60
975	1.00	.60
976	5.25	.60
977	.65	.60
978	.70	.60

Scott No.	Pl. Blk.	FDC
979	.65	.60
980	.75	.60
	1949	
981	.50	.60
982	.50	.60
983	.50	.60
984	.50	.60
985	.50	.60
986	.60	.60
	1950	
987	.50	.60
988	.55	.60
989	.50	.60
990	.50	.60
991	.50	.60
992	.50	.60
993	.50	.60
994	.50	.60
995	.55	.60
996	.50	.60
997	.50	.60
	1951	
998	.50	.60
999	.50	.60
1000	.50	.60
1001	.50	.60
1002	.50	.60
1003	.50	.60
	1952	
1004	.50	.60
1005	.50	.60
1006	.50	.60
1007	.50	.60
1008	.50	.60
1009	.50	.60
1010	.50	.60
1011	.50	.60
1012	.50	.60
1013	.50	.60
1014	.50	.60
1015	.50	.60
1016	.50	.60
	1953-54	
1017	.50	.60
1018	1.00	.60
1019	.55	.60
1020	.50	.60
1021	2.00	.60
1022	.50	.60
1023	.50	.60
1024	.50	.60
1025	.50	.60
1026	.50	.60
1027	.50	.60
1028	.50	.60
1029	.50	.60
	1954-68	
1030	.30	.60
1031	.25	.60
1031A	1.75	.60
1032	7.50	.60
1033	.25	.60
1034	2.00	.60
1035	.40	.60
1036	.50	.60
1037	1.50	.60
1038	.65	.65
1039	1.00	.65

Scott No.	Pl. Blk.	Sheet	FDC
1040	1.00		.70
1041	5.75		.80
1042	1.25		.60
1042A	1.25		.60
1043	1.25		.90
1044	1.35		.90
1044A	1.50		.90
1045	2.50		.90
1046	2.75		1.00
1047	3.25		1.20
1048	7.50		1.30
1049	8.50		1.50
1050	13.50		1.75
1051	16.00		4.50
1052	42.50		8.50
1053	625.00		55.00
	1954		
1060	.50		.60
1061	.50		.60
1062	.60		.60
1063	.50		.60
	1955		
1064	.50		.60
1065	.50		.60
1066	1.75		.60
1067	.50		.60
1068	.50		.60
1069	.50		.60
1070	1.50		.60
1071	.50		.60
1072	.60		.60
	1956		
1073	.50		.60
1074	.50		.60
1076	.50		.60
1077	.65		.60
1078	.65		.60
1079	.65		.60
1080	.50		.60
1081	.50		.60
1082	.50		.60
1083	.50		.60
1084	.50		.60
1085	.50		.60
	1957		
1086	.50		.60
1087	.50		.60
1088	.50		.60
1089	.50		.60
1090	.50		.60
1091	.50		.60
1092	.90		.60
1093	.50		.60
1094	.70	5.50	.60
1095	.70	7.25	.60
1096	1.90	11.50	.65
1097	.50	5.00	.60
1098	.65	5.25	.60
1099	.50	5.00	.60
	1958		
1100	.50	5.00	.60
1104	.50	5.00	.60
1105	.60	7.25	.60
1106	.50	5.00	.60
1107	1.50	8.50	.60
1108	.50	5.00	.60
1109	.50	5.00	.60
1110	.60	7.25	.60

Scott No.	Pl. Blk.	Sheet	FDC
1111	6.00	23.00	.65
1112	.50	5.00	.60
	1958-59		
1113	.40	2.75	.60
1114	.60	5.25	.60
1115	.55	5.25	.60
1116	.65	5.25	.60
	1958		
1117	.60	7.25	.60
1118	4.25	18.50	.65
1119	.50	5.00	.60
1120	.50	5.00	.60
1121	.50	7.00	.60
1122	.60	5.25	.60
1123	.50	5.00	.60
	1959		
1124	.50	5.00	.60
1125	.55	7.25	.60
1126	2.25	15.00	.65
1127	.50	7.00	.60
1128	.85	6.75	.60
1129	1.50	10.75	.60
1130	.50	5.00	.60
1131	.50	5.00	.60
1132	.50	5.00	.60
1133	.65	5.25	.60
1134	.50	5.00	.60
1135	.50	5.00	.60
1136	.60	7.25	.60
1137	2.25	15.00	.65
	1960-61		
1138	.50	7.00	.60
1139	1.00	9.25	.75
1140	1.00	9.25	.75
1141	1.00	9.25	.75
1142	1.00	9.25	.75
1143	1.00	9.25	.75
1144	1.00	9.25	.75
	1960		
1145	.50	5.00	.60
1146	.50	5.00	.60
1147	.60	7.25	.60
1148	2.50	15.50	.65
1149	.50	5.00	.60
1150	.65	5.25	.60
1151	.50	7.00	.60
1152	.50	5.00	.60
1153	.50	5.00	.60
1154	.50	5.00	.60
1155	.50	5.00	.60
1156	.50	5.00	.60
1157	.50	5.00	.60
1158	.50	5.00	.60
1159	.55	7.25	.60
1160	2.00	15.25	.65
1161	.50	7.00	.60
1162	.50	5.00	.60
1163	.50	5.00	.60
1164	.50	5.00	.60
1165	.55	7.25	.60
1166	2.25	15.25	.65
1167	.50	5.00	.60
1168	.55	7.25	.60
1169	2.25	15.25	.65
1170	.50	7.00	.60
1171	.50	7.00	.60
1172	.55	7.25	.60
1173	4.00	30.00	.75

Scott No.	Pl. Blk.	Sheet	FDC
	1961		
1174	.55	7.25	.60
1175	2.25	16.00	.65
1176	.65	5.25	.60
1177	.55	7.25	.60
	1961-65		
1178	1.25	9.50	.60
1179	1.00	8.00	.60
1180	1.00	8.00	.60
1181	1.00	8.00	.60
1182	1.10	9.50	.60
	1961		
1183	.60	5.25	.60
1184	.55	5.25	.60
1185	.55	5.25	.60
1186	.55	5.25	.60
1187	1.20	8.00	.60
1188	.55	5.25	.60
1189	.55	5.25	.60
1190	.70	5.25	.60
	1962		
1191	.55	5.25	.60
1192	1.00	8.25	.60
1193	1.50	11.00	.60
1194	.55	5.25	.60
1195	.55	5.25	.60
1196	.70	5.25	.60
1197	.55	5.25	.60
1198	.55	5.25	.60
1199	.55	5.25	.60
1200	1.00	8.00	.60
1201	.55	5.25	.60
1202	.55	5.25	.60
1203	.70	6.25	.60
1204	5.00	13.00	6.00
1205	.50	10.00	.60
1206	.55	5.25	.60
1207	1.50	8.50	.60
	1962-63		
1208	.55	12.00	.60
1209	.25	5.00	.60
1213	.65	12.00	.60
	1963		
1230	.60	6.00	.60
1231	.60	6.00	.60
1232	.60	6.00	.60
1233	.60	6.00	.60
1234	.60	6.00	.60
1235	.60	6.00	.60
1236	.60	6.00	.60
1237	1.35	10.50	.60
1238	.60	6.00	.60
1239	.60	6.00	.60
1240	.60	12.00	.60
1241	1.25	8.25	.60
	1964		
1242	.60	6.00	.60
1243	1.20	8.25	.60
1244	1.65	9.00	.60
1245	.60	6.00	.60
1246	.60	6.00	.60
1247	.60	6.00	.60
1248	.60	6.00	.60
1249	.60	6.00	.60
1250	.60	6.00	.60
1251	.60	6.00	.60
1252	.60	6.00	.60
1253	.60	6.00	.60

Scott No.		Pl. Blk.	Sheet	FDC
1254-1257		5.00	112.50	.60
1258		.60	6.00	.60
1259		.75	6.25	.60
1260		.75	6.25	.60
		1965		
1261		.75	6.25	.60
1262		.75	6.25	.60
1263		.75	6.25	.60
1264		.75	6.25	.60
1265		.75	6.25	.60
1266		.75	6.25	.60
1267		.75	6.25	.60
1268		.75	6.25	.60
1269		.75	6.25	.60
1270		.75	6.25	.60
1271		1.00	6.50	.60
1272		1.00	6.50	.60
1273		1.25	9.50	.60
1274		13.50	37.50	.75
1275		.75	6.25	.60
1276		.60	12.00	.60
		1965-73		
1278		.20	3.00	.35
1279		20.00	40.00	.35
1280		.30	4.25	.35
1281		.50	6.75	.35
1282		.40	8.00	.35
1283		.50	10.00	.45
1283B		1.00	12.00	.45
1284		.65	12.50	.45
1285		1.25	17.00	.50
1286		1.00	20.00	.60
1286A		1.50	25.00	.50
1287		1.50	26.50	.65
1288		1.50	31.00	.60
1289		2.00	40.00	.80
1290		2.50	50.00	1.00
1291		3.00	60.00	1.20
1292		4.00	80.00	1.60
1293		5.00	100.00	2.50
1294		10.00	200.00	5.00
1295		50.00	1,000.00	45.00
		1966		
1306		1.00	8.00	.60
1307		.90	7.75	.60
1308		.75	6.50	.60
1309		.90	6.50	.60
1310		.90	6.50	.60
1312		.75	6.50	.60
1313		.90	8.00	.60
1314		.75	6.50	.60
1315		1.00	6.75	.60
1316		1.00	6.75	.60
1317		1.00	6.75	.60
1318		1.75	8.75	.60
1319		1.00	6.75	.60
1320		1.00	6.75	.60
1321		.75	12.50	.60
1322		2.75	12.50	.60
		1967		
1323		.90	6.50	.60
1324		.90	6.50	.60
1325		.90	6.50	.60
1326		.90	6.50	.60
1327		.90	6.50	.60
1328		.90	6.50	.60
1329		1.20	6.75	.60
1330		1.00	6.75	.60

Scott No.		Pl. Blk.	Sheet	FDC
1331a		17.50	125.00	5.50
1333		3.00	10.50	.60
1334		3.50	11.00	.60
1335		3.00	11.50	.60
1336		.60	6.25	.60
1337		2.50	10.00	.60
		1968-71		
1338		.60	13.00	.60
1338D	(20)	3.25	13.00	.60
1338F	(20)	3.50	16.50	.60
		1968		
1339		1.00	9.50	.60
1340		1.00	9.50	.60
1341		19.00	192.50	5.00
1342		1.00	9.50	.60
1343		1.00	9.50	.60
1344		1.00	9.50	.60
1345-1354	(20)	22.50	52.50	2.00ea.
1355		1.75	11.50	.60
1356		1.10	10.50	.60
1357		1.10	10.50	.60
1358		1.10	10.50	.60
1359		1.20	10.50	.60
1360		1.65	11.00	.60
1361		2.75	14.00	.60
1362		3.50	17.50	.60
1363	(10)	2.75	10.75	.60
1364		3.50	18.00	.60
		1969		
1365-1368		13.50	110.00	1.50ea.
1369		1.10	10.50	.60
1370		1.35	13.00	.60
1371		3.50	17.00	.60
1372		1.00	10.50	.60
1373		1.00	10.50	.60
1374		1.00	10.50	.60
1375		1.00	10.50	.60
1376-1379		15.00	152.50	1.75ea.
1380		1.35	10.50	.60
1381		1.75	13.25	.60
1382		1.85	13.25	.60
1383		1.00	6.75	.60
1384	(10)	2.25	9.50	.60
1385		1.00	9.50	.60
1386		1.20	6.25	.60
		1970		
1387-1390		3.75	13.50	1.25
1391		1.10	9.50	.60
1392		1.10	9.50	.60
		1970-74		
1393		.60	12.00	.60
1393D		1.35	15.00	.60
1394		1.00	16.50	.60
1396	(12	7.50	30.00	.60
1397		2.35	30.00	.85
1398		2.35	33.50	.65
1399		1.80	36.50	1.00
1400		2.10	42.50	1.00
		1970		
1405		1.00	9.50	.60
1406		1.00	9.50	.60
1407		1.00	9.50	.60
1408		1.00	9.50	.60
1409		1.00	9.50	.60
1410-1413	(10)	9.00	47.50	1.25ea.
1414	(8)	3.00	12.00	1.20
1415-1418	(8)	12.00	60.00	1.20

Scott No.		Pl. Blk.	Sheet	FDC
1419		1.25	9.75	.60
1420		1.25	9.75	.60
1421-1422		7.00	25.00	.60ea.
		1971		
1423		1.00	9.50	.60
1424		1.00	9.50	.60
1425		1.00	9.50	.60
1426	(12)	3.50	11.50	.60
1427-1430		2.25	11.00	1.25ea.
1431		1.65	13.25	.60
1432		7.50	46.50	.75
1433		1.65	12.00	.60
1434a		2.25	16.50	1.00
1436		1.25	9.75	.60
1437		1.25	9.75	.60
1438	(6)	1.85	10.00	.60
1439	(8)	2.10	10.00	.60
1440-1443		2.25	11.50	1.00ea.
1444	(12)	2.50	9.50	.60
1445	(12)	2.50	9.50	.60
		1972		
1446		1.00	9.50	.60
1447		1.50	9.75	.60
1451a		2.50	9.00	.60
1452		1.25	8.75	.60
1453		1.00	6.25	.60
1454		2.50	19.00	.60
1455		1.00	8.50	.60
1456-1459		3.00	17.50	.85ea.
1460	(10)	2.00	7.00	.75
1461	(10)	2.25	8.75	.85
1462	(10)	4.00	16.00	1.00
1463		1.00	9.25	.60
1464-1467		1.25	8.00	1.25ea.
1468	(12)	2.75	9.25	.60
1469	(6)	1.35	9.25	.60
1470		1.00	8.50	.60
1471	(12)	2.75	9.00	.60
1472	(12)	2.75	9.00	.60
1473		1.00	8.50	.60
1474		1.00	6.75	.60
		1973		
1475		1.35	8.50	.60
1476		1.35	10.75	.60
1477		1.35	10.75	.60
1478		1.35	10.75	.60
1479		1.35	10.75	.60
1480-1483		1.35	11.50	1.50ea.
1484	(12)	2.75	6.25	.60
1485	(12)	2.75	6.25	.60
1486	(12)	2.75	6.25	.60
1487	(12)	2.75	6.25	.60
1488		.80	8.25	.60
1489-1498	(10)	2.25	12.00	.90ea.
1499		1.00	5.50	.60
1500		1.25	6.75	.65
1501		1.00	8.50	.65
1502		2.25	16.00	.75
1503	(12)	2.50	5.75	.60
		1973-74		
1504		1.00	8.50	.60
1505		1.00	10.50	.60
1506		1.00	10.50	.60
1507	(12)	2.10	8.25	.60
1508	(12)	2.10	8.25	.60
1509	(20)	4.00	20.00	.60
1510		1.00	20.00	.60
1511	(8)	1.80	20.00	.60

Scott No.		Pl. Blk.	Sheet	FDC
		1974		
1525		1.25	10.50	.60
1526		1.00	10.50	.60
1527	(12)	2.60	8.25	.60
1528	(12)	2.60	10.50	.60
1529		1.00	10.50	.60
1530-1537	(6)	3.40	6.75	.90ea.
1538-1541		1.25	9.75	1.25ea.
1542		1.00	10.50	.60
1543-1546		1.20	10.75	.90ea.
1547		1.00	10.50	.60
1548		1.00	10.50	.60
1549		1.00	10.50	.60
1550	(10)	2.20	10.50	.60
1551	(12)	2.60	10.50	.60
1552	(20)	5.50	12.50	.60
		1975		
1553	(10)	2.20	10.50	.60
1554	(10)	2.20	10.50	.60
1555		1.00	10.50	.60
1556		1.00	10.50	.75
1557		1.00	10.50	.75
1558	(8)	1.80	10.50	.60
1559	(10)	1.75	8.25	.60
1560	(10)	2.20	10.50	.60
1561	(10)	2.20	10.50	.60
1562	(10)	4.00	19.00	.70
1563	(12)	2.60	8.25	.60
1564	(12)	2.60	8.25	.60
1565-1568	(12)	2.60	10.50	.75ea.
1569-1570	(12)	2.60	5.00	.85ea.
1571	(6)	1.40	10.75	.60
1572-1575	(12)	2.60	10.50	.60ea.
1576		1.00	10.50	.60
1577-1578		1.00	8.50	.60ea.
1579	(12)	2.60	10.50	.60
1580	(12)	2.60	10.50	.60
		1975-79		
1581		.15	3.00	.40
1582		.20	4.00	.40
1584		.30	6.00	.40
1585		.40	8.00	.40
1591		.90	18.50	.60
1592		1.00	20.50	.60
1593		1.10	19.50	.60
1596	(12)	3.38	26.50	.60
1597	(6)	2.10	30.50	.65
1599		1.60	32.50	.65
1603		2.40	50.00	.75
1604		2.80	56.50	1.20
1605		2.90	59.00	1.10
1606		3.00	61.00	
1608		5.00	101.00	
1610		10.00	202.50	
1611		20.00	405.00	
1612		50.00	1,010.00	
1619				.60
1622	(20)	5.50	26.50	.65
		1976		
1629-1631	(12)	3.40	13.50	.65ea.
1632		1.30	13.50	.65
1633-1682	(50)	25.00	25.00	1.50ea.
1683		1.30	13.50	.65
1684	(10)	2.90	13.50	.65
1685	(12)	3.40	13.50	.65
1690		1.30	13.50	.65
1691-1694	(20)	5.50	14.00	.65ea.
1695-1698	(12)	3.40	14.00	.65ea.
1699	(12)	3.40	11.00	.65

Scott No.		Pl. Blk.	Sheet	FDC
1700		1.30	9.00	.65
1701	(12)	3.40	13.50	.65
1702	(10)	2.86	13.50	.65
1703	(20)	5.70	13.50	.65
		1977		
1704	(10)	2.90	10.75	.65
1705		1.30	13.50	.65
1706-1709	(10)	3.00	11.00	.65ea.
1710	(12)	3.65	13.50	.65
1711	(12)	3.65	13.50	.65
1712-1715	(12)	3.65	13.50	.65ea.
1716		1.30	11.00	.65
1717-1720	(12)	3.65	13.50	.65ea.
1721		1.30	13.50	.65
1722	(10)	3.10	11.00	.65ea.
1723-1724	(12)	3.65	11.00	.65ea.
1725		1.30	13.50	.65
1726		1.30	13.50	.65
1727		1.30	13.50	.65
1728	(10)	3.10	11.00	.65
1729	(20)	5.70	26.50	.65
1730	(10)	3.10	26.50	.65
		1978		
1731		1.30	13.50	.65
1732		1.30		.65
1733		1.30		.65
1732-1733	(20)	5.75	13.50	
1734		1.30	39.00	.65
1735		1.50	30.00	.65
1744	(12)	3.65	13.50	.65
1745-1748	(12)	3.65	13.00	.65ea.
1749-1752	(12)	3.65	13.00	.65ea.
1753		1.30	13.50	.65
1754		1.30	13.50	.65
1755	(12)	3.65	13.00	.65
1756	(12)	4.20	15.50	.65
1758	(12)	4.20	12.50	.65
1759		1.50	15.50	.65
1760-1763		1.50	15.50	.65ea.
1764-1767	(12)	4.20	12.50	.65ea.
1768	(12)	4.20	30.50	.65
1769	(12)	4.20	30.50	.65
		1979		
1770		1.50	15.00	.65
1771	(12)	4.20	15.50	.65
1772		1.50	15.50	.65
1773		1.50	15.50	.65
1774		1.50	15.50	.65
1775-1778	(10)	3.50	12.50	.65ea.
1779-1782			15.00	.65ea.
1783-1786			15.50	.65ea.
1787		1.50	15.50	.65
1788			15.50	.65
1789			15.50	.65
1790			10.50	.60
1791-1794			15.50	.65ea.
1799			30.50	.65
1800			30.50	.65
1801			15.50	.65
		Air Post		
		1918		
C1	(6)	1,250.00		*9,000.00*
C2	(6)	2,750.00		*9,000.00*
C3		650.00		*10,000.00*
		1923		
C4	(6)	750.00		250.00
C5	(6)	3,500.00		525.00
C6	(6)	4,250.00		625.00
		1926-28		
C7	(6)	87.50		50.00
C8	(6)	90.00		55.00
C9	(6)	210.00		60.00
C10	(6)	250.00		30.00
C11	(6)	75.00		40.00
		1930		
C12	(6)	300.00		12.50
C13	(6)	4,500.00		650.00
C14	(6)	9,500.00		700.00
C15	(6)	13,500.00		1,000.00
		1931-34		
C16		190.00		225.00
C17		67.50		17.50
C18	(6)	1,300.00		110.00
C19		35.00		175.00
		1935-39		
C20	(6)	65.00		12.00
C21	(6)	275.00		15.00
C22	(6)	275.00		17.50
C23		12.50		3.50
C24	(6)	275.00		15.00
		1941-44		
C25		1.00		1.50
C26		1.50		1.50
C27		14.50		2.00
C28		18.50		2.50
C29		17.50		3.25
C30		20.00		4.50
C31		160.00		11.50
		1946-47		
C32		.75		1.00
C33		.75		.75
C34		2.50		1.00
C35		2.85		1.10
C36		6.75		1.50
		1948-49		
C38		20.00		1.10
C39		.85		.75
C40		.95		.75
C42		4.75		.85
C43		3.75		.95
C44		15.00		1.35
C45		.85		.55
		1952-54		
C46		75.00		8.00
C47		.85		.55
C48		6.00		.50
		1957-59		
C49		1.50	10.75	.55
C50		4.00	24.00	.65
C51		1.30	22.50	.65
C53		1.75	13.25	.50
C54		1.75	13.25	.50
C55		1.75	13.25	.50
C56		8.00	26.50	.75
		1959-62		
C57		13.50	152.50	.75
C58		4.75	39.50	.90
C59		4.00	34.00	1.25
C60		1.35	28.00	.55
C62		6.00	29.00	.65
C63		2.25	20.50	.90
C64		1.10	18.50	.60
		1963-64		
C66		14.00	83.00	1.15
C67		4.50	19.00	.50
C68		5.25	21.50	1.10

Scott No.		Pl. Blk.	Sheet	FDC
C69		7.50	54.00	1.20
		1967-69		
C70		10.00	46.00	.55
C71		9.00	60.00	1.25
C72		2.00	26.00	.50
C74		13.50	52.50	.60
C75		6.00	45.00	.90
C76		2.50	10.00	.65
		1971-73		
C77		2.00	19.75	.50
C78		1.35	22.50	.50
C79		1.50	26.50	.55
C80		2.75	21.50	.60
C81		2.50	22.25	.75
C84		2.75	17.00	.50
C85	(10)	3.50	13.75	.50
C86		1.75	16.00	.50
		1974-76		
C87		2.25	23.50	.65
C88		2.85	31.50	.85
C89		2.50	26.00	.85
C90		3.10	32.00	1.10
		1978-79		
C91-C92		3.10	62.50	1.15ea.
C93-C94		2.10	42.50	1.00ea.
C95-C96		2.50	50.50	1.10ea.
C97			31.50	1.15
		Air Post Special Delivery 1934-36		
CE1	(6)	45.00		10.00
CE2		12.50		8.00
		Special Delivery 1885-95		
E1	(8)	*6,500.00*		*6,000.00*
E2	(8)	*6,500.00*		
E3	(8)	*3,750.00*		
E4	(6)	*7,500.00*		
E5	(6)	*2,000.00*		
		1902-17		
E6	(6)	1,350.00		
E7	(6)	700.00		
E8	(6)	*1,650.00*		
E9	(6)	*3,250.00*		
E10	(6)	*4,500.00*		
E11	(6)	225.00		
		1922-25		
E12	(6)	400.00		375.00
E13	(6)	135.00		150.00
E14	(6)	47.50		90.00
		1927-51		
E15		5.00		75.00
E16		5.00		85.00
E17		4.25		7.50
E18		25.00		7.50
E19		6.75		5.00
		1954-57		
E20		4.50		2.50
E21		5.00		2.25
		1969-71		
E22		14.50		4.00
E23		6.00		4.00
		Registration		
F1	(6)	1,100.00		*3,250.00*
		Certified Mail		
FA1		6.25		2.50

Scott No.		Pl. Blk.
		Postage Due 1910-12
J45	(6)	125.00
J46	(6)	100.00
J47	(6)	1,000.00
J48	(6)	225.00
J49	(6)	250.00
J50	(6)	2,750.00
		1914-15
J52	(6)	250.00
J53	(6)	100.00
J54	(6)	1,150.00
J55	(6)	110.00
J56	(6)	150.00
J57	(6)	650.00
J58	(6)	*12,000.00*
		1916
J59	(6)	*3,500.00*
J60	(6)	175.00
		1917-25
J61	(6)	4.75
J62	(6)	6.50
J63	(6)	16.00
J64	(6)	15.00
J65	(6)	17.50
J66	(6)	70.00
J67	(6)	90.00
J68	(6)	2.50
		1930-31 Perforated 11
J69	(6)	12.50
J70	(6)	7.00
J71	(6)	14.00
J72	(6)	60.00
J73	(6)	42.50
J74	(6)	50.00
J75	(6)	210.00
J76	(6)	250.00
J77	(6)	85.00
J78	(6)	185.00
		1931-56 Perforated 11X10½
J79		6.00
J80		1.50
J81		1.50
J82		2.00
J83		2.50
J84		4.00
J85		15.00
J86		20.00
J87		75.00
		1959
J88		65.00
J89		.50
J90		.60
J91		.70
J92		1.25
J93		.75
J94		1.40
J95		1.60
J96		1.75
J97		1.25
J98		5.50
J99		6.50
J100		10.00
J101		40.00
		1978
J102		1.10
J103		1.30

FIRST DAY COVERS

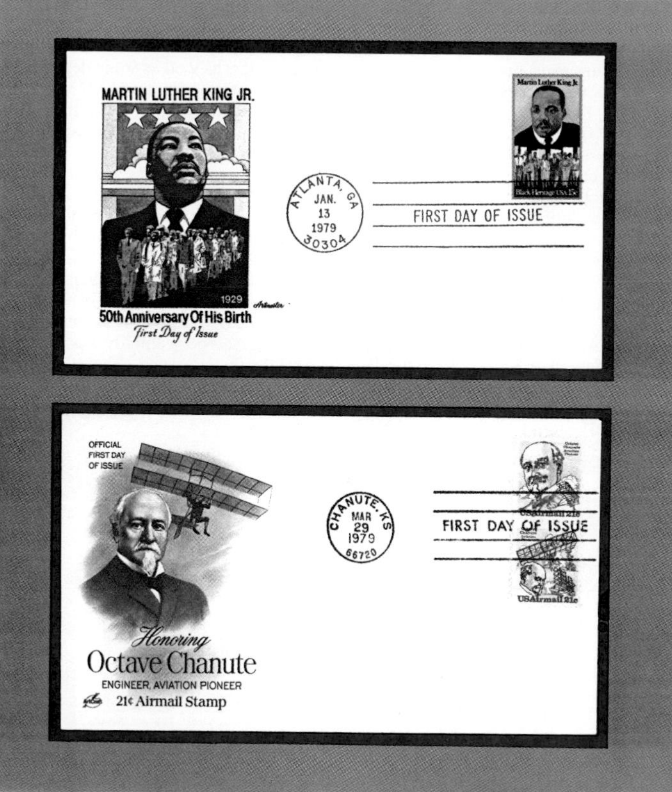

Were you watching TV on August 2, 1971, when astronaut David Scott stood on the surface of the moon and canceled the twin stamps issued to mark a decade of space achievements? It was probably the most widely seen first-day ceremony in the history of philately. But that doesn't mean there isn't plenty of interest in the earthbound ceremonies marking a new stamp's first day of issue.

There's a kind of collectible that, enthusiasts feel, is very nearly as good as owning the very first stamp sold of a new issue. It's called a first-day cover. A first-day cover is an envelope that bears a new stamp canceled on the first-day of issue at the post office designated to conduct the first-day ceremonies.

For each new stamp or postal stationery issue, the Postal Service designates one post office where the item is first placed on sale. Usually it's a post office that is in some way related to the subject the stamp commemorates. Other post offices place the stamp on sale the following day.

You don't have to rely completely on dealers to keep a first-day cover collection current, however. Even if you live thousands of miles away from the first-day post office, you can secure a first-day cover through the Postal Service. Here's how.

Keep your eyes open. The date and place of issue of new stamps are announced by the Postal Service in the press and on post office bulletin board posters.

When the stamps go on sale at your post office, you can buy them and affix them to your envelopes. Your stamped and addressed envelopes (peelable labels are permitted) should be mailed inside another envelope to "First Day Cover," care of the Postmaster of the designated first day city. The Post Office will cancel the envelope and return it to you through the mail. All envelopes must be postmarked no later than 15 days from the date of issuance to qualify for cancellation service.

Or you can send your addressed envelope to the Postmaster and the first day post office will affix the new stamp. You must send payment for the stamps that will be affixed. Payment can be by check or money order, but do not send cash.

The envelope you send can be plain or cacheted. A cacheted envelope carries a special design at the left. The Postal Service doesn't provide cacheted envelopes, but you can buy them from stamp dealers as well as some department stores and stationery stores. If you ever receive a damaged cover in the mail, though, you can send it right back and it will be replaced.

First-day cover service is one way the Postal Service accommodates collectors, and they spare no effort to get the covers in the mail without delay. But sometimes you have to be a little patient. The volume of requests for first-day covers on the average new issue numbers between 400,000 and 600,000—a heavy extra load to handle. And occasionally a post office is completely swamped. The 10¢ Moon Landing Airmail Stamp of 1969, for example, was affixed to 8,700,000 first-day covers.

POSTAL STATIONERY

There are three items in the category of collectibles called postal stationery: (1) embossed stamped envelopes, (2) postal cards and (3) aerogrammes. They're all available at post offices, and the number of Americans who collect them is growing all the time. Let's consider the three items, one by one.

Postal Cards

Plain and simple one-color Government postal cards were first issued May 1, 1873. They stayed plain and simple until 1956, when the first U.S. commemorative postal card came out. Things have been looking up for postal card collectors ever since.

"Visit the USA" was the theme of the first pictorial postal card, issued in 1966. Six years later, a series of five picture postal cards hailed "Tourism Year of the Americas". The backs of the cards featured twenty different U.S. scenic attractions. More recently, a Bicentennial celebration series saluted colonial patriots.

Postal cards are manufactured at the Government Printing Office in Washington D.C. Regular one-color cards can come off the four high-speed rotary web presses at a rate of 250,000 an hour. The Government Printing Office's two-color sheet-fed offset presses produce the two-color air mail and multi-color commemorative cards. Some 800 million postal cards are issued each year by the Postal Service, accounting for approximately 2,500 tons of paper annually.

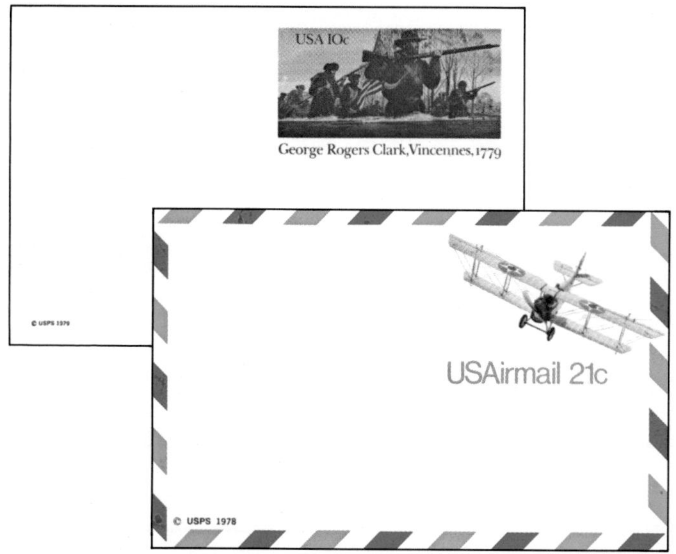

Stamped Envelopes

In the case of stamped envelopes, the stamp is embossed and printed right onto the envelope rather than separately affixed. In recent years the number of commemorative stamped envelopes issued by the United States has been on the increase. And so have the number of collectors.

Multicolor was recently introduced to embossed stamped envelopes with the issuance of the envelopes honoring Golf and Tennis. More of these colorful envelopes are promised for the future.

Stamped envelopes are manufactured for the Postal Service under private contract, awarded to the lowest bidder for a term of four years. They're issued in a number of sizes and styles, including the window type.

Stamped envelopes were first issued in June, 1853. In 1865 envelopes bearing the purchaser's printed return address were authorized by law. The average annual issues of stamped envelopes today is in excess of 1 billion. That represents about 150 million dollars in sales. Obviously, a popular item.

The record for the largest number of stamped envelopes manufactured in a single day goes all the way back to 1932. A new postal rate was going into effect, and an enormous quantity of envelopes was needed to stock the post offices of the nation. To meet that monumental need, the contractor produced, in a single day, a total of 19,168,000 stamped envelopes.

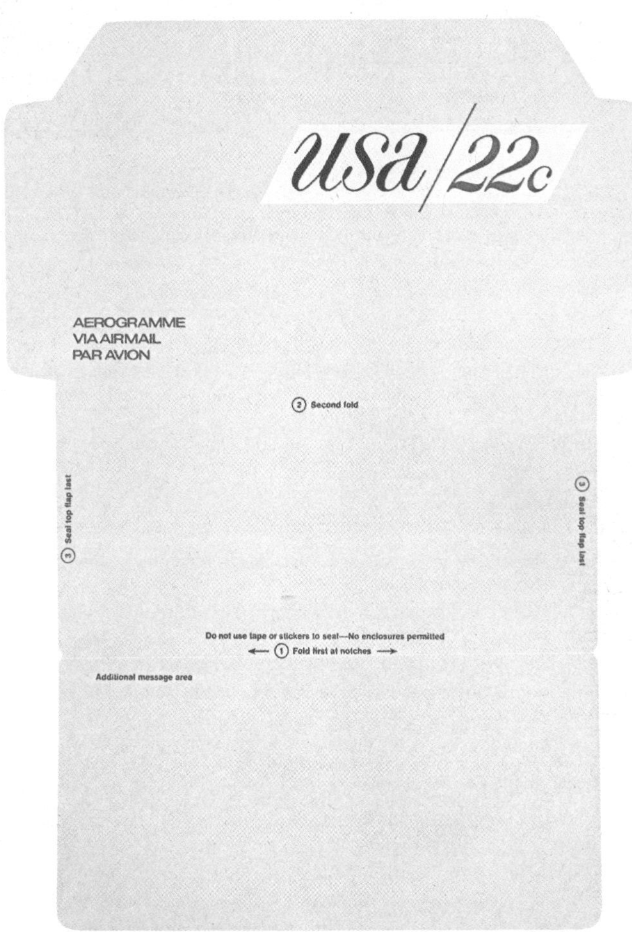

Aerogrammes

An aerogramme is a flat sheet of paper that's specially shaped, fold-marked and gummed so that, after the message is written, it can be sealed for privacy in transit. It's letter and envelope in one, it's intended for air mail only, and it carries a message anywhere in the world at a lower postage rate than air mail.

Aerogrammes are produced by the Bureau of Engraving and Printing on a Seven-Color press. It can execute multicolor stamp designs, apply a phosphor tag and gum the sealing flaps.

Just as is the case with stamped envelopes and postal cards, the Postal Service has stepped up its issuance of commemorative aerogrammes in recent years. And that's good news for collectors.

IMPORTANT DATES IN UNITED STATES POSTAL HISTORY

1707: Postal service in the colonies becomes a function of the British Crown, which appoints deputy postmasters general to manage the mail. Benjamin Franklin, the most important person to hold this position (1753-74), greatly improves postal finances and mail service to and from major cities.

1775: Ben Franklin appointed First Postmaster General by Continental Congress.

1787: The U.S. Constitution authorizes Congress to "establish Post Offices."

1842: Postage stamps are introduced in the United States by a private firm, Greig's City Despatch Post of New York.

1845: Some United States postmasters begin to provide special stamps of local origin to show prepayment of mail. These stamps are called postmasters' provisionals and are usually very rare.

1847: The U.S. government issues its first postage stamps (Scott Nos. 1 and 2).

1864: Railway Mail Service inaugurated.

1885: Special delivery service is inaugurated.

1896: At the request of farmers, rural free delivery is established.

1918: Air mail service is begun. By 1924 the United States has 24-hour transcontinental air mail service.

1969: On July 20, the first postage stamp was cancelled on the moon by Apollo 11 Astronaut Neil Armstrong.

1970: Mailgram established combination letter-telegram.

1971: The first Post Office was established on the moon by Apollo 15 Astronauts David Scott and James Irwin.

1971: The United States Postal Service, an independent establishment of the Executive Branch of the Government, assumes operation of the United States Post Office Department.

1972: Stamps by Mail Program inaugurated.

1974: Highway Post Offices terminated.

1974: First satellite transmission of Mailgrams.

1975: America's postal service celebrated its 200th anniversary.

1977: Airmail abolished as a separate rate category.

1977: Express mail becomes a permanent new class of mail.

1977: The Railway Mail Service, established in 1864 made its final run June 30.

1978: Postage stamps and other philatelic items are copyrighted by U.S. Postal Service.

SOUVENIR CARDS
United States Post Office & United States Postal Service

These cards were issued as souvenirs of the philatelic gatherings at which they were distributed by the United States Postal Service, its predecessor the United States Post Office Department, or the Bureau of Engraving and Printing. They were not valid for postage.

Most of the cards bear reproductions of United States stamps with the design enlarged or altered. The U.S. reproductions are engraved except stamps Nos. 914, 1396, 1460-1462 and C85. The cards are not perforated.

Cards for international exhibitions are issued by the U.S.P.S. and are given to visitors without charge. Cards for National exhibitions are issued by the Bureau and are usually sold at the event.

For information regarding current availability of souvenir cards, send postal card following Page 208.

NAPOSTA '78

Frankfurt am Main, Deutschland — 20.-25. Mai 1978

Viele Menschen deutschen Ursprungs haben zum Aufbau der Vereinigten Staaten beigetragen. Einen von ihnen — Carl Schurz — hat die Bundesrepublik Deutschland durch Herausgabe der abgebildeten Briefmarke anlässlich der 200-Jahr-Feier der amerikanischen Unabhängigkeit geehrt.

Diese Erinnerungskarte wird anlässlich der NAPOSTA '78 herausgegeben. Sie stellt Reproduktionen von US-Briefmarken mit Porträts der Präsidenten Abraham Lincoln und Rutherford B. Hayes dar. Carl Schurz diente in der Armee unter Lincolns Kommando und war später Innenminister im Kabinett von Hayes.

©UNITED STATES POSTAL SERVICE 1978

Generalpostmeister

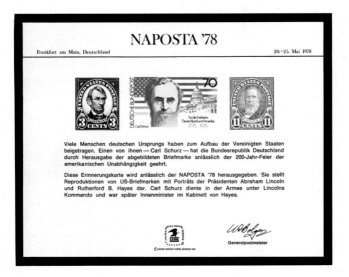

A forerunner of the souvenir cards is the 1938 Philatelic Truck souvenir sheet which the Post Office Department issued and distributed in various cities visited by the Philatelic Truck. It shows the White House, printed in blue on white paper. Issued with and without gum. Price, with gum, $35, without gum, $12.

1960

Barcelona, 1st International Philatelic Congress, Mar. 26-Apr. 5. Enlarged vignette, Landing of Columbus from No. 231. Printed in black. 225.00

1968

EFIMEX, International Philatelic Exhibition, Nov. 1-9, Mexico City. Card of 1. No. 292, inscribed in Spanish. 5.00

1970

PHILYMPIA, London International Stamp Exhibition, Sept. 18-26. Card of 3. Nos. 548-550. 4.00

1971

EXFILIMA 71, 3rd Inter-American Philatelic Exhibition, Nov. 6-14, Lima, Peru. Card of 3. Nos. 1111 and 1126, Peru No. 360. Card inscribed in Spanish. 4.00

1972

BELGICA 72, Brussels International Philatelic Exhibition, June 24-July 9. Brussels, Belgium. Card of 3. Nos. 914, 1026 and 1104. Card inscribed in Flemish and French. 2.00

Olympia Philatelic München 72, Aug. 18-Sept. 10, Munich, Germany. Card of 4. Nos. 1460-1462 and C85, Card inscribed in German. 2.00

ROCPEX '78

中國郵票發行百年紀念郵展

一九七八年三月廿至廿九日

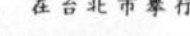

郵票為一宇宙性語言，傳達一國之理想，文化及其成就。此項紀念卡之發行目的在祝賀中國郵票發行百年紀念郵展，所採選複印之中美郵票顯示之藝術成就，殆為中華民國及美利堅合衆國所尊崇。

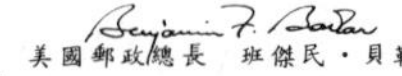

美國郵政總長 班傑民・貝勒

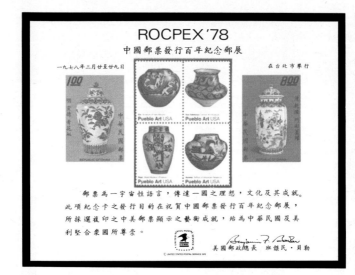

EXFILBRA 72, 4th Inter-American Philatelic Exhibition, Aug. 26-Sept. 2, Rio de Janeiro, Brazil. Card of 3. No. C14, Brazil Nos. C18-C19. Card inscribed in Portuguese.	2.00
National Philatelic Forum VI, Aug. 28-30, Washington, D.C. Card of 4 No. 1396.	2.00

1973

IBRA 73 Internationale Briefmarken Ausstellung, May 11-20, Munich, Germany. With one No. C13.	2.00
APEX 73, International Airmail Exhibition, July 4-7, Manchester, England. Card of 3. Newfoundland No. C4, U.S. No. C3a and Honduras No. C12.	2.00

REPUBBLICA DI SAN MARINO **SAN MARINO 77** 28 AGOSTO-4 SETTEMBRE 1977

Ogni volta che si riuniscono filatelici di varie nazioni del mondo, si rafforzano i legami di amicizia internazionale. Quindi, per rendere omaggio alla Mostra Internazionale Filatelica "San Marino 77" ed a tutte le nazioni partecipanti, e per celebrare il centenario dell'emissione dei primi francobolli sammarinesi, distribuiamo come ricordo questo cartoncino filatelico. In questa occasione, abbiamo deciso di riprodurre il francobollo sammarinese da due centesimi, il quale fu catalogato per primo fra i cinque francobolli sammarinesi emessi il 1º agosto 1877. E' appropriatamente affiancato dai primi due francobolli statunitensi, emessi il 1º luglio 1847 in onore del nostro primo Presidente, George Washington, e del nostro primo Direttore Generale delle Poste, Benjamin Franklin.

Direttore Generale
delle Poste

POLSKA 73, Swiatowa Wystawa Filatelisyczna, Aug. 19-Sept. 2, Poznan, Poland. Card of 3. No. 1488 and Poland Nos. 1944-1945. Card inscribed in Polish. 2.00

1974

HOBBY, The Hobby Industry Association of America Convention and Trade Show, February 3-6, Chicago, Illinois. Card of 4. Nos. 1456-1459. 2.00

INTERNABA, International Philatelic Exhibition, June 7-16, Basel, Switzerland. Card of 8, strip of Nos. 1530-1537. Card inscribed in 4 languages. 2.00

STOCKHOLMIA '74, International frimarksustallning, September 21-29, Stockholm, Sweden. Card of 3. No. 836, Sweden Nos. 300 and 765. Card inscribed in Swedish. 2.00

EXFILMEX 74 UPU, Philatelic Exposition Interamericana, October 26-November 3, Mexico City, Mexico. Card of 2. No. 1157 and Mexico No. 910. Card inscribed in Spanish and English. 2.00

1975

ESPANA 75, World Stamp Exhibition, Apr. 4-13, Madrid, Spain. Card of 3. Nos. 233, 1271 and Spain No. 1312. Card inscribed in Spanish. 2.00

ARPHILA 75, June 6-16, Paris, France. Card of 3. Nos. 1187, 1207 and France No. 1117. Card inscribed in French. 2.00

1976

WERABA 76, Third International Space Stamp Exhibition, April 1-4, Zurich, Switzerland. Card of 2. Nos. 1434 and 1435 setenant. 2.50

Bicentennial Exposition on Science and Technology, May 30-Sept. 6, Kennedy Space Center, Fla. Card of one, No. C76. 2.50

Colorado Statehood Centennial, August 1, Card of 3. Nos. 743, 288 and 1670. 2.50

HAFNIA 76, International Stamp Exhibition, Aug. 20-29, Copenhagen, Denmark. Card of 2. No. 5 and Denmark No. 2. Card inscribed in Danish and English. 2.50

ITALIA 76, International Philatelic Exhibition, Oct. 14-24, Milan, Italy. Card of 3. No. 1168 and Italy Nos. 578 and 601. Card inscribed in Italian. 2.50

NORDPOSTA 76, North German Stamp Exhibition, Oct. 30-31, Hamburg, Germany. Card of 3. No. 689 and Germany Nos. B366 and B417. Card inscribed in German. 2.50

1977

AMPHILEX 77, International Philatelic Exhibition, May 26-June 5, Amsterdam, Netherlands. Card of 3. No. 1027 and Netherlands Nos. 41 and 294. Card inscribed in Dutch. 2.50

SAN MARINO 77, International Philatelic Exhibition, Aug. 28-Sept. 4, San Marino, Card of 3. Nos. 1-2 and San Marino No. 1. Card inscribed in Italian. 4.00

1978

ROCPEX 78, International Philatelic Exhibition, Mar. 20-29, Taipei, Taiwan, Card of 6. Nos. 1706-1709 and Taiwan Nos. 1812 and 1816. Card inscribed in Chinese. 2.50

NAPOSTA 78, Philatelic Exhibition, May 20-25, Frankfurt, Germany. Card of 3. Nos. 555, 563 and Germany No. 1216. Card inscribed in German. 3.50

ITALIA 76

Milano, Italia 14-24 ottobre 1976

Noi celebriamo "ITALIA 76" con un'emissione di tre francobolli che rappresentano italiani di grande coraggio, vedute e genialità.

Il 25 lire italiano onora Leonardo da Vinci, la cui immensa creatività continua ad ispirare il mondo civile. Il 4 centesimi U.S.A. onora Giuseppe Garibaldi, il patriota tanto venerato che unificò l'Italia moderna. Il 20 lire italiano onora Cristoforo Colombo, la cui risolutezza aprì un nuovo mondo in cui, sotto tante forme diverse ed in tanti paesi, è venuta a fiorire la libertà.

Benjamin F. Bailar
Postmaster General

Bureau of Engraving & Printing

1954

Postage Stamp Design Exhibition, National Philatelic Museum, Mar. 13, Philadelphia. Card of 4. Monochrome views of Washington, D.C. Inscribed: "Souvenir sheet designed, engraved and printed by members, Bureau, Engraving and Printing. / Reissued by popular request". 600.00

1966

SIPEX, 6th International Philatelic Exhibition, May 21-30, Washington, D.C. Card of 3. Multicolored views of Washington, D.C. Inscribed "Sixth International Philatelic Exhibition / Washington, D.C. / Designed, Engraved, and Printed by Union Members of Bureau of Engraving and Printing". 165.00

1969

SANDIPEX, San Diego Philatelic Exhibition, July 16-20, San Diego, Cal. Card of 3. Multicolored views of Washington, D.C. Inscribed: "Sandipex—San Diego 200th Anniversary—1769-1969". 55.00

A.S.D.A. National Postage Stamp Show, Nov. 21-23, 1969, New York. Card of 4 No. E4. 20.00

1970

INTERPEX, Mar. 20-22, New York. Card of 4. Nos. 1027, 1035, C35 and C38. 45.00

COMPEX, Combined Philatelic Exhibition of Chicagoland, May 29-31, Chicago. Card of 4 No. C18. 15.00

HAPEX, American Philatelic Society Convention, Nov. 5-8, Honolulu, Hawaii. Card of 3. Nos. 799, C46 and C55. 17.50

1971

INTERPEX, Mar. 12-14, New York. Card of 4 No. 1193. Background includes Nos. 1331-1332, 1371 and C76. 4.00

WESTPEX, Western Philatelic Exhibition, Apr. 23-25, San Francisco. Card of 4. Nos. 740, 852, 966 and 997. 4.00

NAPEX 71, National Philatelic Exhibition, May 21-23, Washington, D.C. Card of 3. Nos. 990, 991, 992. 4.00

TEXANEX 71. Texas Philatelic Association and American Philatelic Society conventions, Aug. 26-29, San Antonio, Tex. Card of 3. Nos. 938, 1043 and 1242. 4.00

A.S.D.A. National Postage Stamp Show, Nov. 19-21, New York. Card of 3. Nos. C13-C15. 4.00

ANPHILEX '71, Anniversary Philatelic Exhibition, Nov. 26-Dec. 1, New York. Card of 2. Nos. 1-2. 2.00

1972

INTERPEX, Mar. 17-19, New York. Card of 4 No. 1173. Background includes Nos. 976, 1434-1435 and C69. 2.00

NOPEX, Apr. 6-9, New Orleans. Card of 4 No. 1020. Background includes Nos. 323-327. 2.00

SEPAD '72, Oct. 20-22, Philadelphia. Card of 4 No. 1044. 2.00

A.S.D.A. National Postage Stamp Show, Nov. 17-19, New York. Card of 4. Nos. 883, 863, 868 and 888. 2.00

STAMP EXPO, Nov. 24-26, San Francisco. Card of 4 No. C36. 2.00

1973

INTERPEX, March 9-11, New York. Card of 4 No. 976. 2.00

COMPEX 73, May 25-27, Chicago. Card of 4 No. 245. 2.00

NAPEX 73, Sept. 14-16, Washington, D.C. Card of 4 No. C3. Background includes Nos. C4-C6. 2.00

A.S.D.A. National Postage Stamp Show, Nov. 16-18, New York. Card of 4 No. 908. Foreground includes Nos. 1139-1144. 2.00

STAMP EXPO NORTH, Dec. 7-9, San Francisco. Card of 4 No. C20. 2.00

1974

MILCOPEX, March 8-10, Milwaukee, Wisconsin. Card of 4. No. C43. Background depicts U.P.U. monument at Berne, Switzerland. 2.00

1975

NAPEX 75, May 9-11, Washington, D.C. Card of 4 No. 708. 2.00

International Women's Year. Card of 3. Nos. 872, 878 and 959. Reproduction of 1886 dollar bill. 20.00

A.S.D.A. National Postage Stamp Show, Nov. 21-23, New York. Bicentennial series. Card of 4 No. 1003. ". . . and maintain the liberty which we have derived from our ancestors." 2.00

1976

INTERPHIL 76, Seventh International Philatelic Exhibition, May 29-June 6, Philadelphia. Bicentennial series. Card of 4. No. 120. "that all men are created equal." 2.50

STAMP EXPO 76, June 11-13, Los Angeles. Bicentennial series. Card of 4. Nos. 1351, 1352, 1345 and 1348 se-tenant vertically. "when we assumed the soldier, we did not lay aside the citizen". 2.50

1977

MILCOPEX, Milwaukee Philatelic Society, Mar. 4-6, Milwaukee. Card of 2. Nos. 733 and 1128. 2.50

ROMPEX 77, Rocky Mountain Philatelic Exhibition, May 20-22, Denver. Card of 4 No. 1001. 2.50

PURIPEX 77, Silver Anniversary Philatelic Exhibit, Sept. 2-5, San Juan, Puerto Rico. Card of 4 No. 801. 2.50

A.S.D.A. National Postage Stamp Show, Nov. 15-20, New York. Card of 4 No. C45. 2.50

1978

CENJEX 78, Federated Stamp Clubs of New Jersey, 30th annual exhibition, June 23-25, Freehold, N.J. Card of 9. Nos. 646, 680, 689, 1086, 1716 and 4 No. 785. 3.50

COMMEMORATIVE PANELS

The Postal Service offers American Commemorative Panels for each new commemorative stamp and special Christmas stamps issued. The series first began September 20, 1972 with the issuance of the Wild Life Commemorative Panel and will total over 100 panels by the end of 1979 . The panels feature stamps in mint condition complemented by reproductions of steel line engravings and stories behind the commemorated subject.

Scott No.		Price
	1972	
1CP	Wildlife	4.00
2CP	Mail Order	4.00
3CP	Osteopathic Medicine	4.00
4CP	Tom Sawyer	4.00
5CP	Pharmacy	4.00
6CP	Christmas 1972	4.00
7CP	'Twas the Night Before Christmas	4.00
8CP	Stamp Collecting	4.00
	1973	
9CP	Love	4.00
10CP	Pamphleteers	4.00
11CP	George Gershwin	4.00
12CP	Posting Broadside	4.00
13CP	Copernicus	4.00
14CP	Postal People	4.00
15CP	Harry S. Truman	4.00
16CP	Post Rider	4.00
17CP	Boston Tea Party	4.00
18CP	Electronics	4.00
19CP	Robinson Jeffers	4.00
20CP	Lyndon B. Johnson	4.00
21CP	Henry O. Tanner	4.00
22CP	Willa Cather	4.00
23CP	Drummer	4.00
24CP	Angus Cattle	4.00
25CP	Christmas 1973	4.00
26CP	Needlepoint	4.00
	1974	
27CP	Veterans of Foreign Wars	4.00
28CP	Robert Frost	4.00
29CP	EXPO '74	4.00
30CP	Horse Racing	4.00
31CP	Slylab	4.00
32CP	Universal Postal Union	4.00
33CP	Mineral Heritage	4.00
34CP	Fort Harrod	4.00
35CP	Continental Congress	4.00
36CP	Chautauqua	4.00
37CP	Kansas Wheat	4.00
38CP	Energy Conservation	4.00
39CP	Sleepy Hollow	4.00
40CP	Retarded Children	4.00
41CP	"The Road-Winter"	4.00
42CP	Angel Altarpiece	4.00
	1975	
43CP	Benjamin West	4.00
44CP	Pioneer	4.00
45CP	Collective Bargaining	4.00

Scott No.		Price
46CP	Contributors to the Cause	4.00
47CP	Mariner	4.00
48CP	Lexington & Concord	4.00
49CP	Paul Laurence Dunbar	4.00
50CP	D W Griffith	4.00
51CP	Bunker Hill	4.00
52CP	Military Services	4.00
53CP	Apollo Soyuz	4.00
54CP	World Peace Through Law	4.00
55CP	International Women's Year	4.00
56CP	Postal Bicentennial	4.00
57CP	Banking and Commerce	4.00
58CP	Early Christmas Card	4.00
59CP	Ghirlandaio Madonna	4.00
	1976	
60CP	Spirit of '76	4.00
61CP	Interphil 76	4.00
62CP	State Flags	4.00
63CP	Telephone Centennial	4.00
64CP	Commercial Aviation	4.00
65CP	Chemistry	4.00
66CP	Benjamin Franklin	4.00
67CP	Declaration of Independence	4.00
68CP	Olympics	4.00
69CP	Clara Maas	4.00
70CP	Adolph S. Ochs	4.00
71CP	Currier Winter Pastime	5.00
72CP	Copley Nativity	5.00
	1977	
73CP	Washington at Princeton	5.00
74CP	Sound Recording	8.00
75CP	Pueblo Art	8.00
76CP	Lindbergh Flight	8.00
77CP	Colorado Centennial	8.00
78CP	Butterflies	8.00

Scott No.		Price
79CP	Lafayette	8.00
80CP	Skilled Hands	8.00
81CP	Peace Bridge	8.00
82CP	Herkimer at Oriskany	8.00
83CP	Energy Conservation & Development	8.00
84CP	Alta California	8.00
85CP	Articles of Confederation	8.00
86CP	Talking Pictures	8.00
87CP	Surrender at Saratoga	8.00
88CP	Washington at Valley Forge	8.00
89CP	Rural Mailbox	8.00
	1978	
90CP	Carl Sandburg	8.00
91CP	Captain Cook	8.00
92CP	Harriet Tubman	8.00
93CP	American Quilts	8.00
94CP	American Dance	8.00
95CP	French Alliance	8.00
96CP	Dr. Papanicolaou	8.00
97CP	Jimmie Rodgers	8.00
98CP	Photography	8.00
99CP	George M. Cohan	8.00
100CP	Viking Missions	8.00
101CP	American Owls	8.00
102CP	American Trees	8.00
103CP	Madonna and Child	8.00
104CP	Hobby Horse	8.00
	1979	
105CP	Robert F. Kennedy	8.00
106CP	Martin Luther King, Jr.	8.00
107CP	Year of the Child	8.00
108CP	John Steinbeck	8.00
109CP	Albert Einstein	8.00
110CP	Pennsylvania Toleware	8.00
111CP	American Architecture	8.00
112CP	Endangered Flora	8.00
113CP	Seeing Eye Dogs	8.00
114CP	Special Olympics	8.00
115CP	John Paul Jones	8.00
116CP	15c Olympic Games	8.00
117CP	Virgin and Child	8.00
118CP	Santa Claus	8.00
119CP	Will Rogers	8.00

STAMP CLUBS

**JOIN A STAMP CLUB . . .
IT'S EASIER THAN EVER!**

The United States Postal Service started a schools program several years ago. The objective was to introduce Stamp Clubs into school systems around the country at the fourth, fifth and sixth grade levels. To date, over 35,000 clubs have been established, offering many, many hours of fun and education.

**THE BENJAMIN FRANKLIN
STAMP CLUB**

You know all about Ben Franklin's key and kite experiment, his Franklin stove, his bifocals and his ***Poor Richard's Almanac.*** But did you know that, besides everything else, Franklin was the Father of the postal service. That's why it's his face that appears on the first postage stamp the U.S. ever issued. And that's why, when the Postal Service decided to help establish stamp clubs in schools all over the country, they thought of calling them Benjamin Franklin Stamp Clubs.

The Postal Service has prepared a lot of exciting material to introduce the idea of a school stamp club and to support its activities there's even a filmstrip. The idea has already been presented and approved in elementary schools throughout the country and the enthusiasm of the kids is tremendous. As of April, 1979 approximately 900,000 girls and boys were members of 36,000 different Benjamin Franklin Stamp Clubs. The Postal Service estimates a national membership of 1.1 million by April, 1980. So watch for an announcement in ***your*** school. It should be happening soon!

WHY A STAMP CLUB?

Because if it's fun to collect stamps, it's twice as much fun to share ideas about the hobby, trade stamps, and learn from others who share your philatelic interests. So if a Benjamin Franklin Stamp Club gets started in your school, join. If not, join a community stamp club. And if there's no community stamp club, start one!

STARTING A CLUB

If you think you'd like to start a stamp club, your first task is to find members. So publicize your club with announcements on your school's bulletin boards and in the school newspapers . . . with posters in the windows of cooperating stores, banks and restaurants . . . with announcements in local newspapers and over local radio stations, if they're willing to carry club activity news without charge. Your announcements should tell when the club will meet, where, and how a prospective member can get additional information. Bear in mind that successful stamp clubs usually have a good mix of younger and older members.

You'll want a conveniently located place for meetings, available at little or no cost. Try local schools, libraries, museums, churches, the "Y". There are always the homes of clubs members if all else fails.

During the club's first official meeting, club officers should be elected. Start out with as few officers as are necessary to keep the club functioning. You can always elect more as the club's membership increases and the need arises. It's important for both younger and older members to take leadership positions in the club.

The entire membership should have a hand in developing the rules that will govern club activities. A club constitution or by-laws might be written so it can be duplicated and distributed to all members. Do make the rules during one of the early meetings. And don't make them too strict.

WHAT TO DO AT MEETINGS

The entire membership should participate in planning club activities. And planning should start at the very first meeting. Make it a rule to keep the business part of your meeting short, and the pleasure part long.

The pleasure part consists of trading, buying and selling stamps—that happens spontaneously when stamp collectors get together. Other than that, members can exhibit their collections. Guest speakers can be invited to lecture or conduct question and answer sessions. Films can be shown. Stamp auctions can be organized. Group discussions can be set up. You'll all enjoy stamp quiz shows—like the quiz shows on television, but with questions that deal exclusively with stamps and collecting.

But with all that going on, how will members ever remember what's coming up and when? They'll read about it in your club newsletter, of course! Many clubs issue a weekly or monthly bulletin to keep members informed. It doesn't have to be an elaborate publication, and the duplication method you use can be the least expensive. A single sheet of paper would do very nicely, with pertinent club information on one side and a calendar of meetings and upcoming events on the other.

Does the idea of starting a stamp club sound a little scary? It shouldn't—not if you organize well, share the work fairly, and take things step by carefully planned step.

So become a member of a stamp club somehow—whether you join a new Benjamin Franklin Stamp Club at school or an ongoing stamp club in your community or start a stamp club of your own. The joy of collecting is multiplied many times over when you share it.

POSTMASTERS GENERAL OF THE UNITED STATES

1789 Samuel Osgood, MA
1791 Timothy Pickering, PA
1795 Joseph Habersham. GA
1801 Gideon Granger, CT
1814 Return J. Meigs, Jr., OH
1823 John McLean, OH
1829 William T. Barry, KY
1835 Amos Kendall, KY
1840 John M. Niles, CT
1841 Francis Granger, NY
1841 Charles A. Wickliffe, KY
1845 Cave Johnson, TN
1849 Jacob Collamer, VT
1850 Nathan K. Hall, NY
1852 Samuel D. Hubbard, CT
1853 James Campbell, PA
1857 Aaron V. Brown, TN
1859 Joseph Holt, KY
1861 Horatio King, ME
1861 Montgomery Blair, DC
1864 William Dennison, OH
1866 Alexander W. Randall, WI
1869 John A. J. Creswell, MD
1874 Jas. W. Marshall, NJ
1874 Marshall Jewell, CT
1876 James N. Tyner, IN
1877 David McK. Key, TN
1880 Horace Maynard, TN
1881 Thomas L. James, NY
1882 Timothy O. Howe, WI
1883 Walter Q. Gresham, IN
1884 Frank Hatton, IA
1885 Wm. F. Vilas, WI
1888 Don M. Dickinson, MI
1889 John Wanamaker, PA
1893 Wilson S. Bissell, NY
1895 William L. Wilson, WV
1897 James A. Gary, MD
1898 Charles Emory Smith, PA
1902 Henry C. Payne, WI
1904 Robert J. Wynne, PA
1905 Geo. B. Cortelyou, NY
1907 Geo. von L. Meyer, MA
1909 Frank H. Hitchcock, MA
1913 Albert S. Burleson, TX
1921 Will H. Hays, IN
1922 Hubert Work, CO
1923 Harry S. New, IN
1929 Walter F. Brown, OH
1933 James A. Farley, NY
1940 Frank C. Walker, PA
1945 Robert E. Hannegan, MO
1947 Jesse M. Donaldson, IL
1953 Arthur E. Summerfield, MI
1961 J. Edward Day, CA
1963 John A. Gronouski, WI
1965 Lawrence F. O'Brien, MA
1968 W. Marvin Watson, TX
1969 Winton M. Blount, AL
1972 E. T. Klassen, MA
1975 Benjamin Franklin Bailar, MD
1978 William F. Bolger, CT

STAMP COLLECTING KITS

U.S. Postal Service Stamp Collecting Kits come in an exciting range of subjects. One will give you a garden. Others will help you discover the world, and learn about strange geometric shapes. All without leaving home. Sound like fun?

Every Collecting Kit contains:

- A 20-page, color illustrated stamp album.
- A selection of exciting, colorful, genuine stamps to mount in the stamp album.
- A packet of stamp hinges.
- The ABC's of Stamp Collecting—a 32-page booklet with colorful illustrations and information about starting your own stamp collection.

Pick your kit or kits from these topicals: • World of Sports • Animal Kingdom • Masterworks • Flowers • Flags, Maps and Coats of Arms • Diamonds and Triangles • and Travel Through the Ages. Each one is so great you'll probably want them all. Price $2.00 each kit.

Prices subject to change.

For additional information, send postal card following page 208.

COMMEMORATIVE MINT SETS

Each year, the United States Postal Service issues a new Commemorative Mint Set, a collection of commemoratives issued that year. Every stamp in the set is in mint condition, held by an acetate strip to keep it mint-fresh. The album created to contain the stamps is handsomely designed, with a new design for each year's set. In it, you will find the story behind each commemorated subject. What an exciting way to collect America's commemoratives. Each set is a thrilling window on our country's past and present.

1979 contains twenty-nine commemorative stamps including the exciting 1980 Olympics set and the beautiful blocks of four on Endangered Flora, Pennsylvania Toleware and American Architecture. **$5.25**

1978 contains twenty-six Commemorative and two Special Issue stamps for a total of twenty-eight Mint Stamps. In addition to the beautiful blocks of four American owls and American trees, this year initiates the first of the Black Heritage and the Performing Arts series. **$4.50**

1977 Contains twenty-seven mint stamps. Among the many exciting stamps is the Lindbergh Flight issue. Also included are the popular Blocks of four of Pueblo Indian Pottery and beautifully designed Butterfly stamps. **$4.00**

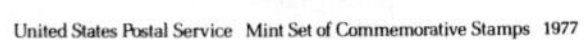

UNITED STATES POSTAL SERVICE MINT SET OF COMMEMORATIVE STAMPS 1

1976 American Revolution Bicentennial stamps dominate this year's mint set. Ben Franklin, the Spirit of '76 strip of three and the Declaration of Independence strip of four join the '76 Olympics to round out the year. **$3.50**

1975 Twenty-eight commemoratives complete the 1975 mint set. In addition to the many Bicentennial issues, this set includes Mariner 10, Pioneer Jupiter and the much sought after Apollo-Soyuz pair. **$3.50**

Prices subject to change

For additional information, send postal card following page 208.

AMERICAN COMMEMORATIVE PANEL SERIES

These are dramatically beautiful and important panels that do far more than simply display newly minted commemoratives. Each panel, a handsomely designed 8½″ x 11¼″ page, features an actual block of four or more stamps in mint condition, protected by a transparent mylar mount. And complementing the stamps are intaglio-printed reproductions of old steel engravings which illustrate subjects related to the commemorative. Enriching the sheet further is the written story of the commemorated subject, documented expressly for the series. These limited-edition panels—all of heirloom quality—make superb gifts and awards, as well as being unique showpieces for the collector.

For additional information, send postal card following page 208.

SOUVENIR PAGES
With First Day Cancellations

The Postal Service offers Souvenir Pages for new stamps. The series began with a page for the Yellowstone Park Centennial stamp issued March 1, 1972. The pages feature one or more stamps tied by the first day cancel, technical data and information on the subject of the issue.

Scott No.		Price
	1972	
1SP	Yellowstone Park	1.25
2SP	Cape Hatteras	1.25
3SP	Fiorello La Guardia	1.25
4SP	City of Refuge	1.50
5SP	Wolf Trap Farm	1.25
6SP	Colonial Craftsman	2.00
7SP	Mount McKinley	1.25
8SP	Olympic Games	2.50
9SP	Parent Teachers Association	1.25
10SP	Wildlife Conservation	2.50
11SP	Mail Order	1.25
12SP	Osteopathic Medicine	1.25
13SP	Tom Sawyer	1.25
14SP	Benjamin Franklin	1.25
15SP	Christmas	1.25
16SP	Pharmacy	1.25
17SP	Stamp Collecting	1.25
	1973	
18SP	Eugene O'Neill coil	3.50
19SP	Love	1.25
20SP	Pamphleteer	1.25
21SP	George Gershwin	1.25
22SP	Posting Broadside	1.25
23SP	Copernicus	1.25
24SP	Postal Service Employees	5.00
25SP	Harry S Truman	1.25
26SP	Postrider	1.25
27SP	Giannini	1.50
28SP	Boston Tea Party	3.25
29SP	Progress in Electronics	3.00
30SP	Robinson Jeffers	1.25
31SP	Lyndon B. Johnson	1.25
32SP	Henry O. Tanner	1.25

Scott No.		Price
33SP	Willa Cather	1.25
34SP	Colonial Drummer	1.25
35SP	Angus Cattle	1.25
36SP	Christmas	1.25
37SP	13c Airmail sheet stamp	1.25
38SP	10c Crossed Flags	1.25
39SP	Jefferson Memorial	1.25
40SP	13c Airmail coil	1.25
	1974	
41SP	Mount Rushmore	1.50
42SP	ZIP Code	1.25
43SP	Statue of Liberty	1.35
44SP	Elizabeth Blackwell	1.35
45SP	Veterans of Foreign Wars	1.25
46SP	Robert Frost	1.25
47SP	EXPO '74	1.25
48SP	Horse Racing	1.25
49SP	Skylab	1.25
50SP	Universal Postal Union	3.50
51SP	Mineral Heritage	2.50
52SP	Fort Harrod	1.25
53SP	Continental Congress	2.50
54SP	Chautauqua	1.25
55SP	Kansas Wheat	1.25
56SP	Energy Conservation	1.25
57SP	6.3c Bulk Rate	1.25
58SP	Sleepy Hollow	1.25
59SP	Retarded Children	1.25
60SP	Christmas, two dates	1.75
	1975	
61SP	Benjamin West	1.25
62SP	Pioneer	1.25
63SP	Collective Bargaining	1.25
64SP	Sybil Ludington	1.25
65SP	Salem Poor	1.25
66SP	Haym Salomon	1.25
67SP	Peter Francisco	1.35
68SP	Mariner	1.25
69SP	Lexington & Concord, both cities	1.35
70SP	Paul Laurence Dunbar	1.25

Scott No.		Price
71SP	D.W. Griffith	1.25
72SP	Bunker Hill	1.25
73SP	Military Services	2.00
74SP	Apollo Soyuz	1.50
75SP	International Women's Year	1.25
76SP	Postal Bicentennial	2.00
77SP	World Peace Through Law	1.25
78SP	Banking & Commerce	1.35
79SP	Christmas	1.35
80SP	Francis Parkman	1.25
81SP	Freedom of the Press	1.25
82SP	Old North Church	
83SP	Flag & Independence Hall	1.50
84SP	Freedom to Assemble	1.35
85SP	Liberty Bell coil	1.25
86SP	American Eagle & Shield	1.25
	1976	
87SP	Spirit of '76	1.75
88SP	25c & 31c Airmails	2.00
89SP	Interphil	1.25
90SP	Freedom to Assemble coil	1.35
91SP	Telephone Centennial	1.25
92SP	Commercial Aviation	1.25
93SP	Chemistry	1.25
94SP	7.9c Bulk Rate	1.25
95SP	13c Souvenir Sheet	6.00
96SP	18c Souvenir Sheet	7.50
97SP	24c Souvenir Sheet	8.50
98SP	31c Souvenir Sheet	9.50
99SP	Benjamin Franklin	1.25
100SP	Declaration of Independence	2.00
101SP	Olympics	2.00
102SP	Clara Maass	1.25
103SP	Adolph S. Ochs	1.25
104SP	Christmas	1.75
105SP	7.7c Bulk rate	1.25

Scott No.		Price
	1977	
106SP	Washington at Princeton	1.25
107SP	$1 Vending Machine Booklet Pane, perf. 10	5.00
108SP	Sound Recording	1.25
109SP	Pueblo Art	2.00
110SP	Lindbergh Flight	1.25
111SP	Colorado Centennial	1.25
112SP	Butterflies	2.00
113SP	Lafayette	1.25
114SP	Skilled Hands	2.00
115SP	Peace Bridge	1.25
116SP	Herkimer at Oriskany	1.25
117SP	Alta California	1.25
118SP	Articles of Confederation	1.25
119SP	Talking Pictures	1.25
120SP	Surrender at Saratoga	1.25
121SP	Energy	1.50
122SP	Christmas, Valley Forge	1.50
123SP	Christmas, Omaha	1.50
124SP	Petition for Redress coil	1.65
125SP	Petition for Redress sheet stamp	1.50
126SP	1c, 2c, 3c, 4c Americana	1.50
	1978	
127SP	Carl Sandburg	1.50
128SP	Indian Head Penny	1.50
129SP	Captain Cook, Honolulu	2.00
130SP	Captain Cook, Anchorage	2.00
131SP	Harriet Tubman	1.75
132SP	American Quilts	2.00
133SP	16c Statue of Liberty	2.00
134SP	Sandy Hook Lighthouse	2.00
135SP	American Dance	2.50
136SP	French Alliance	1.75

Scott No.		Price
137SP	Dr. Papanicolaou	1.75
138SP	"A" Stamp	2.00
139SP	Jimmie Rodgers	1.75
140SP	CAPEX '78	4.00
141SP	Oliver Wendell Holmes	1.75
142SP	Photography	1.75
143SP	Fort McHenry Flag	2.00
144SP	George M. Cohan	1.75
145SP	Rose booklet single	1.75
146SP	8.4c Bulk Rate	1.75
147SP	Viking Missions	1.75
148SP	Remote Outpost	2.00
149SP	American Owls	2.75
150SP	Wright Brothers	2.75
151SP	American Trees	2.75
152SP	Andrea della Robbia	1.75
153SP	Hobby Horse	1.75
154SP	$2 Kerosene Lamp	5.00
	1979	
155SP	Robert F. Kennedy	1.75
156SP	Martin Luther King, Jr.	1.75
157SP	International Year of the Child	1.75
158SP	John Steinbeck	1.75
159SP	Albert Einstein	1.75
160SP	Octave Chanute	2.25
161SP	Pennsylvania Toleware	2.75
162SP	American Architecture	2.75
163SP	Endangered Flora	2.75
164SP	Seeing Eye Dogs	1.75
165SP	$1 Americana	3.50
166SP	Special Olympics	1.75
167SP	$5 Americana	10.00
168SP	30c Americana	2.00
169SP	50c Americana	2.50
170SP	John Paul Jones	1.75
171SP	Olympics	2.00
172SP	Gerard David Madonna	1.75
173SP	Santa Claus	1.75
174SP	Will Rogers	1.75
175SP	Viet Nam Veterans	1.75
176SP	Wiley Post	2.50
177SP	31c Olympic	2.00

U.S. STAMP PRODUCTION

Letters requesting commemorative and other postage stamps originate with individuals and organizations, and are sent to the Postmaster General. A Citizens' Stamp Advisory Committee makes recommendations for new stamp issues from the thousands of requests on file. The Postmaster General makes the final determination based on the Committee's recommendations.

The U.S. Postal Service commissions an artist to design the stamp. It's a great honor to be chosen, of course. Such famous American artists as Norman Rockwell, Robert McCall and Jamie Wyeth have designed U.S. postage stamps.

From the artist's design, the Treasury Department's Bureau of Engraving and Printing prepares a model. They follow the design and any other suggestions the Postal Service may provide. They may have to make several models if the first one isn't just right. But eventually a model is approved and returned to the Bureau so a master die can be engraved.

To engrave a master die, the design of the stamp is cut into a piece of soft steel. From this, completed prints (called "die proofs") are pulled in various colors. The Postmaster General looks them over and gives final approval to the design and the ink colors. Now the master die is heated to an extremely high temperature. This hardens it, so it can be impressed into a soft steel roll, transferring the master impression. The roll is hardened and the design impressed into a soft steel plate a predetermined number of times. When the plate is hardened, it is attached to a press. The press rolls. And here comes the latest commemorative stamp issue.

But that's not the only way stamp plates are made. They can be produced by the electrolytic process (electroplating), too. Through the making of the master plate, the process is the same. But in this case, the master plate is immersed in a plating tank. Metallic plating is deposited on the master. When the plating is thick enough, it's separated from the master. The result is a "working alto". The part of the design that is engraved or incised below the surface of the master plate is reversed, so it stands above the surface of the working alto. Next, the working alto goes in the plating tank, and the process is repeated. The image is reversed once again to its original condition, and press plates are produced.

In a third method of plate making, the stamp design is transferred to a metal cylinder by photography. The cylinder is put through an etching process, and a rotogravure cylinder is produced.

PRODUCTION TECHNIQUES AND EQUIPMENT USED

The Bureau of Engraving and Printing is the main source of supply of U.S. postage stamps. Their printing equipment is in a continual program of modernization. It's hard to imagine what improvements may lie in store, though. Right now, the Bureau's incredible presses do everything but talk! Consider their capabilities:

Single Color Intaglio Press

These presses are used to print single color stamps on a continuous web of ungummed paper. This equipment applies gum and phosphor to the stamps during the printing operaiton. These presses produce most of our regular postage stamp issues. They also have precanceling capabilities.

3-Color Intaglio Press

This press utilizes an engraved, concentric, seamless printing surface, called a "printing sleeve" which contains 936 coil size stamps (18 across and 52 around). A pregummed paper web passes through the three-color intaglio unit, a phosphor tagging unit, and finally to an automatic rewind unit. The press does not have perforating or sheeting capabilities as it is primarily a coil printing press. The operational speed of 300 feet per minute provides a production capacity of 15-20 million stamps per shift.

Multicolor Intaglio

Two of these presses are designed to operate with two printing plates while the third uses four plates. The Giori presses print on pregummed sheets of paper and print up to three colors with one pass through the press. A phosphor coating is later applied by the offset process. Many colorful commemorative issues are produced on the Giori presses, particularly those that combine the intaglio (engraved) impression printed over the offset underlay colors. Six offset (lithographing) presses are used to print background colors on some Giori-printed stamps.

Seven Color Press

This press can print on either gummed or ungummed rolls. It is capable of printing in seven colors, and can apply phosphor and deliver the finished printings in sheet or roll form. It can produce stamps at speeds up to 900 feet per minute.

8-Color Gravure/Intaglio Press

This press is capable of printing five colors gravure and three colors line intaglio with one pass through the press. The press, when fully employed, is capable of printing regular, commemorative, or book stamps on a web of pregummed, coated paper, phosphor tagging them, precanceling them, and printing on the back if desired. It also perforates, cuts, and delivers the stamps in stacks of 100 sheets.

Automatic Book Forming Machines

The Bureau is presently using an automatic process for book stamps. Booklet forming machines perforate the stamps, imprint the covers, apply a cohesive to the covers, collate covers and stamps, cut books to finished size, and fold the covers over the stamps.

Format of Plates

Postage stamps are produced in sheet, coil and book form. Sheet stamps are printed from 96 to 600 subject plates, depending on the size of the individual stamp. Sheets of regular stamps are printed from 400-subject plates and the majority of commemoratives from 200-subject plates. Sheets of international airmail stamps are printed in 200-subject size. Coil stamps are produced from 432 or 936-subject plates, and book stamps from plates having 360, 400, or 832-subjects. All coil and book stamps are printed on web-fed presses.

Perforating

Presently, the gravure press and the 8-color gravure/intaglio press are the only pieces of Bureau equipment capable of in-line perforating. Stamps produced on all other presses must be perforated separately. Single color intaglio printed stamps are perforated on electric eye perforators which also trim and sheet the stamps from a web. Coil stamps are perforated by equipment which reduced rolls of stamps into coils of 100, 500, and 3,000 stamps. Stamps printed on the Giori presses are perforated on an L-type perforator. Sheets are automatically fed into the machine, perforated in both directions, and delivered at the output end in a pile. Finally, the finished postage stamps are examined and packaged for delivery to the U.S. Postal Service.

Tagging

How would a machine that has no eyes turn a batch of letters right side up, cancel the stamps and sort the mail? By means of an ingenious process most people never even heard of. It's called tagging.

During the printing process, stamps are coated with an invisible compound that shows up only when it's exposed to shortwave ultraviolet light. A tagged stamp is one that has that special invisible coating. A piece of post office equipment can't see the letters it handles, but it can sense tagging once it's been activated by ultraviolet light, and it can process the mail accordingly. And if you think it will never work, think again. It's been working since 1963.

Two different luminescent qualities are found in U.S. postage stamps and postal stationery - fluorescence and phosphorescence. They both glow when exposed to short wave ultraviolet light. But only the phosphorescent items have a brief afterglow when the ultraviolet light is turned off.

In August, 1963, in Dayton, Ohio, the U.S. Post Office began testing mail handling equipment that automatically faced, canceled and sorted mail by sensing the afterglow of phosphorescence activated by ultraviolet light. The first stamps tagged with an invisible phosphorescent compound were the 8¢ carmine airmails of 1963. The test was a resounding success. By January, 1967, all air mail stamps would be tagged with the special orange-red glowing phosphor.

But the spectrum has other colors. And in the Dayton area, from 1963 through 1965, other experimental tests were conducted. First, a limited number of issues was tagged with a yellow-green phosphor to distinguish surface mail from air mail. More and more issues followed. In 1964 testing was expanded to the Cincinnati Postal Region. With each new success, tagging became more and more common. By 1967, most regular issues through the 16¢, all commemoratives, and additional items of postal stationery were tagged. During 1973 tagging was ordered for the higher denominations of regular postage, too.

Are there still stamps that aren't tagged? There are.

Stamps that are precanceled by the Bureau of Engraving and Printing aren't usually tagged. That's because precancel permit holders have to post such mail already faced. In some postal stationery the luminescent element is in the ink with which the stamp design is printed, but in others a vertical phosphorescent bar or panel is placed to the left of the imprinted stamp. And then there are stamps from which the tagging is left off by mistake.

Since tagging is generally invisible to the naked eye, the only way you can tell whether or not it's there is to examine the stamp under an ultraviolet lamp. BUT BEWARE!

Prolonged exposure to ultraviolet light can permanently damage the eyes. You'll get some protection from sunglasses or prescription eyeglasses. But play it safe. Keep your exposures brief. And never, NEVER look directly into the ultraviolet light for any reason whatsoever.

COMMEMORATIVE STAMPS QUANTITIES ISSUED

The latest figures represent the quantities of stamps distributed to post offices through December 31, 1978.

Cat. No.	Quantity
230	449,195,550
231	1,464,588,750
232	11,501,250
233	19,181,550
234	35,248,250
235	4,707,550
236	10,656,550
237	16,516,950
238	1,576,950
239	617,250
240	243,750
241	55,050
242	45,550
243	27,650
244	26,350
245	27,350
285	70,993,400
286	159,720,800
287	4,924,500
288	7,694,180
289	2,927,200
290	4,629,760
291	530,400
292	56,900
293	56,200
294	91,401,500
295	209,759,700
296	5,737,100
297	7,201,300
298	4,921,700
299	5,043,700
323	79,779,200
324	192,732,400
325	4,542,600
326	6,926,700
327	4,011,200
328	77,728,794
329	149,497,994
330	7,980,594
367	148,387,191
368	1,273,900
369	637,000
370	152,887,311
371	525,400
372	72,634,631
373	216,480
397 410	334,796,926
398 402	503,713,086
399 403	29,088,726
400 404	16,968,365
537	99,585,200
548	137,978,207

Cat. No.	Quantity
549	196,037,327
550	11,321,607
610	1,459,487,085
611	770,000
612	99,950,300
614	51,378,023
615	77,753,423
616	5,659,023
617	15,615,000
618	26,596,600
619	5,348,800
620	9,104,983
621	1,900,983
627	307,731,900
628	20,280,500
629	40,639,485
630 *(sheet of 25)*	107,398
643	39,974,900
644	25,628,450
645	101,330,328
646	9,779,896
647	5,519,897
648	1,459,897
649	51,342,273
650	10,319,700
651	16,684,674
654	31,679,200
655	210,119,474
656	133,530,000
657	51,451,880
658	13,390,000
659	8,240,000
660	87,410,000
661	2,540,000
662	2,290,000
663	2,700,000
664	1,450,000
665	1,320,000
666	1,530,000
667	1,130,000
668	2,860,000
669	8,220,000
670	8,990,000
671	73,220,000
672	2,110,000
673	1,600,000
674	1,860,000
675	980,000
676	850,000
677	1,480,000
678	530,000
679	1,890,000
680	29,338,274
681	32,680,900
682	74,000,774
683	25,215,574

Cat. No.	Quantity
688	25,609,470
689	66,487,000
690	96,559,400
702	99,074,600
703	25,006,400
704	87,969,700
705	1,265,555,100
706	304,926,800
707	4,222,198,300
708	456,198,500
709	151,201,300
710	170,565,100
711	111,739,400
712	83,257,400
713	96,506,100
714	75,709,200
715	147,216,000
716	51,102,800
717	100,869,300
718	168,885,300
719	52,376,100
724	49,949,000
725	49,538,500
726	61,719,200
727	73,382,400
728	348,266,800
729	480,239,300
730 *(sheet of 25)*	456,704
731 *(sheet of 25)*	441,172
732	1,978,707,300
733	5,735,944
734	45,137,700
735 *(sheet of six)*	811,404
736	46,258,300
737	193,239,100
738	15,432,200
739	64,525,400
740	84,896,350
741	74,400,200
742	95,089,000
743	19,178,650
744	30,980,100
745	16,923,350
746	15,988,250
747	15,288,700
748	17,472,600
749	18,874,300
750 *(sheet of six)*	511,391
751 *(sheet of six)*	793,551
752	3,274,556
753	2,040,760
754	2,389,288
755	2,294,948
756	3,217,636
757	2,746,640
758	2,168,088

Cat. No.	Quantity	Cat. No.	Quantity	Cat. No.	Quantity
759	1,822,684	*877*	23,779,000	*950*	131,968,000
760	1,724,576	*878*	15,112,580	*951*	131,488,000
761	1,647,696	*879*	57,322,790	*952*	122,362,000
762	1,682,948	*880*	58,281,580	*953*	121,548,000
763	1,638,644	*881*	56,398,790	*954*	131,109,500
764	1,625,224	*882*	21,147,000	*955*	122,650,500
765	1,644,900	*883*	13,328,000	*956*	121,953,500
766 (pane of 25)	98,712	*884*	54,389,510	*957*	115,250,000
767 (pane of 25)	85,914	*885*	53,636,580	*958*	64,198,500
768 (pane of six)	267,200	*886*	55,313,230	*959*	117,642,500
769 (pane of six)	279,960	*887*	21,720,580	*960*	77,649,600
770 (pane of six)	215,920	*888*	13,600,580	*961*	113,474,500
771	1,370,560	*889*	47,599,580	*962*	120,868,500
772	70,726,800	*890*	53,766,510	*963*	77,800,500
773	100,839,600	*891*	54,193,580	*964*	52,214,000
774	73,610,650	*892*	20,264,580	*965*	53,958,100
775	75,823,900	*893*	13,726,580	*966*	61,120,010
776	124,324,500	*894*	46,497,400	*967*	57,823,000
777	67,127,650	*895*	47,700,000	*968*	52,975,000
778 (sheet of four)	2,809,039	*896*	50,618,150	*969*	77,149,000
782	72,992,650	*897*	50,034,400	*970*	58,332,000
783	74,407,450	*898*	60,943,700	*971*	56,228,000
784	269,522,200	*902*	44,389,550	*972*	57,832,000
785	105,196,150	*903*	54,574,550	*973*	53,875,000
786	93,848,500	*904*	63,558,400	*974*	63,834,000
787	87,741,150	*906*	21,272,800	*975*	67,162,200
788	35,794,150	*907*	1,671,564,200	*976*	64,561,000
789	36,839,250	*908*	1,227,334,200	*977*	64,079,500
790	104,773,450	*909*	19,999,646	*978*	63,388,000
791	92,054,550	*910*	19,999,646	*979*	62,285,000
792	93,291,650	*911*	19,999,646	*980*	57,492,610
793	34,552,950	*912*	19,999,646	*981*	99,190,000
794	36,819,050	*913*	19,999,646	*982*	104,790,000
795	84,825,250	*914*	19,999,646	*983*	108,805,000
796	25,040,400	*915*	19,999,646	*984*	107,340,000
797	5,277,445	*916*	14,999,646	*985*	117,020,000
798	99,882,300	*917*	14,999,646	*986*	122,633,000
799	78,454,450	*918*	14,999,646	*987*	130,960,000
800	77,004,200	*919*	14,999,646	*988*	128,478,000
801	81,292,450	*920*	14,999,646	*989*	132,090,000
802	76,474,550	*921*	14,999,646	*990*	130,050,000
835	73,043,650	*922*	61,303,000	*991*	131,350,000
836	58,564,368	*923*	61,001,450	*992*	129,980,000
837	65,939,500	*924*	60,605,000	*993*	122,315,000
838	47,064,300	*925*	50,129,350	*994*	122,170,000
852	114,439,600	*926*	53,479,400	*995*	131,635,000
853	101,699,550	*927*	61,617,350	*996*	121,860,000
854	72,764,550	*928*	75,500,000	*997*	121,120,000
855	81,269,600	*929*	137,321,000	*998*	119,120,000
856	67,813,350	*930*	128,140,000	*999*	112,125,000
857	71,394,750	*931*	67,255,000	*1000*	114,140,000
858	66,835,000	*932*	133,870,000	*1001*	114,490,000
859	56,348,320	*933*	76,455,400	*1002*	117,200,000
860	53,177,110	*934*	128,357,750	*1003*	116,130,000
861	53,260,270	*935*	135,863,000	*1004*	116,175,000
862	22,104,950	*936*	111,616,700	*1005*	115,945,000
863	13,201,270	*937*	308,587,700	*1006*	112,540,000
864	51,603,580	*938*	170,640,000	*1007*	117,415,000
865	52,100,510	*939*	135,927,000	*1008*	2,899,580,000
866	51,666,580	*940*	260,339,100	*1009*	114,540,000
867	22,207,780	*941*	132,274,500	*1010*	113,135,000
868	11,835,530	*942*	132,430,000	*1011*	116,255,000
869	52,471,160	*943*	139,209,500	*1012*	113,860,000
870	52,366,440	*944*	114,684,450	*1013*	124,260,000
871	51,636,270	*945*	156,540,510	*1014*	115,735,000
872	20,729,030	*945*	156,540,510	*1015*	115,430,000
873	14,125,580	*946*	120,452,600	*1016*	136,220,000
874	59,409,000	*947*	127,104,300	*1017*	114,894,600
875	57,888,600	*948*	10,299,600	*1018*	118,706,000
876	58,273,180	*949*	132,902,000	*1019*	114,190,000

Cat. No.	Quantity
1020	113,990,000
1021	89,289,600
1022	114,865,000
1023	115,780,000
1024	115,244,600
1025	123,709,600
1026	114,798,600
1027	115,759,600
1028	116,134,600
1029	118,540,000
1060	115,810,000
1061	113,603,700
1062	128,002,000
1063	116,078,150
1064	116,139,800
1065	120,484,800
1066	53,854,750
1067	176,075,000
1068	125,944,400
1069	122,284,600
1070	133,638,850
1071	118,664,600
1072	112,434,000
1073	129,384,550
1074	121,184,600
1075	2,900,731
1076	119,784,200
1077	123,159,400
1078	123,138,800
1079	109,275,000
1080	112,932,200
1081	125,475,000
1082	117,855,000
1083	122,100,000
1084	118,180,000
1085	100,975,000
1086	115,299,450
1087	186,949,627
1088	115,235,000
1089	106,647,500
1090	112,010,000
1091	118,470,000
1092	102,230,000
1093	102,410,000
1094	84,054,400
1095	126,266,000
1096	39,489,600
1097	122,990,000
1098	174,372,800
1099	114,365,000
1100	122,765,200
1104	113,660,200
1105	120,196,580
1106	120,805,200
1107	125,815,200
1108	108,415,200
1109	107,195,200
1110	115,745,280
1111	39,743,640
1112	114,570,200
1113	120,400,200
1114	91,160,200
1115	114,860,200
1116	126,500,000
1117	120,561,280
1118	44,064,576
1119	118,390,200
1120	125,770,200
1121	114,114,280
1122	156,600,200

Cat. No.	Quantity
1123	124,200,200
1124	120,740,200
1125	133,623,280
1126	45,569,088
1127	122,493,280
1128	131,260,200
1129	47,125,200
1130	123,105,000
1131	126,105,050
1132	209,170,000
1133	120,835,000
1134	115,715,000
1135	118,445,000
1136	111,685,000
1137	43,099,200
1138	115,444,000
1139	126,470,000
1140	124,560,000
1141	115,455,000
1142	122,060,000
1143	120,540,000
1144	113,075,000
1145	139,325,000
1146	124,445,000
1147	113,792,000
1148	44,215,200
1149	113,195,000
1150	121,805,000
1151	115,353,000
1152	111,080,000
1153	153,025,000
1154	119,665,000
1155	117,855,000
1156	118,185,000
1157	112,260,000
1158	125,010,000
1159	119,798,000
1160	42,696,000
1161	106,610,000
1162	109,695,000
1163	123,690,000
1164	123,970,000
1165	124,796,000
1166	42,076,800
1167	116,210,000
1168	126,252,000
1169	42,746,400
1170	124,117,000
1171	119,840,000
1172	117,187,000
1173	124,390,000
1174	112,966,000
1175	41,644,200
1176	110,850,000
1177	98,616,000
1178	101,125,000
1179	124,865,000
1180	79,905,000
1181	125,410,000
1182	112,845,000
1183	106,210,000
1184	110,810,000
1185	116,995,000
1186	121,015,000
1187	111,600,000
1188	110,620,000
1189	109,110,000
1190	145,350,000
1191	112,870,000
1192	121,820,000

Cat. No.	Quantity
1193	289,240,000
1194	120,155,000
1195	124,595,000
1196	147,310,000
1197	118,690,000
1198	122,730,000
1199	126,515,000
1200	130,960,000
1201	120,055,000
1202	120,715,000
1203	121,440,000
1204	40,270,000
1205	861,970,000
1206	120,035,000
1207	117,870,000
1230	129,945,000
1231	135,620,000
1232	137,540,000
1233	132,435,000
1234	135,520,000
1235	131,420,000
1236	133,170,000
1237	130,195,000
1238	128,450,000
1239	118,665,000
1240	1,291,250,000
1241	175,175,000
1242	125,995,000
1243	128,925,000
1244	145,700,000
1245	120,310,000
1246	511,750,000
1247	123,845,000
1248	122,825,000
1249	453,090,000
1250	123,245,000
1251	123,355,000
1252	126,970,000
1253	121,250,000
1254-1257	1,407,760,000
1258	120,005,000
1259	125,800,000
1260	122,230,000
1261	115,695,000
1262	115,095,000
1263	119,560,000
1264	125,180,000
1265	120,135,000
1266	115,405,000
1267	115,855,000
1268	115,340,000
1269	114,840,000
1270	116,140,000
1271	116,900,000
1272	114,085,000
1273	114,880,000
1274	26,995,000
1275	128,495,000
1276	1,139,930,000
1306	116,835,000
1307	117,470,000
1308	123,770,000
1309	131,270,000
1310	122,285,000
1311	14,680,000
1312	114,160,000
1313	128,475,000
1314	119,535,000
1315	125,110,000
1316	114,853,200

Cat. No.	Quantity
1317	124,290,000
1318	128,460,000
1319	127,585,000
1320	115,875,000
1321	1,173,547,420
1322	114,015,000
1323	121,105,000
1324	132,045,000
1325	118,780,000
1326	121,985,000
1327	111,850,000
1328	117,225,000
1329	111,515,000
1330	114,270,000
1331-1332	120,865,000
1333	110,675,000
1334	110,670,000
1335	113,825,000
1336	1,208,700,000
1337	113,330,000
1339	141,350,000
1340	144,345,000
1342	147,120,000
1343	130,125,000
1344	158,700,000
1345-1354	231,530,000
1355	153,015,000
1356	132,560,000
1357	130,385,000
1358	132,265,000
1359	128,710,000
1360	124,775,000
1361	128,295,000
1362	142,245,000
1363	1,410,580,000
1364	125,100,000
1365-1368	192,570,000
1369	148,770,000
1370	139,475,000
1371	187,165,000
1372	125,555,000
1373	144,425,000
1374	135,875,000
1375	151,110,000
1376-1379	159,195,000
1380	129,540,000
1381	130,925,000
1382	139,055,000
1383	150,611,200
1384	1,709,795,000
1385	127,545,000
1386	145,788,800
1387-1390	201,794,200
1391	171,850,000
1392	142,205,000
1405	137,660,000
1406	135,125,000
1407	135,895,000
1408	132,675,000
1409	134,795,000
1410-1413	161,600,000
1414-1414a	683,730,000
1415-1418 1415a-1418a	489,255,000
1419	127,610,000
1420	129,785,000
1421-1422	134,380,000
1423	135,305,000
1424	134,840,000
1425	130,975,000
1426	161,235,000
1427-1430	175,680,000
1431	138,700,000
1432	138,165,000
1433	152,125,000
1434-1435	176,295,000
1436	142,845,000
1437	148,755,000
1438	139,080,000
1439	130,755,000
1440-1443	170,208,000
1444	1,074,350,000
1445	979,540,000
1446	137,355,000
1447	150,400,000
1448-1451	172,730,000
1452	104,090,000
1453	164,096,000
1454	53,920,000
1455	153,025,000
1456-1459	201,890,000
1460	67,335,000
1461	179,675,000
1462	46,340,000
1463	180,155,000
1464-1467	198,364,800
1468	185,490,000
1469	162,335,000
1470	162,789,950
1471	1,003,475,000
1472	1,017,025,000
1473	165,895,000
1474	166,508,000
1475	330,055,000
1476	166,005,000
1477	163,050,000
1478	159,005,000
1479	147,295,000
1480-1483	196,275,000
1484	139,152,000
1485	128,048,000
1486	146,008,000
1487	139,608,000
1488	159,475,000
1489-1498	486,020,000
1499	157,052,800
1500	53,005,000
1501	159,775,000
1502	39,005,000
1503	152,624,000
1504	145,840,000
1505	151,335,000
1506	141,085,000
1507	885,160,000
1508	939,835,000
1525	143,930,000
1526	145,235,000
1527	135,052,000
1528	156,750,000
1529	164,670,000
1530-1537	190,156,800
1538-1541	167,212,800
1542	156,265,000
1543-1546	195,585,000
1547	148,850,000
1548	157,270,000
1549	150,245,000
1550	835,180,000
1551	882,520,000
1552	213,155,000
1553	156,995,000
1554	146,365,000
1555	148,805,000
1556	173,685,000
1557	158,600,000
1558	153,355,000
1559	63,205,000
1560	157,865,000
1561	166,810,000
1562	44,825,000
1563	144,028,000
1564	139,928,000
1565-1568	179,855,000
1569-1570	161,863,200
1571	145,640,000
1572-1575	168,655,000
1576	146,615,000
1577-1578	146,196,000
1579	739,430,000
1580	878,690,000
1629-1631	219,455,000
1632	157,825,000
1633-1682	436,005,000
1683	159,915,000
1684	156,960,000
1685	158,470,000
1686	1,990,000
1687	1,983,000
1688	1,953,000
1689	1,903,000
1690	164,890,000
1691-1694	204,035,000
1695-1698	185,715,000
1699	130,592,000
1700	158,332,800
1701	809,955,000
1702-1703	963,370,000
1704	150,328,000
1705	176,830,000
1706-1709	195,976,000
1710	208,820,000
1711	192,250,000
1712-1715	219,830,000
1716	159,852,000
1717-1720	188,310,000
1721	163,625,000
1722	156,296,000
1723-1724	158,676,000
1725	154,495,000
1726	168,050,000
1727	156,810,000
1728	153,736,000
1729	882,260,000
1730	921,530,000
1731	156,560,000
1733	202,155,000
1744	156,525,000
1745-1748	165,182,400
1749-1752	157,598,400
1753	102,856,000
1754	152,270,000
1755	94,600,000
1756	151,570,000
1757	15,170,400
1758	161,228,000
1759	158,880,000
1760-1763	186,550,000
1764-1767	168,136,000
1768	963,120,000
1769	916,800,000

INDEX OF COMMEMORATIVE STAMPS & STORIES

Stamps having related stories are indicated in **boldface** type.
The numbers in this index are the Scott numbers of the stamps.

Special Olympics 1788
Spirit of Independence 1476-1479